McDougal Littell

MATH

Course 3

Larson Boswell Kanold Stiff

Notetaking Guide

The Notetaking Guide contains a lesson-by-lesson framework that allows students to take notes on and review the main concepts of each lesson in the textbook. Each Notetaking Guide lesson features worked-out examples and Guided Practice exercises similar to those found in the textbook. Each example has a number of write-in boxes for students to complete, either in class as the example is discussed or at home as part of a review of the lesson. Each chapter concludes with a review of the main vocabulary of the chapter. Upon completion, each chapter of the Notetaking Guide can be used by students to help review for the test on that particular chapter.

McDougal Littell
A DIVISION OF HOUGHTON MIFFLIN COMPANY
Evanston, Illinois • Boston • Dallas

ISBN 13: 978-0-618-74192-2
ISBN 10: 0-618-74192-5

56789–0956–12 11 10 09

Contents

Notetaking Guide

Contents

Contents

Contents

Interpreting Graphs

Goal: Use graphs to analyze data.

Vocabulary

Bar graph: ______

Data: ______

Frequency table: ______

Histogram: ______

EXAMPLE 1 Interpreting a Bar Graph

State Parks The bar graph shows the number of state parks in four states. Use the bar graph to answer the question, or explain why you can't answer the question using the graph.

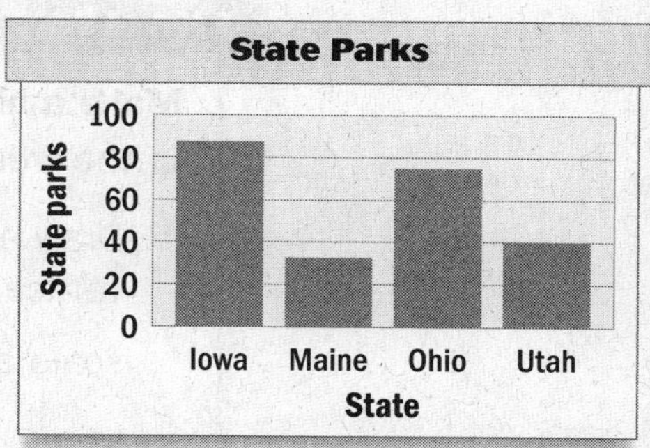

a. Which state has the most state parks?

b. Which state has the largest state park?

Solution

a. The vertical axis in the bar graph is labeled ______, so the tallest bar represents the ______ with the most state parks. Because ______ has the tallest bar, it has the most state parks.

b. The sizes of the bars do not represent the sizes of the state parks. So, you ______ this question using the bar graph.

Guided Practice **Use the bar graph about state parks.**

1. About how many more state parks does Ohio have than Utah?	**2.** Which state has the least number of state parks?

EXAMPLE 2 Making a Frequency Table

Waterfalls The data show the heights, in meters, of the 23 tallest waterfa in the world. Make a frequency table of the data.

Think: What are the smallest and largest heights?

365, 491, 739, 703, 423, 610,
979, 850, 655, 561, 300, 370,
503, 360, 300, 762, 468, 580,
774, 647, 800, 357, 311

Height (m)	Tally	Fr
300–399		
400–499		
500–599		
600–699		
700–799		
800–899		
900–999		

1. Choose a scale and ______ of equal size for the data.

2. Use ______ to record each occurrence of a height in its interval.

Think: In what interval is 365?

3. Write the ______ for each interval by totaling the tally marks.

EXAMPLE 3 Making a Histogram

Make a histogram of the data shown in the frequency table in Example 2.

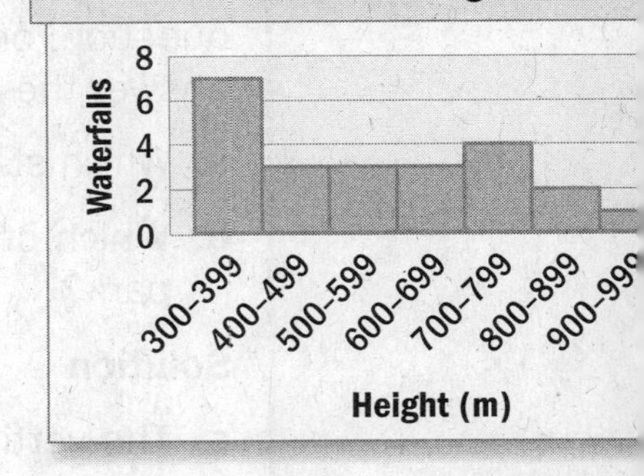

1. Draw and label the horizontal and vertical axes. Start the vertical scale at ___ and end at ___. Use increments of ___.

2. Draw a bar to represent the ______ of each interval. The bars of neighboring intervals should touch.

3. Write a title.

Guided Practice **Use the data in Example 3.**

3. Which interval has the greatest number of waterfalls?

4. If you include the next five tallest waterfalls, in what interval do you think they will be? Explain.

Order of Operations

Goal: Use order of operations to evaluate numerical expressions.

Vocabulary

Numerical expression:

Evaluate:

Order of operations:

Verbal model:

Order of Operations

To ______ an expression that has more than one operation:

1. Evaluate expressions inside ______ symbols.

2. ______ and divide from left to right.

3. Add and ______ from left to right.

ink: Are there
ny expressions
side grouping
symbols?

EXAMPLE 1 Using the Order of Operations

Evaluate the expression 9 − 18 ÷ 6 × 2.

$9 - 18 \div 6 \times 2 = 9 -$ ______ $\times 2$ Divide ______ by ______.

$= 9 -$ ______ Multiply ______ by ______.

$=$ ______ Subtract ______ and ______.

u can express
plication by using
entheses or the
mbols • or ×.
6(3) = 18
6 • 3 = 18
6 × 3 = 18

EXAMPLE 2 Using Grouping Symbols

WATCH OUT!
You can express division using either the symbol ÷ or a fraction bar. In an expression with a fraction bar, the numerator is the dividend and the denominator is the divisor.

a. $(16 + 9) \cdot 4 = \square \cdot 4$ Add inside parentheses first.

$= \square$ Then multiply.

b. $\frac{6 \times 10}{7 + 5} = \frac{\square}{7 + 5}$ Evaluate numerator.

$= \frac{\square}{\square}$ Evaluate denominator.

$= \square$ Divide.

c. $48 \div [120 \div (4 \cdot 5)] = 48 \div [120 \div \square]$ Multiply inside the innermost set of grouping symbols.

$= 48 \div \square$ Divide inside brackets.

$= \square$ Divide.

Guided Practice **Evaluate the expression.**

1. $15 + 9 \div 3$	**2.** $32 - 9 \times 2 + 7$	**3.** $5 \cdot 8 - 2 \cdot 14$
4. $64 \div (9 + 7)$	**5.** $11 \cdot [(15 - 3) \div 3]$	**6.** $\frac{41 + 13}{9 \times 3}$

EXAMPLE 3 Writing an Expression

Sporting Goods A sporting goods store has a sale. Roller skates are on sale for \$24.50, and in-line skates are on sale for \$50. The store sells 5 pairs of the roller skates and 12 pairs of the in-line skates. How much money does the store take in from the sale?

Solution

To find the total taken in, you can use a verbal model to write and evaluate an expression.

Total taken in = Pairs of roller skates × ______ + ______ × Cost of in-line skates

= 5 × ______ + 12 × ______ Substitute values.

= ______ + ______ Multiply first.

= ______ Then add.

ANSWER The store takes in \$ ______.

Variables and Expressions

Goal: Evaluate and write variable expressions.

Vocabulary

Variable:

Variable expression:

EXAMPLE 1 **Using a Variable Expression**

Biking You are taking a bike trip. After riding 8 miles, you change your s to 12 miles per hour. What is the total distance you travel if you stay at speed for 2 hours? for 3 hours?

Solution

Let t represent the time, in hours that you ride at 12 miles per hour. So, the total distance you travel is *original distance* + *speed* × *time*, which is $8 + 12t$.

1. Write hours traveled, t.	**2.** Substitute for t in the expression $8 + 12t$.	**3.** Evaluate to fir the total dista
2	$8 + 12(\quad)$	
3	$8 + 12(\quad)$	

ANSWER If you ride at 12 miles per hour for 2 hours, you travel a total ______. After 3 hours, you travel a total of ______.

Guided Practice **Use the information in Example 1.**

1. If you travel for 4 hours, what is the total distance?

2. If you travel for $1\frac{1}{2}$ hours, what is the total distance?

EXAMPLE 2 Evaluating Variable Expressions

Evaluate the expression when $x = 6$ and $y = 3$.

a. $9x - 14 = 9(\square) - 14$ Substitute $\square$ for x.

$= \square - 14$ Multiply.

$= \square$ Subtract.

b. $4x + 7y = 4(\square) + 7(\square)$ Substitute $\square$ for x and $\square$ for y.

$= \square + \square$ Multiply.

$= \square$ Add.

Writing Expressions

The following common words and phrases indicate addition, subtraction, multiplcation and division.

Addition	Subtraction	Multiplication	Division
plus the sum of increased by total more than added to	minus the difference of decreased by fewer than less than subtracted from	times the product of multiplied by of	divided by the quotient of per

EXAMPLE 3 Translating Verbal Phrases

Verbal Phrase	Variable Expression
The sum of 8 and a number	$\square + n$
The difference of 24 and a number	$\square$
The $\square$ of 5 and a number	$5n$
The $\square$ of 35 and a number	$\frac{\square}{\square}$
$\square$ $\square$ a number	$\frac{2}{3}n$

der is important
translating verbal
ssions that suggest
action and division.
e difference of a
ber and 10 means
10, not $10 - n$.
e quotient of a
ber and 9 means
÷ 9, not $9 \div n$.

Guided Practice Evaluate the expression when $a = 14$ and $b = 4$.

3. $7a$	4. ba
5. $b(a + 6)$	6. $\frac{5a}{a - b}$

Write the phrase as a variable expression using x.

7. A number decreased by 16	8. 72 divided by a number

EXAMPLE 4 Writing and Evaluating Expressions

Fundraising Your school's fundraising committee is making team banner The committee can make n banners in 15 minutes. Multiply by 4 to find number of banners the committee can make per hour.

a. Use n to write an expression for the number of banners the committe can make per hour.

b. The committee makes 9 banners in 15 minutes. Find the number of banners the committee can make per hour.

Solution

a. The phrase *multiply by* suggests multiplication. So, the variable express for the number of banners the committee can make per hour is $4n$.

b. Substitute 9 for n in the expression $4n$ to find the number of banners committee can make per hour.

$4n = 4(\ \_\_\_\ )$

$= \_\_\_$

ANSWER The committee can make ____ banners per hour.

Powers and Exponents

Goal: Evaluate expressions with powers.

Vocabulary

Power:

Exponent:

Base:

EXAMPLE 1 **Reading Powers**

Power	Repeated Multiplication	Description in Words
5^2	$5 \cdot 5$	5 to the *second power,* or 5
8^3		8 to the , or 8 *cubed*
$x^{\square}$	$x \cdot x \cdot x \cdot x \cdot x \cdot x$	*x* to the power

EXAMPLE 2 **Evaluating a Power**

Evaluate three to the fourth power.

$3^4 =$ Write as a factor times.

$=$ Multiply.

Guided Practice Write the product as a power.

1. $9 \times 9 \times 9 \times 9 \times 9$	2. $11 \cdot 11 \cdot 11$	3. $t \cdot t$

Describe the power in words and then evaluate.

4. 10^3	5. 2^6	6. 15^2	7. 7^1

Order of Operations

1. Evaluate expressions inside ______.
2. Evaluate powers.
3. Multiply and ______ from left to right.
4. ______ and ______ from left to right.

EXAMPLE 3 Using a Power

Egg Drop Contest In an egg drop contest, you drop your egg from a winc of a building. The egg hits the ground after 2 seconds. From what height you drop your egg?

Solution

To find how high you are from the ground in feet, use the expression $16t$ where t is the time in seconds.

$16t^2 = 16(\_\_)^2$ Substitute ______ for t.

$= 16(\_\_)$ Evaluate the power.

$=$ ______ Multiply.

ANSWER You dropped your egg from a height of ______ feet.

EXAMPLE 4 Using the Order of Operations

Evaluate the expression.

a. $(7 - 3)^3 - 28 + 8^2 = \square - 28 + 8^2$ Evaluate inside grouping symbols.

$= \square - 28 + \square$ Evaluate powers.

$= \square$ Add and subtract from left to right.

b. $3 \cdot (2 + 4)^2 \div 3^2 = 3 \cdot \square \div 3^2$ Evaluate inside grouping symbols.

$= 3 \cdot \square \div \square$ Evaluate powers.

$= \square$ Multiply and divide from left to right.

Guided Practice **Evaluate the expression.**

8. $(6 + 5)^2 + 7 - 5^3$	**9.** $15 + (9 - 2)^2 - 2^5$	**10.** $9^3 + 16 \div (7 - 5)^4$

11. Use the expression in Example 3 to find the height from which you dropped your egg if it hit the ground after 3 seconds.

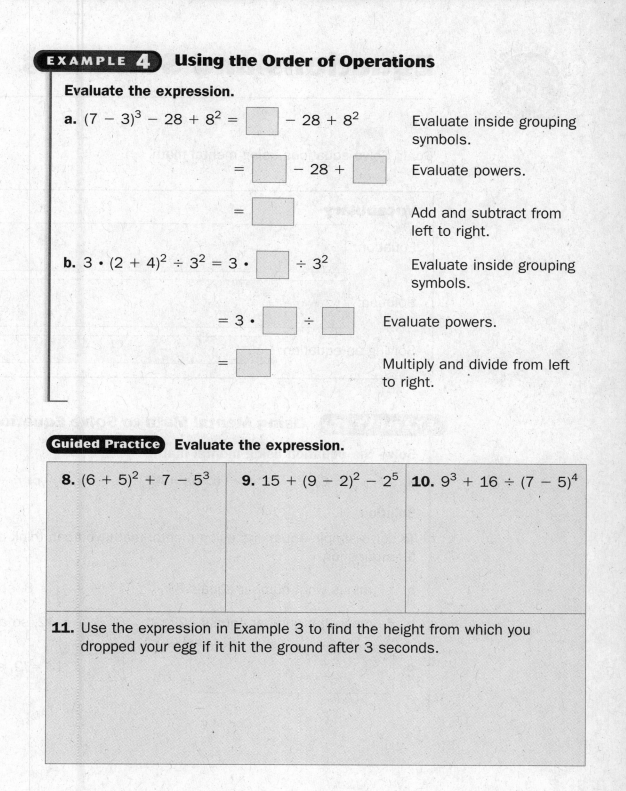

Equations and Solutions

Goal: Solve equations using mental math.

Vocabulary

Equation:

Solution:

Solving an equation:

EXAMPLE 1 **Using Mental Math to Solve Equations**

Solve the equation using mental math.

a. $17 - y = 8$ **b.** $6a = 42$ **c.** $n \div 13 = 2$

Solution

To solve simple equations using mental math, you can think of the equat as a question.

a. 17 minus what number equals 8? $17 - \square = 8$, so $y = \square$.

b. 6 times what number equals 42? $6(\square) = 42$, so $a = \square$.

c. $\square \div 13 = 2$, so $n = \square$

EXAMPLE 2 Checking Solutions of Equations

Tell whether the value of the variable is a solution of $x - 6 = 21$.

a. $x = 15$ **b.** $x = 27$

Solution

Substitute for x and then simplify.

The $\stackrel{?}{=}$ symbol
ns *are these values*
al? The $\neq$ symbol
ns *is not equal to.*

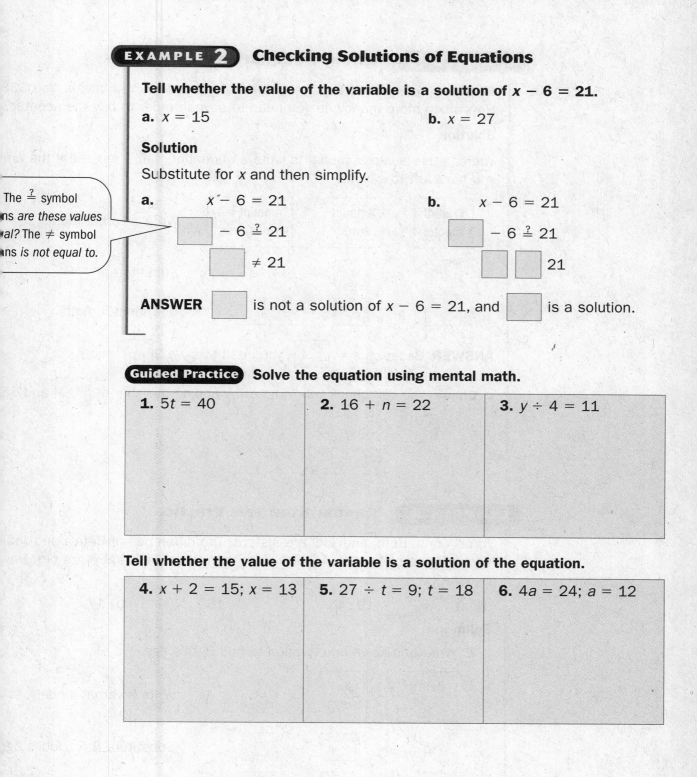

a.

$x - 6 = 21$

$\square - 6 \stackrel{?}{=} 21$

$\square \neq 21$

b.

$x - 6 = 21$

$\square - 6 \stackrel{?}{=} 21$

 21

ANSWER $\square$ is not a solution of $x - 6 = 21$, and $\square$ is a solution.

Guided Practice **Solve the equation using mental math.**

1. $5t = 40$	**2.** $16 + n = 22$	**3.** $y \div 4 = 11$

Tell whether the value of the variable is a solution of the equation.

4. $x + 2 = 15$; $x = 13$	**5.** $27 \div t = 9$; $t = 18$	**6.** $4a = 24$; $a = 12$

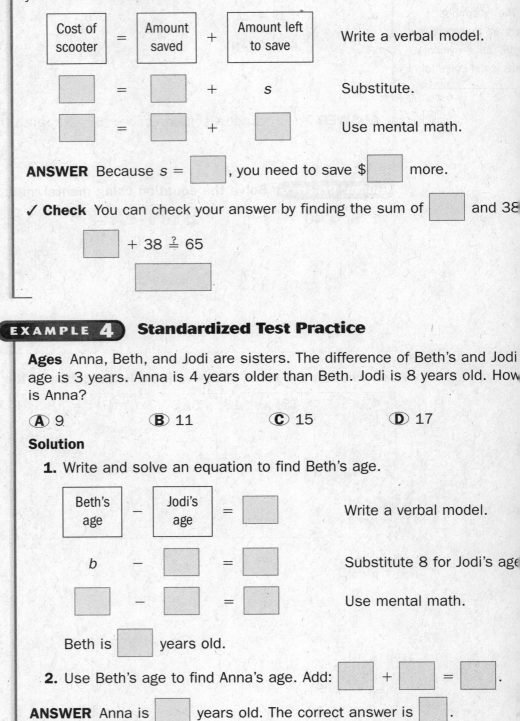

EXAMPLE 3 Writing an Equation

Scooters You want to buy a scooter that costs \$65. You have saved \$38
How much more money do you need to save in order to buy the scooter?

Solution

You can use a verbal model to write an equation. Let s represent the am
you have left to save.

Cost of scooter	=	Amount saved	+	Amount left to save	Write a verbal model.
	=		+	s	Substitute.
	=		+		Use mental math.

ANSWER Because $s =$, you need to save \$ more.

✓ **Check** You can check your answer by finding the sum of and 38

$+ 38 \stackrel{?}{=} 65$

EXAMPLE 4 Standardized Test Practice

Ages Anna, Beth, and Jodi are sisters. The difference of Beth's and Jodi
age is 3 years. Anna is 4 years older than Beth. Jodi is 8 years old. How
is Anna?

Ⓐ 9 Ⓑ 11 Ⓒ 15 Ⓓ 17

Solution

1. Write and solve an equation to find Beth's age.

Beth's age	–	Jodi's age	=		Write a verbal model.
b	–		=		Substitute 8 for Jodi's age
	–		=		Use mental math.

Beth is years old.

2. Use Beth's age to find Anna's age. Add: + = .

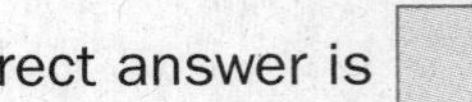

ANSWER Anna is years old. The correct answer is .

Ⓐ Ⓑ Ⓒ Ⓓ

Variables in Familiar Formulas

Goal: Use formulas to find unknown values.

Vocabulary

Formula:

Perimeter:

Area:

Perimeters and Area Formulas

	Diagram	Perimeter	Area
Rectangle	(rectangle with sides l and w)	$P =$ ___ $+ 2w$	$A =$ ___
Square	(square with sides s and s)	$P =$ ___	$A =$ ___

EXAMPLE 1 **Finding Perimeter and Area**

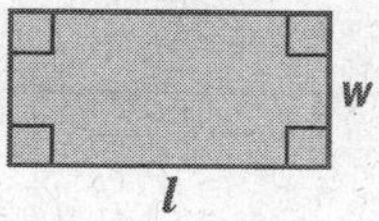

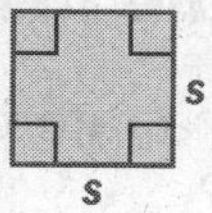

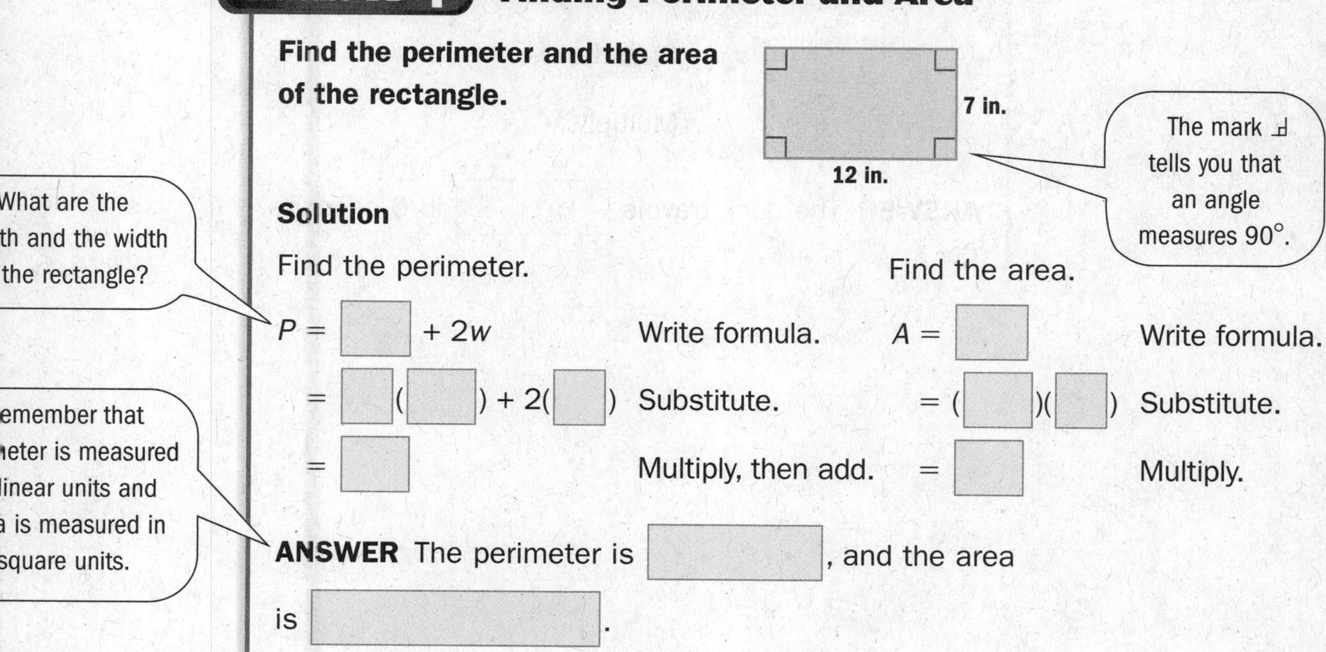

7 in.
12 in.
The mark ⅃ tells you that an angle measures 90°.
What are the th and the width the rectangle?
emember that neter is measured linear units and a is measured in square units.

Find the perimeter and the area of the rectangle.

Solution

Find the perimeter.

$P =$ ___ $+ 2w$ Write formula.

$=$ ___ (___) $+ 2($ ___ $)$ Substitute.

$=$ ___ Multiply, then add.

Find the area.

$A =$ ___ Write formula.

$= ($ ___ $)($ ___ $)$ Substitute.

$=$ ___ Multiply.

ANSWER The perimeter is ___, and the area is ___.

EXAMPLE 2 Finding Side Length

Find the side length of a square with an area of 64 square inches.

Think: What number squared is equal to 64?

$A = s^2$ Write formula for area of a square.

____ $= s^2$ Substitute ____ for A.

____ $= s$ Use mental math.

s
s $A = 64$ in.^{2} s
s

ANSWER The side length of the square is ____.

Distance Formula

Words The distance traveled d is the ____ of the rate r and the time t.

Algebra $d =$ ____ • ____ or $d =$ ____

Numbers $d = \frac{20 \text{ miles}}{\cancel{\text{hour}}} \cdot 4 \cancel{\text{ hours}} =$ ____

EXAMPLE 3 Using the Distance Formula

Ducks A duck is flying at a rate of 55 feet per second. How far does the duck travel in 6 seconds?

Solution

$d =$ ____ • ____ Write distance formula.

$=$ ____ • ____ Substitute.

$=$ ____ Multiply.

ANSWER The duck travels ____ in 6 seconds.

Guided Practice **Solve.**

1. Find the perimeter and area of a square with a 6 inch side length.

2. Find the side length of a square that has an area of 144 square meters.

3. How far does an airplane travel in 3 hours at a rate of 450 miles per hour?

EXAMPLE 4 Standardized Test Practice

Notice that
u can write the
tance formula in
different form to
d time. You can
rate using $r = \frac{d}{t}$.

Geese How long will it take a goose to travel 690 feet at a rate of 46 feet per second?

Ⓐ 0.067 sec Ⓑ 15 sec

Ⓒ 736 sec Ⓓ 31,740 sec

Solution

$t = \frac{d}{r}$ Write distance formula.

$= \frac{\square}{\square}$ Substitute  for *d* and 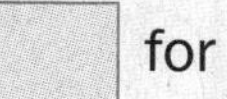 for *r*.

=  Divide.

ANSWER It will take a goose  to travel 690 feet.

The correct answer is .  Ⓑ  Ⓓ

A Problem Solving Plan

Goal: Use a problem solving plan to solve problems.

Vocabulary

Unit Analysis: ____

EXAMPLE 1 **Understanding and Planning**

Shopping The table shows the size and cost of each container of juice. Which juice is the better buy?

	Size (fl oz)	Cost
Juice A	48	3.3
Juice B	64	4.0

Solution

To decide which juice is the better buy, you need to make sure you understand the problem. Then make a plan for solving the problem.

Read and Understand

What do you know?

The table tells you the size and cost of each juice.

The size of Juice A is ____ fluid ounces, and it costs ____.

The size of Juice B is ____ fluid ounces, and it costs ____.

What do you want to find out?

Which juice is the better buy?

Make a Plan

How can you relate what you know to what you want to find out?

Find the unit cost of each juice.

Compare the unit costs.

You will solve the problem in Example 2.

Guided Practice **Use the information at the top of the page.**

1. Which formula can you use to find the unit costs of Juice A and Juice B? Explain your reasoning.

A. $\text{unit cost} = \dfrac{\text{cost of juice}}{\text{size of juice}}$ B. $\text{unit cost} = \dfrac{\text{size of juice}}{\text{cost of juice}}$

EXAMPLE 2 Solving and Looking Back

To solve the problem from Example 1, you need to carry out the plan and then check the answer.

Solve the Problem

To find the unit cost of each juice, use the formula

unit cost = ________ / ________ .

Juice A: unit cost = ________ / ________

= $ ____ / ____ fl oz

≈ $ ____ per fl oz

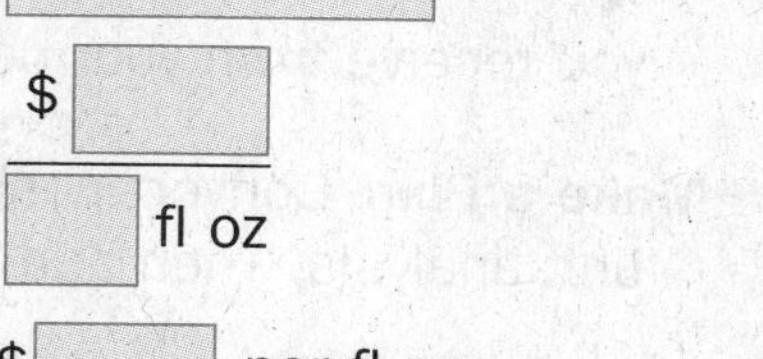

Juice B: unit cost = ________ / ________

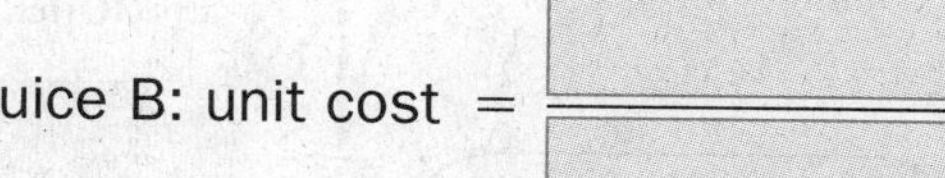

= $ ____ / ____ fl oz

≈ $ ____ per fl oz

The ≈ symbol means *approximately equal to.*

Compare the unit costs to find the better buy.

$ ____ per fl oz > $ ____ per fl oz

ANSWER ________ is the better buy.

Look Back

Does your answer make sense?

Notice that ________ has a greater unit cost than ________, making ________ more expensive than ________. So it makes sense that ________ is the better buy.

Problem Solving Plan

1. **Read and** ______ Read the problem carefully. Identify the question and any important information.
2. **Make a** ______ Decide on a problem solving strategy.
3. ______ Use the problem solving strategy to answer the question.
4. **Look** ______ Check that your ______ is reasonable.

EXAMPLE 3 **Using a Problem Solving Plan**

You have two pen pals. Your pen pal from Mexico sends you 55 pesos. Your pen pal from Japan sends you 725 yen. One U.S. dollar is equivalent to 10.13 pesos. One U.S. dollar is equivalent to 122.63 yen. Find the total amount, in U.S. dollars, you receive from your pen pals.

Solution

Read and Understand You receive ______ pesos and ______ yen. One dollar is equivalent to ______ pesos. One U.S. dollar is equivaler ______ yen. You are asked to find the total amount, in U.S. doll. you receive from your pen pals.

Use unit analysis when converting units of measure and when checking that your answer uses the correct units.

Make a Plan Convert pesos to U.S. dollars and yen to U.S. dollars u unit analysis. Then add to find the total amount.

Solve the Problem Because ______ pesos are equivalent to one U.S. dollar, you can multiply the number of pesos you receive by

$\frac{\quad}{\quad}$ to convert pesos to U.S. dollars.

$$\underline{\quad}\ \cancel{\text{pesos}} \times \frac{\quad}{\quad} \approx \$\underline{\quad}$$

Use the unit rate for yen to convert yen to U.S. dollars.

$$\underline{\quad}\ \cancel{\text{yen}} \times \frac{\quad}{\quad} \approx \$\underline{\quad}$$

ANSWER You receive \$______ + \$______ = \$______ from your pen

Words to Review

Give an example of the vocabulary word.

Bar Graph

Evaluate

Data

Order of Operations

Frequency table

Verbal model

Histogram

Variable

Numerical Expression

Variable Expression

Power

Solving an Equation

Exponent

Formula

Base

Perimeter

Equation

Area

Solution

Unit analysis

Review your notes and Chapter 1 by using the Chapter Review on pages 46–47 of your textbook.

Integers and Absolute Value

Goal: Study integers.

Vocabulary

Integers:

Negative integer:

Positive integer:

Absolute value:

Opposites:

EXAMPLE 1 Graphing and Ordering Integers

Temperature The table shows the low temperatures for five days. Which day had the lowest temperature?

Daily Low Temperatures	
Day	**Temperature (°C)**
Monday	8
Tuesday	−4
Wednesday	−1
Thursday	−8
Friday	6

Remember that negative integers lie to the *left* of 0 and positive integers lie *to the right* of 0.

Solution

To find which day had the lowest temperature, graph each integer on a number line.

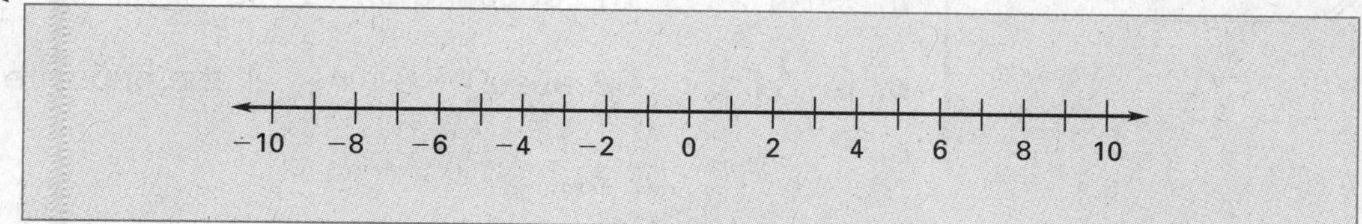

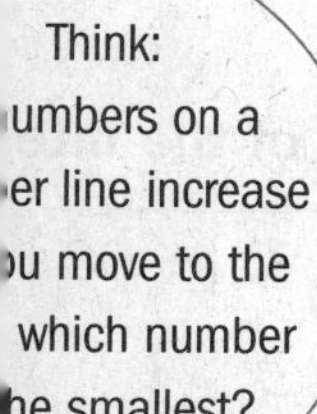

Think: numbers on a number line increase as you move to the right, which number is the smallest?

ANSWER ________ had the lowest temperature, ____ °C.

Guided Practice Order the integers from least to greatest.

1. 7, −5, 9, −10, −2

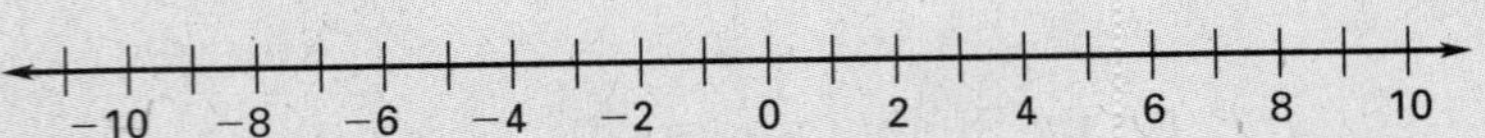

2. 0, −25, 45, −50, 30

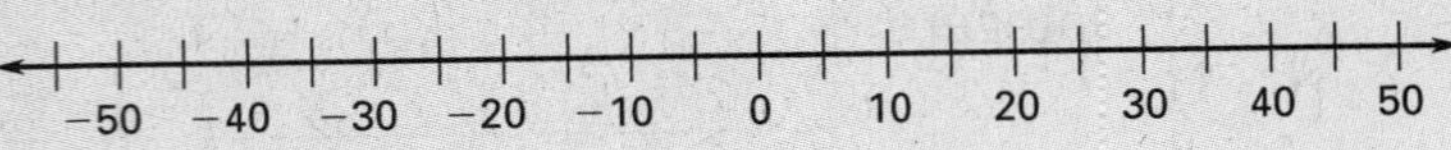

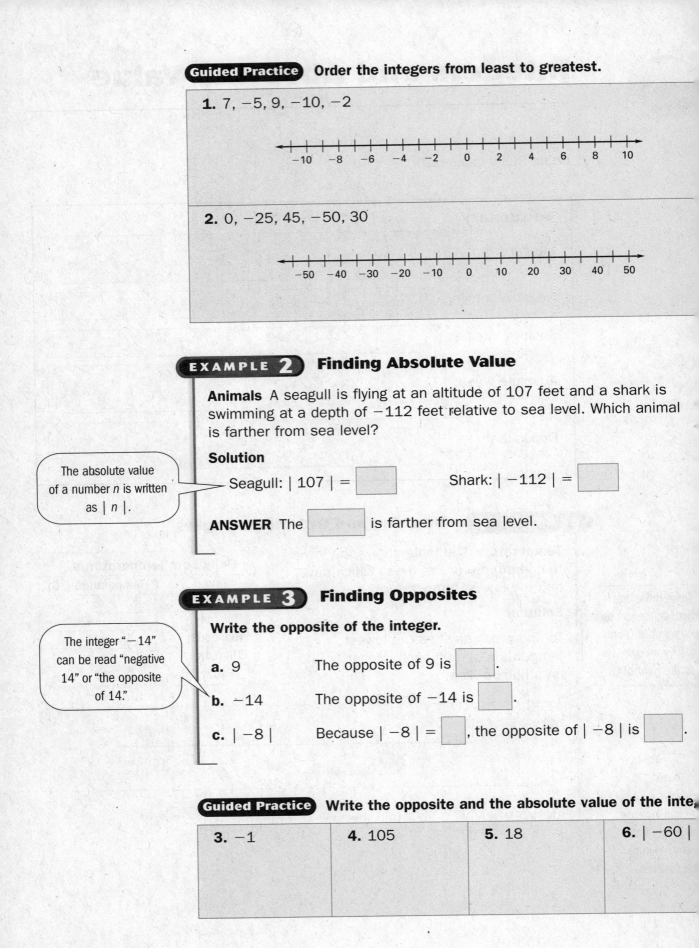

EXAMPLE 2 Finding Absolute Value

Animals A seagull is flying at an altitude of 107 feet and a shark is swimming at a depth of −112 feet relative to sea level. Which animal is farther from sea level?

Solution

The absolute value of a number *n* is written as | *n* |.

Seagull: | 107 | = ☐ Shark: | −112 | = ☐

ANSWER The ☐ is farther from sea level.

EXAMPLE 3 Finding Opposites

Write the opposite of the integer.

The integer "−14" can be read "negative 14" or "the opposite of 14."

a. 9 The opposite of 9 is ☐.

b. −14 The opposite of −14 is ☐.

c. | −8 | Because | −8 | = ☐, the opposite of | −8 | is ☐.

Guided Practice Write the opposite and the absolute value of the inte

3. −1	**4.** 105	**5.** 18	**6.** | −60 |

LESSON 2.2

Adding Integers

Goal: Add integers.

Vocabulary

Additive inverse: ______

EXAMPLE 1 **Adding Integers Using a Number Line**

Use a number line to find the sum.

a. $4 + (-9)$ **b.** $-7 + 8$ **c.** $-5 + (-2)$

Solution

...ember that when ...u add a positive ...ger, you move to ...ght. When you add ...gative integer, you ...ove to the left.

a. Start at 0, move ______ units to the ______. Then move ______ units to the ______.

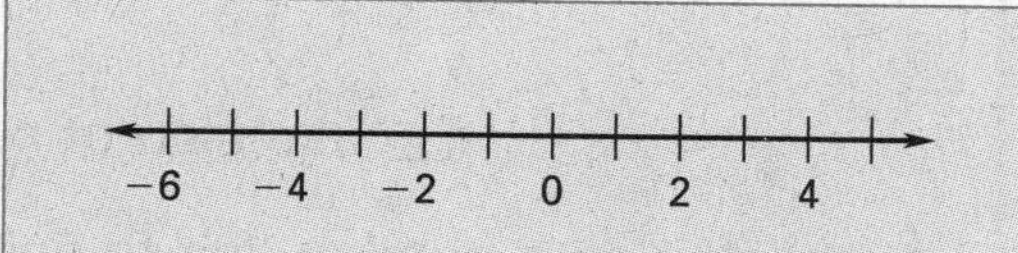

ANSWER The final position is ______. So, $4 + (-9) =$ ______.

b. Start at 0, move ______ units to the ______. Then move ______ units to the ______.

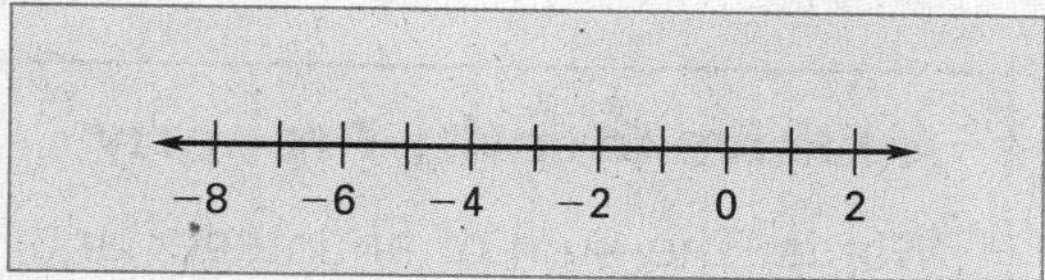

ANSWER The final position is ______. So, $-7 + 8 =$ ______.

c. Start at 0, move ______ units to the ______. Then move ______ units to the ______.

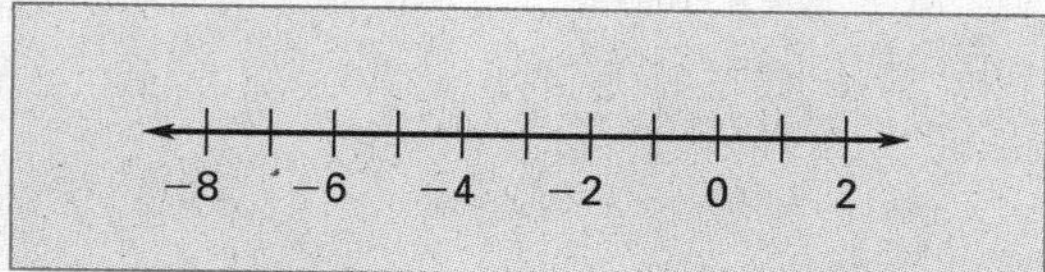

ANSWER The final position is ______. So, $-5 + (-2) =$ ______.

Guided Practice **Use the number line to find the sum.**

1. $11 + (-6)$

0 2 4 6 8 10 12

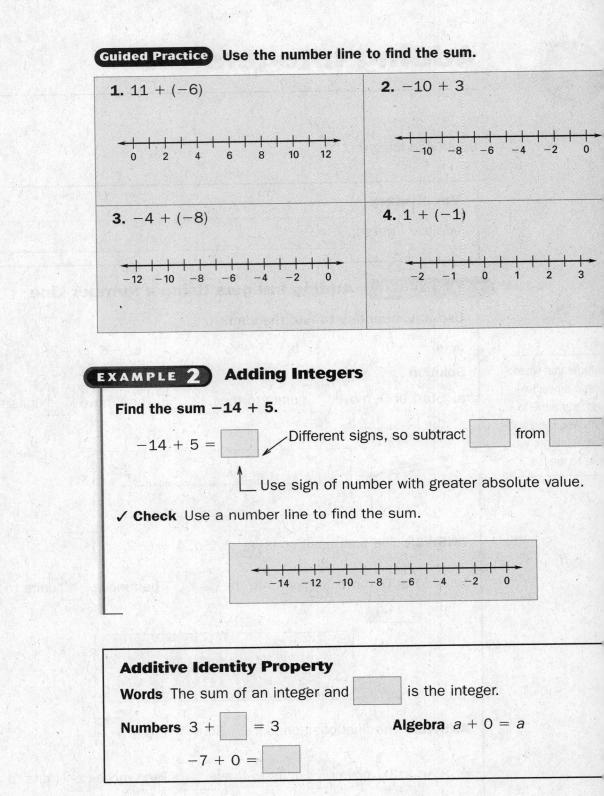

2. $-10 + 3$

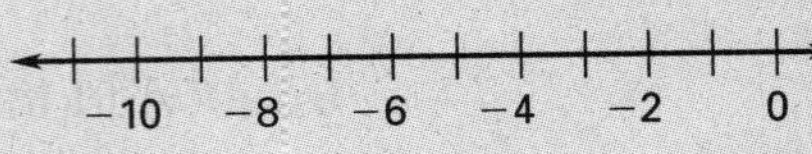

3. $-4 + (-8)$

−12 −10 −8 −6 −4 −2 0

4. $1 + (-1)$

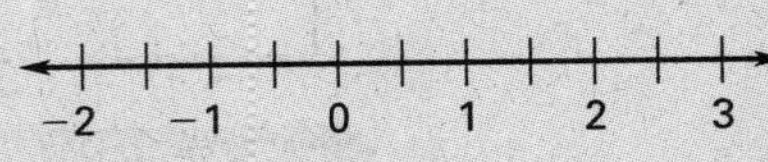

EXAMPLE 2 Adding Integers

Find the sum −14 + 5.

$-14 + 5 =$ ____ ← Different signs, so subtract ____ from ____

↑ Use sign of number with greater absolute value.

✓ **Check** Use a number line to find the sum.

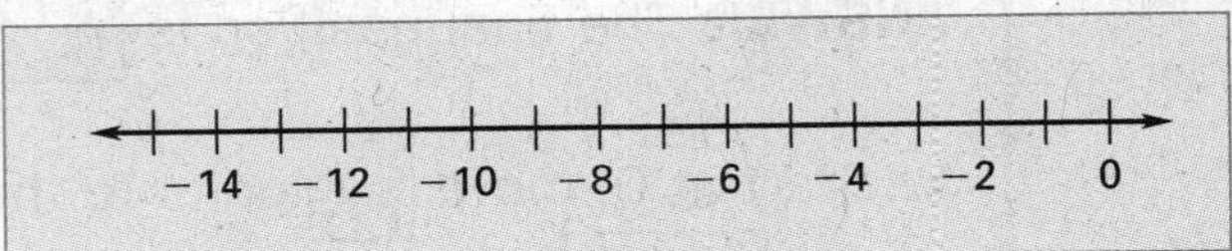

Additive Identity Property

Words The sum of an integer and ____ is the integer.

Numbers $3 +$ ____ $= 3$

$-7 + 0 =$ ____

Algebra $a + 0 = a$

EXAMPLE 3 Adding More Than Two Integers

a. Use the left to right rule of order of operations to find the sum.

$-56 + 0 + (-164) = -56 + (-164)$ ______

$= $ ______ Same sign, so sum has common sign.

b. Use the left to right rule of order of operations to find the sum.

$-39 + (-62) + 76 = $ ______ $+ 76$ Same sign, so sum has common sign.

$= $ ______ Use sign of number with greater absolute value.

EXAMPLE 4 Adding More Than Two Integers

Banking You start a bank account. The table shows the deposits and withdrawals of the account during the first month. How much money is in the account at the end of the month?

January 2	$675
January 9	−$80
January 19	−$25
January 24	$168
January 30	−$40

Solution

$675 + (-80) + (-25) + 168 + (-40) = $ ______ $+ (-25) + 168 + (-40)$

$= $ ______ $+ 168 + (-40)$

$= $ ______ $+ (-40)$

$= $ ______

Think: What operation ould I use to find much money is in account at the end of the month?

ANSWER You have ______ in the account at the end of the month.

Guided Practice **Find the sum.**

5. $-28 + (-12)$	**6.** $19 + 0 + (-51)$
7. $310 + 123 + (-68) + (-365)$	**8.** $-240 + (-516) + 193 + 113$

LESSON 2.3

Subtracting Integers

Goal: Subtract integers.

Subtracting Integers

Words To subtract an integer, ______ its opposite.

Numbers $2 - 9 =$ ______ $=$ ______

$4 - (-5) =$ ______ $=$ ______

Algebra $a - b = a + (-b)$

$a - (-b) = a + b$

EXAMPLE 1 Subtracting Integers

a. $-49 - (-7) =$ ______ ______.

$=$ ______ Add.

b. $-15 - 36 =$ ______ ______.

$=$ ______ Add.

Guided Practice **Find the difference.**

1. 18 − 57	2. −13 − 9	3. 34 − (−25)	4. −62 − (−1

EXAMPLE 2 Evaluating a Variable Expression

Evaluate $x - 33 - y$ when $x = 19$ and $y = -41$.

$x - 33 - y =$ ▭ $- 33 -$ (▭) Substitute ▭ for x and ▭ for y.

$=$ ▭ $+$ ▭ $-$ (▭) Add the opposite of ▭.

$=$ ▭ $-$ (▭) Add ▭ and ▭.

$=$ ▭ $+$ ▭ Add the opposite of ▭.

$=$ ▭ Add.

EXAMPLE 3 Standardized Test Practice

Mining What is the vertical height of the mineshaft?

Ⓐ −273 feet Ⓑ −163 feet

Ⓒ 163 feet Ⓓ 273 feet

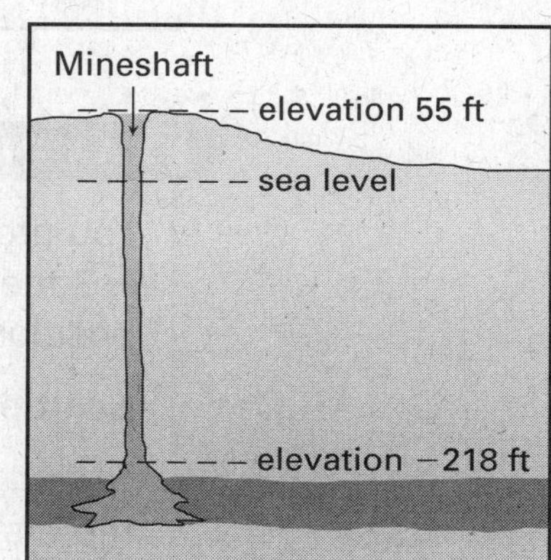

Solution

The vertical height is the difference of the highest and lowest elevations.

Vertical height $= 55 -$ (▭) Write subtraction statement.

$= 55$ ▭ ▭.

$=$ ▭ Add.

ANSWER The vertical height of the mineshaft is ▭. The correct answer is ▭. Ⓐ Ⓑ Ⓒ Ⓓ

Multiplying Integers

Goal: Multiply integers.

Multiplying Integers

Words	Numbers
The product of two integers with the same sign is ______.	$3 \cdot 5 =$ ______ $-4 \cdot (-6) =$ ______
The product of two integers with different signs is ______.	$3 \cdot (-5) =$ ______ $-4 \cdot 6 =$ ______

EXAMPLE 1 **Multiplying Integers**

You drop a rock into the ocean. The rock's depth is changing by −3 feet per second. If you dropped the rock at sea level, what is the position of the rock after 30 seconds?

Solution

To find the position of the rock relative to sea level after 30 seconds, use the distance formula $d = rt$.

Think: Do the integers have the same sign or different signs?

$d = rt$ Write the distance formula.

$d = ($ ______ $)($ ______ $)$ Substitute ______ for r and ______ for t.

$d =$ ______ Different signs, so product is ______.

ANSWER The position of the rock relative to sea level is ______ feet.

Guided Practice **Use the information above.**

1. Find the position of the rock relative to sea level after 45 seconds.

Multiplication Properties

Multiplication Property of Zero

Words The product of a number and 0 is ____.

Numbers $-2 \cdot 0 =$ ____ **Algebra** For any value of a, $a \cdot 0 = 0$.

Identity Property of Multiplication

Words The product of a number and ____ is the integer.

Numbers $7($ ____ $) = 7$ **Algebra** For any value of a, $a(1) = a$.

EXAMPLE 2 Multiplying Two or More Integers

mber that when
ultiply a number
1, the product is
pposite of the
ginal number.

a. $-1(10) =$ ____ Different signs, so product is ____.

b. $-9(-4) =$ ____ Same sign, so product is ____.

c. $-12(0) =$ ____ Product of an integer and 0 is ____.

d. $5(-11)(1) =$ ____ (1) Multiply from left to right.

$=$ ____ Product of an integer and 1 is ____.

n you multiply
than two positive
gative integers:
ere is an *even*
ber of negative
ors then the
uct is *positive*.
ere is an *odd*
ber of negative
ors then the
uct is *negative*.

EXAMPLE 3 Evaluating an Expression with Integers

Evaluate $-4b - a^2$ when $a = -8$ and $b = -12$.

$-4b - a^2 = -4($ ____ $) - ($ ____ $)^2$ Substitute ____ for b and ____ for a.

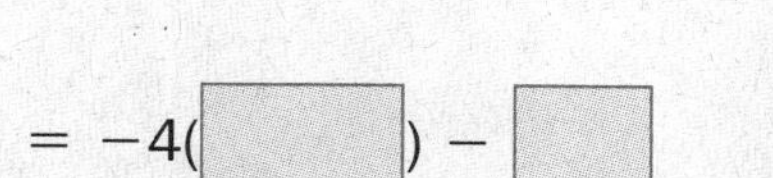

$= -4($ ____ $) -$ ____ Evaluate the power.

$=$ ____ $-$ ____ Multiply.

$=$ ____ $+ ($ ____ $)$ Add the opposite of ____.

$=$ ____ Add.

Guided Practice Find the product.

2. $-1(5)$	3. $8(0)$	4. $-7(-12)$	5. $-2(-10)$

Evaluate the expression when $a = 4$, $b = -5$, and $c = -6$.

6. $ac - b$	7. $ac + b$	8. $a^2 + bc$	9. $ab - c^2$

Dividing Integers

Goal: Divide integers.

Vocabulary

Mean: ______

Dividing Integers

Words	Numbers	
The quotient of two integers with the same sign is ______.	$\frac{20}{4} = \square$	$\frac{-20}{-4} = \square$
The quotient of two integers with different signs is ______.	$\frac{20}{-4} = \square$	$\frac{-20}{4} = \square$
The quotient of zero and any nonzero integer is ______.	$\frac{0}{20} = \square$	$\frac{0}{-20} = \square$

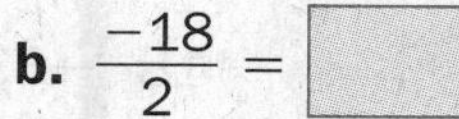

EXAMPLE 1 **Dividing Integers**

a. $\frac{-42}{-7} = \square$ Same sign, so quotient is ______.

b. $\frac{-18}{2} = \square$ Different signs, so quotient is ______.

c. $\frac{32}{-8} = \square$ Different signs, so quotient is ______.

TCH OUT!
:annot divide a
oer by 0. The
ent of any
oer divided by 0
defined.

EXAMPLE 2 Finding a Mean

Golf You golf four rounds of 18 holes. The table shows your score for each round with respect to par. What is the mean of your scores for the four rounds?

Round	Score
1	−6
2	−1
3	2
4	−7

Solution

To find the mean of your scores, first find the sum of the scores.

$-6 + (-1) + 2 + (-7) =$ ______

Then, divide the sum by the number of scores.

$\frac{-12}{\_\_\_} =$ ______

ANSWER The mean of your scores is .

Guided Practice **Find the quotient.**

1. $\frac{-48}{12}$	2. $\frac{-15}{-5}$	3. $\frac{0}{-9}$	4. $\frac{66}{-11}$

Find the mean of the data.

5. −8, 34, −72, −50, −29	6. −1, −5, −16, 21, −4, −18, −33
7. 45, −26, 12, −18, −23	8. 45, −55, −81, −13, −9, 34, −12

EXAMPLE 3 Evaluating Expressions

Evaluate the expression when $a = -30$, $b = 5$, and $c = -2$.

a. $\frac{a}{b}$

b. $\frac{a}{bc}$

Solution

a. $\frac{a}{b} =$ ______ Substitute ______ for a and ______ for b.

$=$ ______ Different signs, so quotient is ______.

b. $\frac{a}{bc} =$ ______ Substitute ______ for a, ______ for b, and ______ for c.

$=$ ______ Multiply.

$=$ ______ Same sign, so quotient is ______.

LESSON 2.6

Number Properties

Goal: Use properties to evaluate expressions.

The Commutative Property

	Addition	Multiplication
Words	You can add numbers of a sum in any order.	You can multiply factors of a product in any order.
Numbers	$4 + (-9) = \square + \square$	$3(-7) = \square(\square)$
Algebra	$a + b = b + a$	$ab = ba$

EXAMPLE 1 **Using the Commutative Property**

Babysitting You have a summer babysitting job. You baby-sit 5 days a w
You work 9 hours each day earning $4 per hour. What is your weekly pay

Solution

You can use a verbal model to find your weekly pay.

Weekly pay = Hourly rate • Hours per day • Number of days

$= 4 \cdot \square \cdot \square$ Substitute known values.

$= 4 \cdot \square \cdot \square$ Commutative property of multiplica

$= \square \cdot \square$ Multiply.

$= \square$ Multiply.

The unit for the result is $\square$. $\frac{\text{dollars}}{\cancel{\text{hour}}} \cdot \frac{\cancel{\text{hours}}}{\cancel{\text{day}}} \cdot \cancel{\text{days}} = \square$

ANSWER Your weekly pay is $\square$.

EXAMPLE 2 Using the Commutative Property

When deciding [what] numbers to add or [multi]ply first, look for pairs [who]se sum or product [en]ds in zero, because [m]ultiples of 10 are [e]asier to work with.

$-63 + 38 - 17 = -63 + 38 \; \square \; (\square)$ Change subtraction to addition.

$= -63 + (\square) + \square$ Commutative property of addition

$= \square + \square$ Add.

$= \square$ Add.

Guided Practice **Use the commutative property to evaluate.**

1. $5 \cdot (-7) \cdot 4$	**2.** $56 + (-115) - (-64)$	**3.** $91 - 32 - 71$

The Associative Property

	Addition	Multiplication
Words	Changing the grouping of numbers will not change the sum.	Changing the grouping of factors will not change the product.
Numbers	$(1 + 3) + 6 = 1 + (\square + \square)$	$(8 \cdot 2) \cdot 4 = 8 \cdot (\square \cdot \square)$
Algebra	$(a + b) + c = a + (b + c)$	$(ab)c = a(bc)$

EXAMPLE 3 Using the Associative Property

$\frac{-3}{8} + \left(\frac{-5}{8} + 10\right) = \square + 10$ Associative property of addition

$= \square + 10$ Add fractions.

$= \square + 10$ Rewrite fraction.

$= \square$ Add.

EXAMPLE 4 Using the Associative Property

Commute means change locations. You can use the *commutative properties* to change the order of numbers. *Associate* means group together. You can use the *associative properties* to group numbers differently.

$6 \cdot (9 \cdot 5) = 6 \cdot (\_\_\_ \cdot \_\_\_)$ ______ prop. of multiplication

$= \_\_\_ \cdot 9$ ______ prop. of multiplication

$= \_\_\_ \cdot 9$ Multiply inside grouping symbols.

$= \_\_\_$ Multiply.

Guided Practice **Evaluate the expression using mental math.**

4. $15 + (-46 + 25)$	**5.** $37 + (-82 - 37)$	**6.** $-5(9 \cdot 40)$
7. $-3\left(-\frac{2}{3} \cdot 14\right)$	**8.** $\frac{2}{5} + \left(10 + \frac{3}{5}\right)$	**9.** $[-74 \cdot (-26)] \cdot$

The Distributive Property

Goal: Use the distributive property.

Vocabulary

Terms:

Like terms:

Coefficient:

Constant term:

EXAMPLE 1 **Finding a Combined Area**

Think: What formula do I need to find the area?

Gardening You are planting a vegetable garden and a flower garden. The diagram shows the dimensions of the two adjacent, rectangular gardens. How can you find the total area of the two gardens?

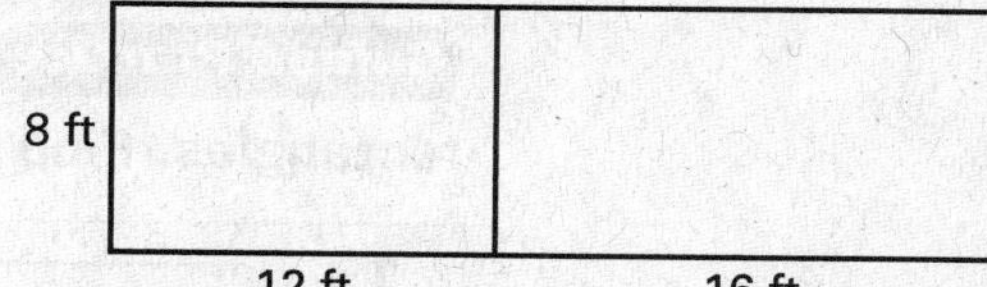

Solution

Method 1 Find the area of each garden, then find the total area.

Area = ______

= ______ + ______

= ______ square feet

Method 2 Find the total length, then multiply by the common width.

Area = ______(______)

= ______(______)

= ______ square feet

ANSWER The total area of the two gardens is ______ square feet.

The Distributive Property

Algebra $a(b + c) = ab + ac$ **Numbers** $9(2 + 6) =$ ______

$a(b - c) = ab - ac$ $8(7 - 1) =$ ______

EXAMPLE 2 Using the Distributive Property

a. $-4(a + 13) =$ ______ Distributive property

$=$ ______ $+$ ______ Multiply.

b. $5[3 - 11 + (-7)] =$ ______ Distributive property

$=$ ______ $-$ ______ $+ ($ ______ $)$ Multiply.

$= 15 + ($ ______ $) + ($ ______ $)$ Add the opposite of

$=$ ______ Add from left to righ

Guided Practice **Write two expressions for the total area of the two rectangles. Find the total area.**

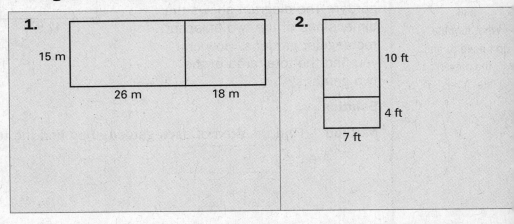

1.

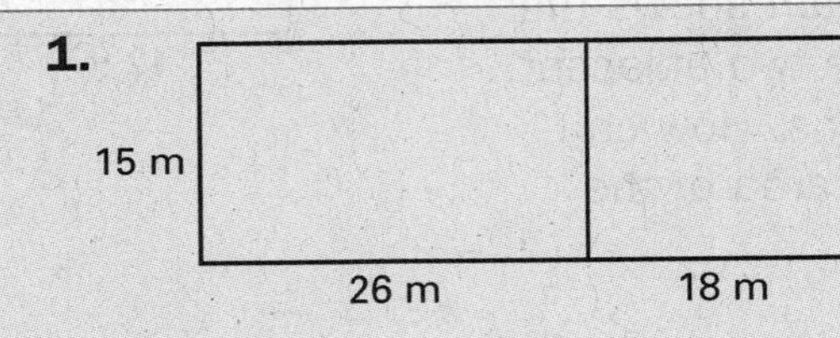

2.

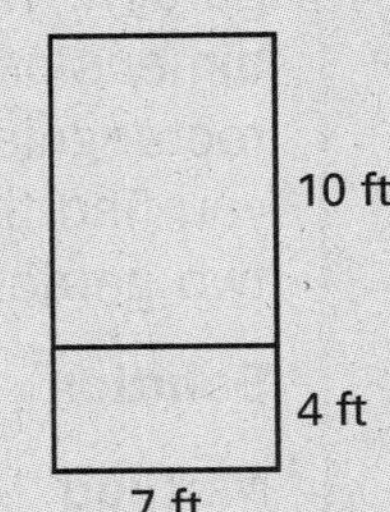

Use the distributive property to evaluate or simplify the expression.

3. $-3(8 + 16)$	**4.** $-5(-2 - 19)$	**5.** $2(x - 7)$	**6.** $-6(t +$

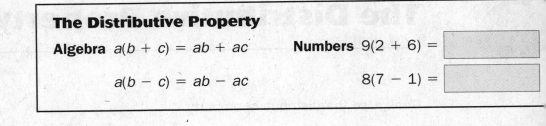

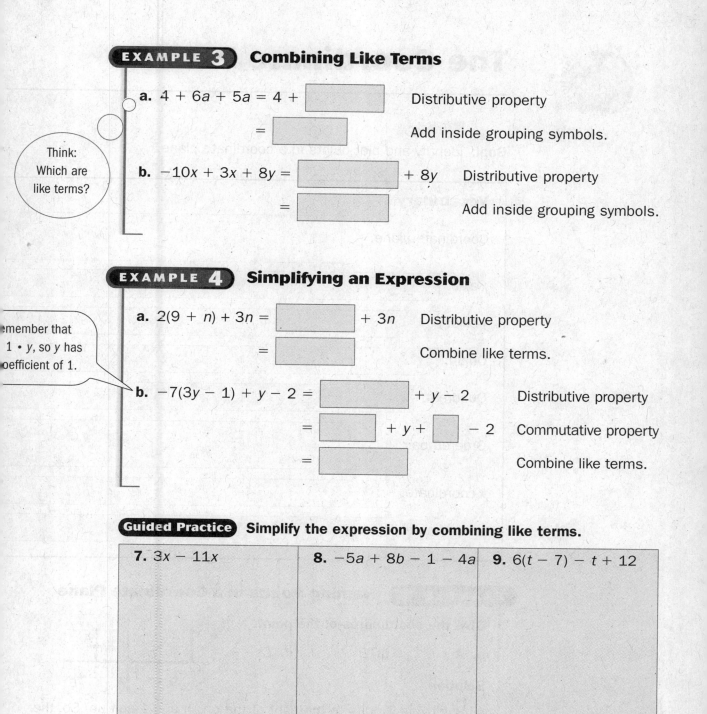

EXAMPLE 3 Combining Like Terms

Think: Which are like terms?

a. $4 + 6a + 5a = 4 +$ ______ Distributive property

$=$ ______ Add inside grouping symbols.

b. $-10x + 3x + 8y =$ ______ $+ 8y$ Distributive property

$=$ ______ Add inside grouping symbols.

EXAMPLE 4 Simplifying an Expression

emember that 1 • *y*, so *y* has oefficient of 1.

a. $2(9 + n) + 3n =$ ______ $+ 3n$ Distributive property

$=$ ______ Combine like terms.

b. $-7(3y - 1) + y - 2 =$ ______ $+ y - 2$ Distributive property

$=$ ______ $+ y +$ ______ $- 2$ Commutative property

$=$ ______ Combine like terms.

Guided Practice **Simplify the expression by combining like terms.**

7. $3x - 11x$	8. $-5a + 8b - 1 - 4a$	9. $6(t - 7) - t + 12$

The Coordinate Plane

Goal: Identify and plot points in a coordinate plane.

Vocabulary

Coordinate plane: ___

x-axis: ___

y-axis: ___

Origin: ___

Quadrant: ___

Ordered pair: ___

x-coordinate: ___

y-coordinate: ___

EXAMPLE 1 Naming Points in a Coordinate Plane

Give the coordinates of the point.

a. *A* **b.** *B* **c.** *C*

Solution

a. Point *A* is 2 units to the right of the origin and 1 unit up. So, the *x*-coordinate is ___ and the *y*-coordinate is ___. The point is *A*(___, ___).

b. Point *B* is ___ units to the ___ of the origin and ___ units ___. Sc

x-coordinate is -4 and the *y*-coordinate is ___. The point is *B*(___,

c. Point *C* is 1 unit ___ from the origin. So, the ___-coordinate is ___

and the ___-coordinate is ___. The point is *C*(___, ___).

Guided Practice **Use the coordinate plane from Example 1 to give the coordinates of the point.**

1. *D*	**2.** *E*	**3.** *F*

EXAMPLE 2 Graphing Points in a Coordinate Plane

Plot the point and describe its location.

a. $A(1, -1)$ **b.** $B(-2, 4)$ **c.** $C(0, 3)$

Solution

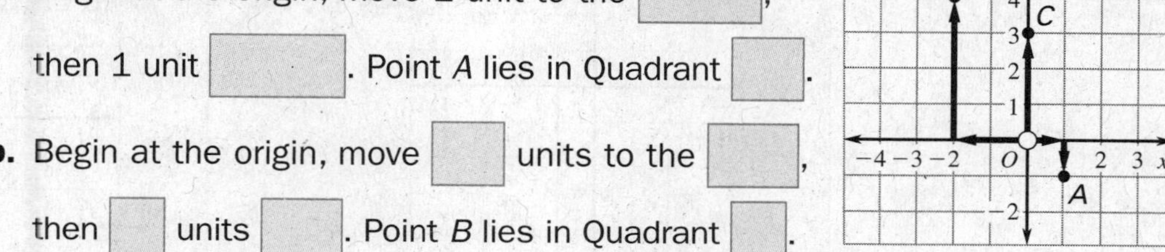

a. Begin at the origin, move 1 unit to the ______, then 1 unit ______. Point *A* lies in Quadrant ______.

b. Begin at the origin, move ______ units to the ______, then ______ units ______. Point *B* lies in Quadrant ______.

c. Begin at the origin, move ______ units ______. Point *C* lies on the ______.

Remember that
ints on the *x*-axis
-axis do not lie in
any quadrant.

EXAMPLE 3 Solve a Multi-Step Problem

Identify the figure and find its perimeter.

Solution

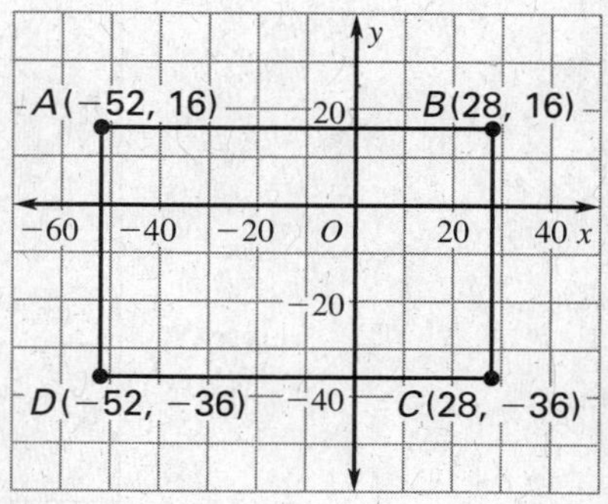

1. Points *A*, *B*, *C*, and *D* form a ______.
2. Find the *horizontal* distance from *A* to *B* to find the length *l*.

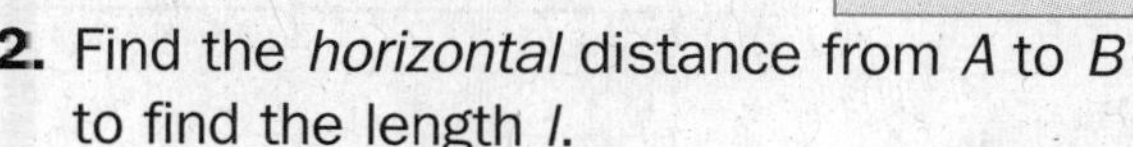

$l = |$ *x*-coordinate of *A* − *x*-coordinate of *B* $|$

$= |$ ______ − ______ $| = |$ ______ $| =$ ______

3. Find the *vertical* distance from *A* to *D* to find the width *w*.

$w = |$ *y*-coordinate of *A* − *y*-coordinate of *D* $|$

$= |$ ______ − (______) $| = |$ ______ $| =$ ______

4. Perimeter $= 2l + 2w = 2($ ______ $) + 2($ ______ $) =$ ______

ANSWER The rectangle has a perimeter of ______ units.

Guided Practice **Plot the point and describe its location.**

4. $W(1, -3)$

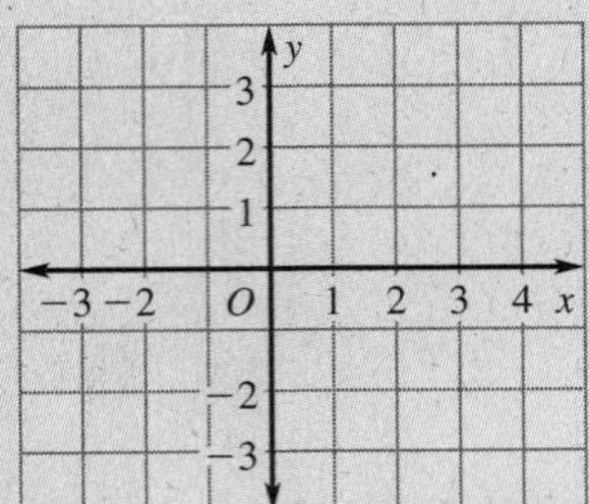

5. $X(-2, -1)$

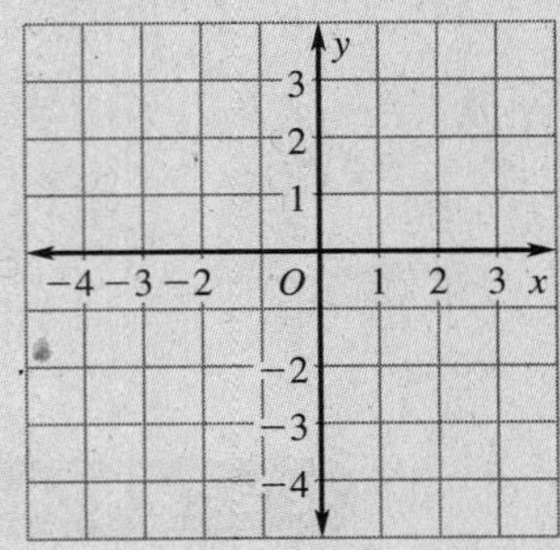

6. $Y(0, -3)$

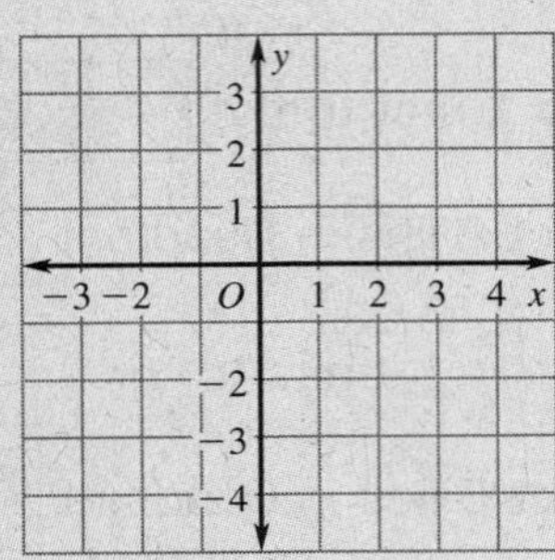

7. $Z(-4, 3)$

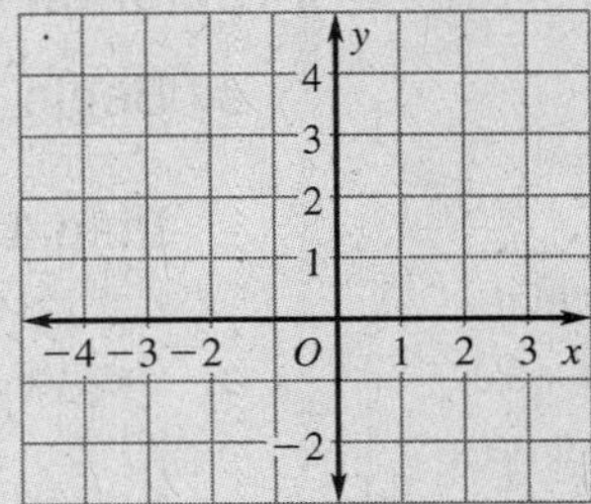

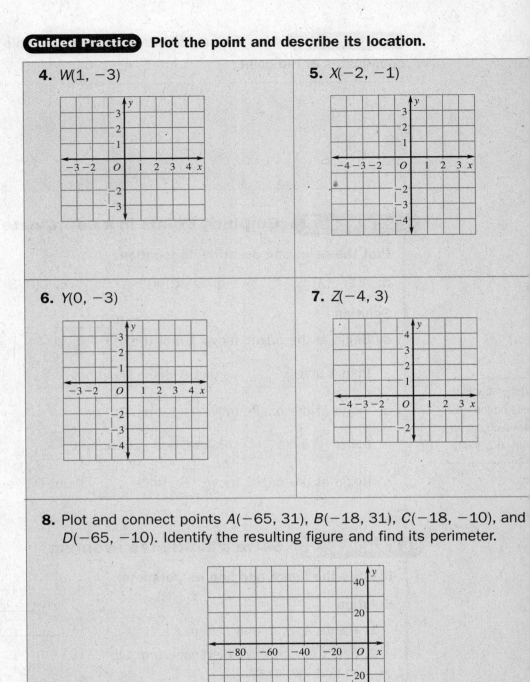

8. Plot and connect points $A(-65, 31)$, $B(-18, 31)$, $C(-18, -10)$, and $D(-65, -10)$. Identify the resulting figure and find its perimeter.

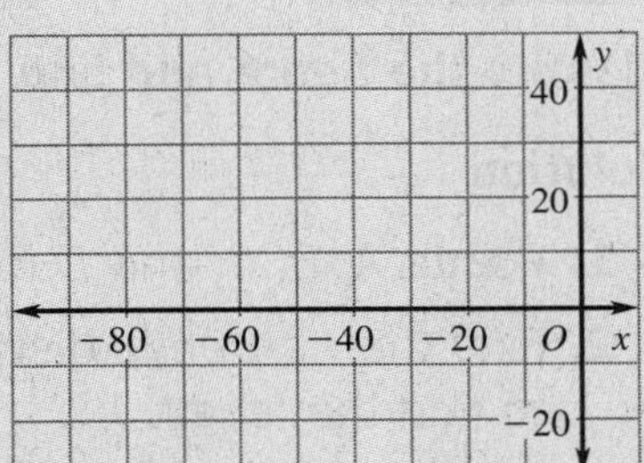

Words to Review

Give an example of the vocabulary word.

Integers

Mean

Negative integer

Terms

Positive integer

Like terms

Absolute value

Coefficient

Opposites

Additive inverse

Constant term

Distributive property

Quadrant

Coordinate plane

Ordered pair

x-axis

x-coordinate

y-axis

y-coordinate

Origin

Review your notes and Chapter 2 by using the Chapter Review on pages 102–10 your textbook.

Solving Equations Using Addition or Subtraction

Goal: Solve equations using addition or subtraction.

Vocabulary

Equivalent equations: ______

Inverse operation: ______

Subtraction Property of Equality

Words Subtracting the same number from each side of an equation produces an equivalent equation.

Numbers If $x + 9 = 12$, then $x + 9 - 9 = 12 - \square$.

Algebra If $x + a = b$, then $x + a - a = \square - a$.

EXAMPLE 1 **Solving an Equation Using Subtraction**

$x + 7$	$=$	-13	Original equation
$\square$	$=$	$\square$	______ from each side to undo addition.
x	$=$	$\square$	Simplify. x is by itself.

ANSWER The solution is ______.

Addition Property of Equality

Words Adding the same number to each side of an equation produces an equivalent equation.

Numbers If $x - 6 = 1$, then $x - 6 + 6 = 1 + \square$.

Algebra If $a = b$, then $a + \square = b + c$.

EXAMPLE 2 Solving an Equation Using Addition

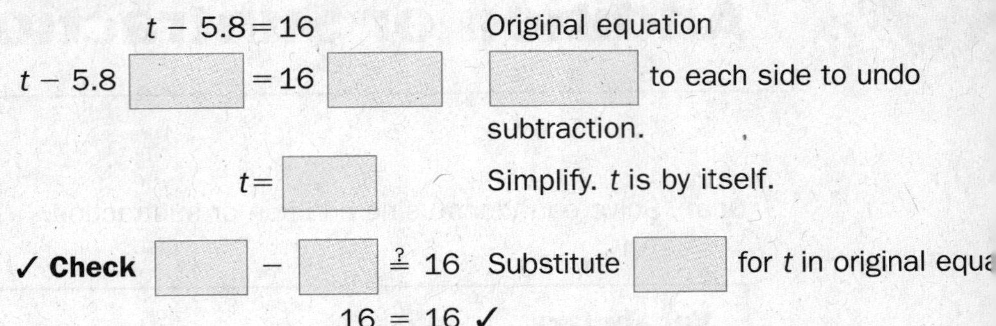

$t - 5.8 = 16$	Original equation
$t - 5.8$ ______ $= 16$ ______	______ to each side to undo subtraction.
$t =$ ______	Simplify. t is by itself.
✓ **Check** ______ − ______ $\stackrel{?}{=}$ 16	Substitute ______ for t in original equa
$16 = 16$ ✓	

WATCH OUT!
You can add or subtract horizontally or vertically to solve equations, but remember that when solving, you must perform the same operation on *each* side.

Guided Practice Solve the equation. Check your solution.

1. $y + 4 = 13$	**2.** $-17 = 7 + t$	**3.** $n - 11 = 14$	**4.** $-2 = s$

EXAMPLE 3 Using a Model

Kites You are flying a kite. The total length of the kite's string is 275 fe So far you have let out 153 feet of string. How much string do you have

Solution

Let s represent the length of string left. Write a verbal model.

______ = ______ + Length of string already let out

______ = ______ + 153 Write an algebraic model.

______ − ______ = ______ + 153 − ______ Subtract ______ from each

______ = ______ Simplify. s is by itself.

ANSWER You have ______ feet of string left.

Think: What part of the verbal model is missing? What values correspond to each part of the verbal model?

Solving Equations Using Multiplication or Division

Goal: Solve equations using multiplication or division.

Multiplication Property of Equality

Words Multiplying each side of an equation by the same nonzero number produces an equivalent equation.

Numbers If $\frac{x}{4} = 6$, then $\frac{x}{4} \cdot 4 = \square \cdot 4$.

Algebra If $a = b$ and $c \neq 0$, then $ac = \square$.

EXAMPLE 1 Solving an Equation Using Multiplication

$\frac{t}{8} = 6$ Original equation

$\frac{t}{8} \cdot \square = 6 \cdot \square$ Multiply each side by $\square$ to undo division.

$t = \square$ Simplify. t is by itself.

✓ **Check** $\frac{\square}{8} = 6$ ✓ Substitute $\square$ for t in original equation.

member to check your answer by bstituting it in the riginal equation.

Division Property of Equality

Words Dividing each side of an equation by the same nonzero number produces an equivalent equation.

Numbers If $3x = 21$, then $\frac{3x}{3} = \frac{21}{\square}$.

Algebra If $a = b$ and $c \neq 0$, then $\frac{a}{c} = \square$.

EXAMPLE 2 Solving an Equation Using Division

WATCH OUT!
When solving an equation, remember to perform the same operation on each side.

$-3.4y = 17$ Original equation

$\frac{-3.4y}{\square} = \frac{17}{\square}$ Divide each side by $\square$.

$y = \square$ Simplify. y is by itself.

Guided Practice **Solve the equation. Check your solution.**

1. $14 = \frac{x}{8}$	2. $\frac{x}{4.5} = 12$	3. $56 = -3.5x$	4. $8x = 72$

EXAMPLE 3 Writing and Solving an Equation

Pizza Three people equally share the cost of a pizza. The total cost of the pizza is \$14.67. Write and solve an equation to find each person's cost.

Think:
What part of the verbal model is missing? What values correspond to each part of the verbal model?

Solution

Let c represent each person's cost.

$\square$ = Number of people • $\square$

$\square = 3\square$ Write an algebraic model.

$\square = \square$ Divide each side by $\square$.

$\square = \square$ Simplify.

ANSWER Each person's cost is $\square$.

Solving Two-Step Equations

Goal: Solve two-step equations.

EXAMPLE 1 Solving a Real-World Problem

Book Club You pay \$15 to join a book club. You pay \$6 for each book. Your cost for joining and buying some books is \$51. How many books did you buy?

Solution

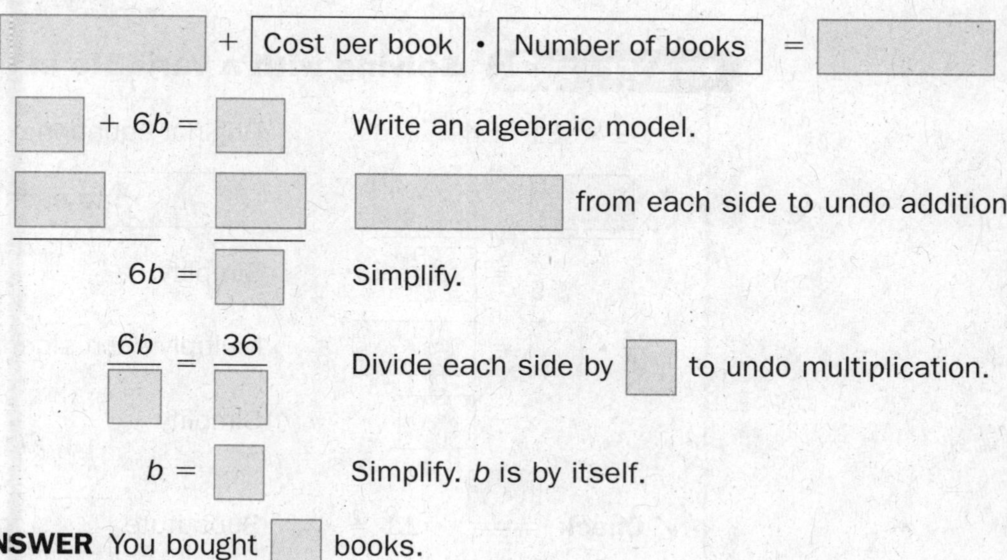

____ + Cost per book • Number of books = ____

____ $+ 6b =$ ____ Write an algebraic model.

____ ____ ____ from each side to undo addition.

$6b =$ ____ Simplify.

$\frac{6b}{\_\_} = \frac{36}{\_\_}$ Divide each side by ____ to undo multiplication.

$b =$ ____ Simplify. b is by itself.

ANSWER You bought ____ books.

Guided Practice **Use the equation in Example 1.**

1. What is the cost to join the club and buy 5 books?

2. Suppose the cost to join and buy books is \$63. How does this change the equation you solve to find the number of books?

Solving a Two-Step Equation

Some equations require two inverse operations to solve.

$3x + 4 = 10$	Original equation.
$3x + 4 \; \square = 10 \; \square$	Undo addition or subtraction.
$3x = \square$	Simplify.
$\frac{3x}{\square} = \frac{6}{\square}$	Undo multiplication or division.
$x = \square$	Simplify.

EXAMPLE 2 Solving with a Variable in the Numerator

$\frac{x}{5} - 11 = 4$	Original equation
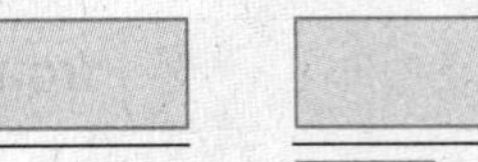	$\square$ to each side to undo subtract
$\frac{x}{5} = \square$	Simplify.
$\frac{x}{5} \cdot \square = \square$	Multiply each side by $\square$ to undo divisio
$x = \square$	Simplify.
✓ **Check** 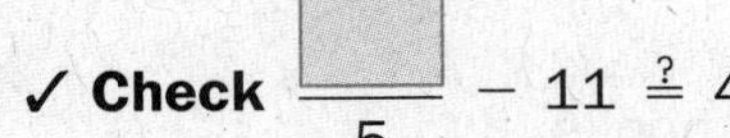 $\frac{\square}{5} - 11 \stackrel{?}{=} 4$	Substitute 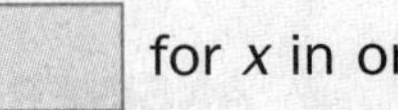 for x in original equatior
$\square - 11 = 4$ ✓	

Remember that you can solve an equation vertically or horizontally.

EXAMPLE 3 **Solving with a Negative Coefficient**

$6 = 18 - 4x$	Original equation
$6 - \square = 18 - 4x - \square$	Subtract $\square$ from each side to undo addition.
$\square = -4x$	Simplify.
$\dfrac{\square}{\square} = \dfrac{-4x}{\square}$	Divide each side by $\square$ to undo multiplication.
$\square = x$	Simplify.

Guided Practice **Solve the equation. Check your answer.**

3. $17 = 10 + \frac{a}{2}$	**4.** $\frac{y}{3} - 1 = 9$	**5.** $-8x + 5 = 29$	**6.** $2 = 11 - t$

Writing Two-Step Equations

Goal: Solve problems by writing two-step equations.

EXAMPLE 1 Standardized Test Practice

Sightseeing Your family paid $180 to rent a plane to tour the Grand Car
The tour company charged $35 per hour, plus a fuel fee of $75. Which equation can be used to find h, the number of hours your family rented the plane?

(A) $180 + 75 = h$ (B) $180 = h + 35$

(C) $180 + 75 = 35h$ (D) $180 = 35h + 75$

Solution

Write and solve a two-step equation to find h, the number of hours your family rented the plane. Begin by writing a verbal model.

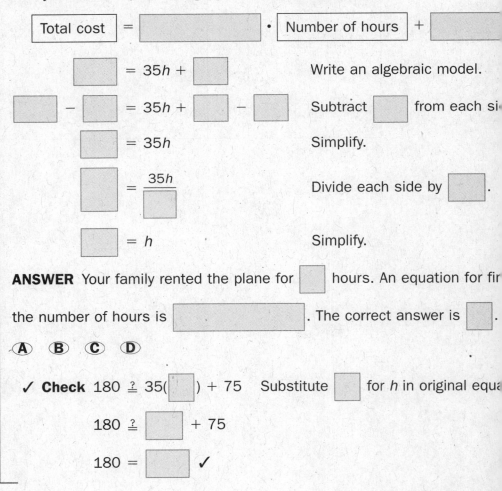

Total cost = ______ • Number of hours + ______

______ = 35h + ______ Write an algebraic model.

______ − ______ = 35h + ______ − ______ Subtract ______ from each si

______ = 35h Simplify.

$\frac{\text{\_\_\_\_\_\_}}{\text{\_\_\_\_\_\_}} = \frac{35h}{\text{\_\_\_\_\_\_}}$ Divide each side by ______.

______ = h Simplify.

ANSWER Your family rented the plane for ______ hours. An equation for fir the number of hours is ______. The correct answer is ______.

(A) (B) (C) (D)

✓ **Check** $180 \stackrel{?}{=} 35($ ______ $) + 75$ Substitute ______ for h in original equa

$180 \stackrel{?}{=}$ ______ $+ 75$

$180 =$ ______ ✓

Guided Practice **Write a two-step equation to solve the problem.**

1. Your family paid $224 to rent a boat to tour Chesapeake Bay. The marina charged $26 per hour plus a fuel fee of $42. For how many hours did your family rent the boat?

EXAMPLE 2 Writing and Solving a Two-Step Equation

The difference of 5 times a number and −12 is 2. What is the number?

Solution

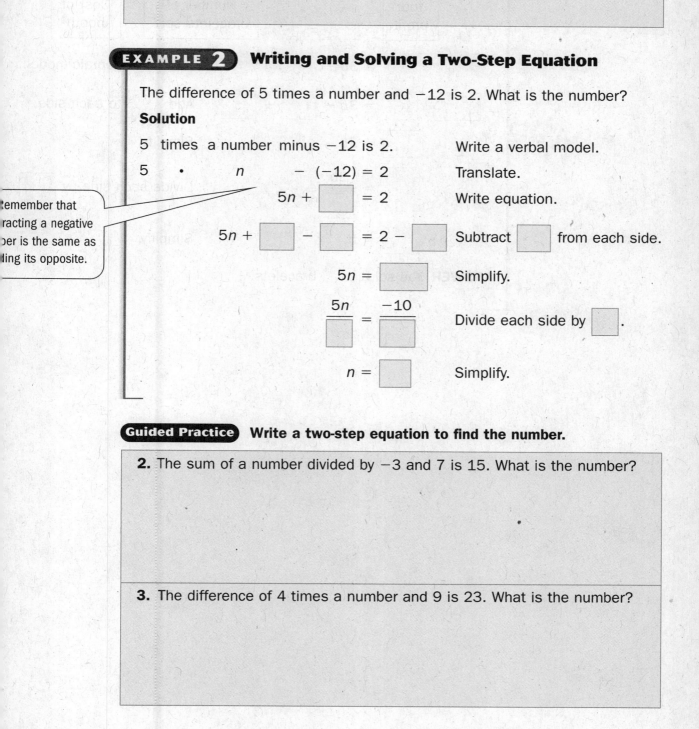

5 times a number minus −12 is 2.	Write a verbal model.
$5 \cdot n - (-12) = 2$	Translate.
$5n + \square = 2$	Write equation.
$5n + \square - \square = 2 - \square$	Subtract $\square$ from each side.
$5n = \square$	Simplify.
$\frac{5n}{\square} = \frac{-10}{\square}$	Divide each side by $\square$.
$n = \square$	Simplify.

emember that racting a negative ber is the same as ling its opposite.

Guided Practice **Write a two-step equation to find the number.**

2. The sum of a number divided by −3 and 7 is 15. What is the number?

3. The difference of 4 times a number and 9 is 23. What is the number?

EXAMPLE 3 Writing and Solving a Two-Step Equation

Fairs At a one-day fair, you sold bracelets. You made \$79. It cost \$17 to rent a booth. You sold the bracelets for \$3 each. How many bracelets did you sell?

Solution

Let b be the number of bracelets you sell.

Your profit	=	______	•	Number of bracelets sold	–	Cost of booth

$\_\_\_ = 3b - \_\_\_$ Write an algebraic model.

$\_\_\_ + \_\_\_ = 3b - \_\_\_ + \_\_\_$ Add ___ to each side.

$\_\_\_ = 3b$ Simplify.

$\_\_\_ = \frac{3b}{\_\_\_}$ Divide each side by ___.

$\_\_\_ = b$ Simplify.

ANSWER You sold ___ bracelets.

Applying Geometric Formulas

Goal: Use formulas for perimeter and area.

Vocabulary

Base: ______

Height: ______

Area and Perimeter of a Triangle

Words The ______ of a triangle is one half the product of its base b and height h.

The ______ of a triangle is the sum of the lengths of all three sides a, b, and c.

Algebra $A = \frac{1}{2}b$ ______

$P = a +$ ______ $+ c$

Diagram

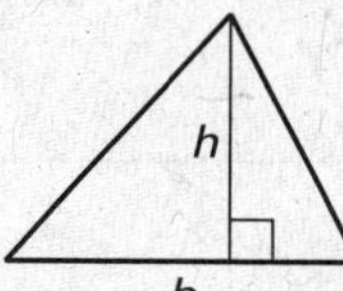

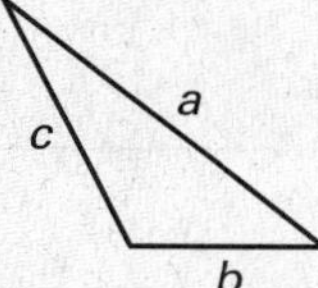

EXAMPLE 1 **Finding Area and Perimeter of a Triangle**

Find the area and perimeter of the triangle.

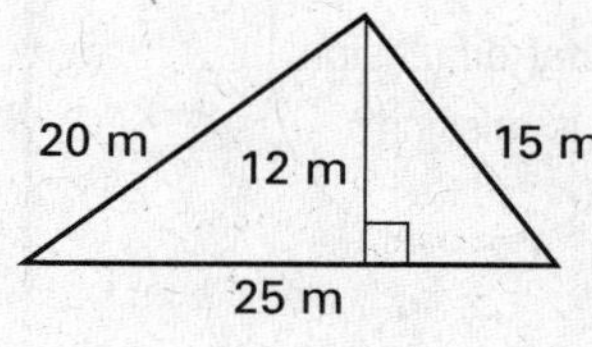

$A = \frac{1}{2}b$ ______

$= \frac{1}{2}($ ______ $)($ ______ $)$

$=$ ______

$P = a +$ ______ $+ c$

$= 15 + 25 +$ ______

$=$ ______

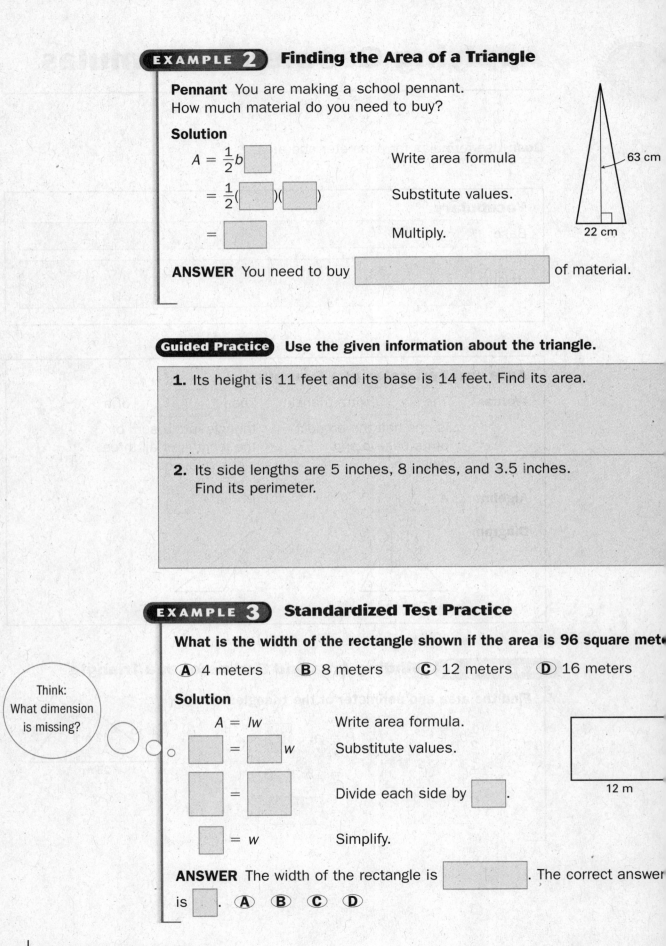

EXAMPLE 2 Finding the Area of a Triangle

Pennant You are making a school pennant. How much material do you need to buy?

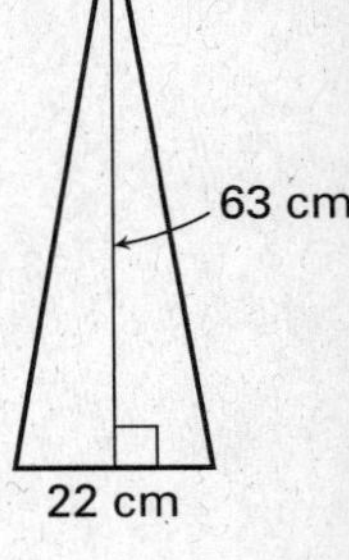

Solution

$A = \frac{1}{2}b$ ☐ Write area formula

$= \frac{1}{2}($ ☐ $)($ ☐ $)$ Substitute values.

$=$  Multiply.

ANSWER You need to buy ☐ of material.

Guided Practice **Use the given information about the triangle.**

1. Its height is 11 feet and its base is 14 feet. Find its area.

2. Its side lengths are 5 inches, 8 inches, and 3.5 inches. Find its perimeter.

EXAMPLE 3 Standardized Test Practice

What is the width of the rectangle shown if the area is 96 square met

Ⓐ 4 meters Ⓑ 8 meters Ⓒ 12 meters Ⓓ 16 meters

Think: What dimension is missing?

Solution

$A = lw$ Write area formula.

 ☐ $=$ ☐ w Substitute values.

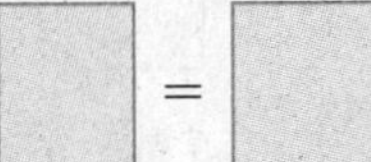 ☐ $=$ ☐ Divide each side by ☐.

☐ $= w$ Simplify.

ANSWER The width of the rectangle is . The correct answer is . Ⓐ  Ⓑ Ⓒ  Ⓓ

EXAMPLE 4 Finding an Unknown Length

The rectangle shown has a perimeter of 20 feet. Find the length of the rectangle.

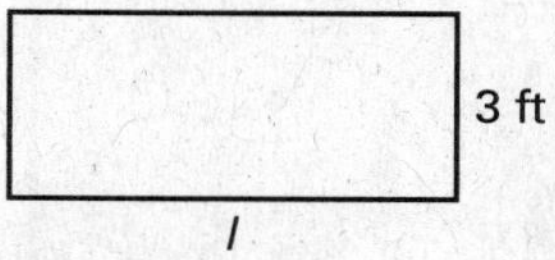

$P = 2l + 2w$	Write perimeter formula.
$\square = 2l + 2(\square)$	Substitute values.
$\square = 2l + \square$	Multiply.
$\square = \square$	$\square$ from each side.
$\square = 2l$	Simplify.
$\dfrac{\square}{\square} = \dfrac{2l}{\square}$	Divide each side by $\square$.
$\square = l$	Simplify.

ANSWER The length of the rectangle is $\square$.

Guided Practice **Find the unknown dimension.**

3. Perimeter = 40 yd

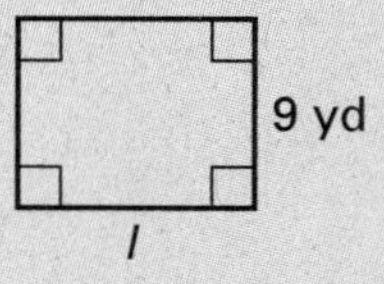

4. Area = 17.5 mm^2

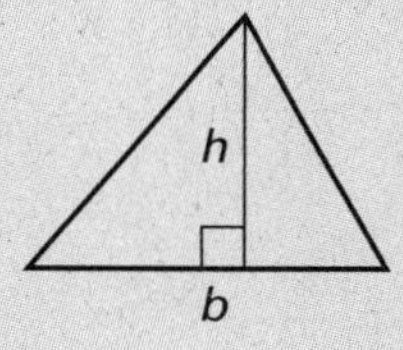

5. Area = 12 $in.^2$

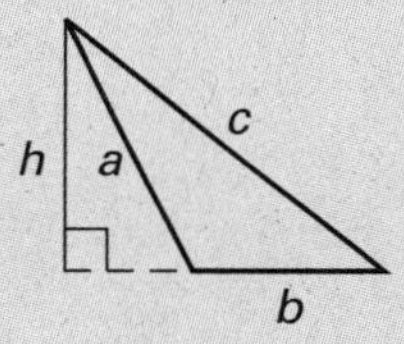

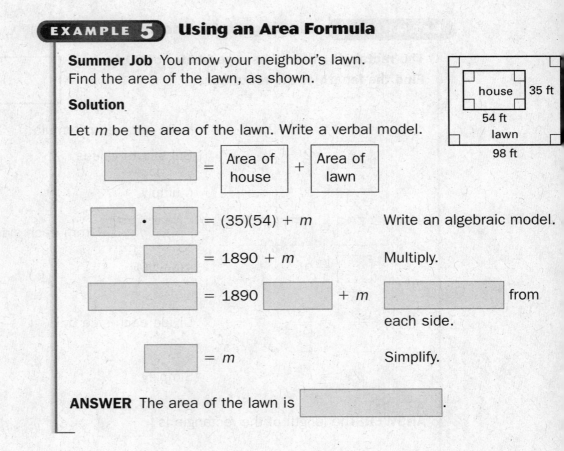

EXAMPLE 5 Using an Area Formula

Summer Job You mow your neighbor's lawn. Find the area of the lawn, as shown.

house
35 ft
54 ft
lawn
98 ft

Solution

Let m be the area of the lawn. Write a verbal model.

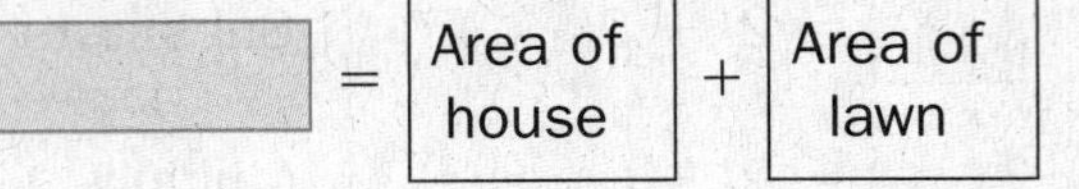

= Area of house + Area of lawn

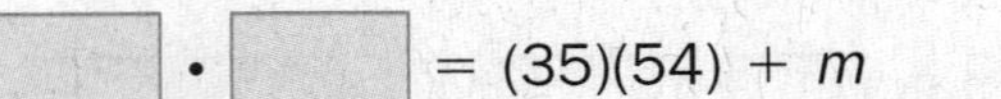

$= (35)(54) + m$ Write an algebraic model.

$= 1890 + m$ Multiply.

$= 1890 \quad + m$ from each side.

$= m$ Simplify.

ANSWER The area of the lawn is .

LESSON 3.6

Solving Inequalities Using Addition or Subtraction

Goal: Solve inequalities using addition or subtraction.

Vocabulary

Inequality:

Solution of an inequality:

Equivalent inequalities:

EXAMPLE 1 Graphing Inequalities

ce that when you an inequality with , you use an open . When you graph quality with ≥ or ≤, se a closed circle.

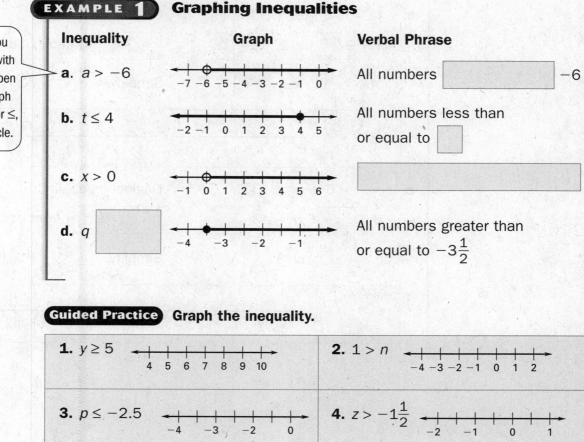

Inequality	Graph	Verbal Phrase
a. $a > -6$	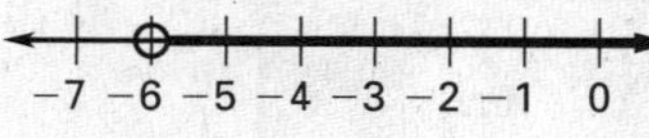	All numbers ____ -6
b. $t \leq 4$	-2 -1 0 1 2 3 4 5	All numbers less than or equal to ____
c. $x > 0$	-1 0 1 2 3 4 5 6	____
d. q ____	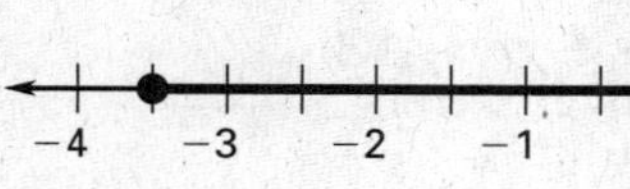	All numbers greater than or equal to $-3\frac{1}{2}$

Guided Practice **Graph the inequality.**

1. $y \geq 5$ 4 5 6 7 8 9 10	**2.** $1 > n$ -4 -3 -2 -1 0 1 2
3. $p \leq -2.5$ -4 -3 -2 0	**4.** $z > -1\frac{1}{2}$ -2 -1 0 1

Addition and Subtraction Properties of Inequality

Words Adding or subtracting the same number on each side of an inequality produces an equivalent inequality.

Algebra If $a > b$, then $a + c >$ ____ $+ c$.

If $a > b$, then $a -$ ____ $> b - c$.

Remember that the inequality symbols can be read as follows:
$>$ "greater than"
$<$ "less than"
$\geq$ "greater than or equal to"
$\leq$ "less than or equal to"

EXAMPLE 2 **Solving Inequalities**

Solve the inequality. Then graph its solution.

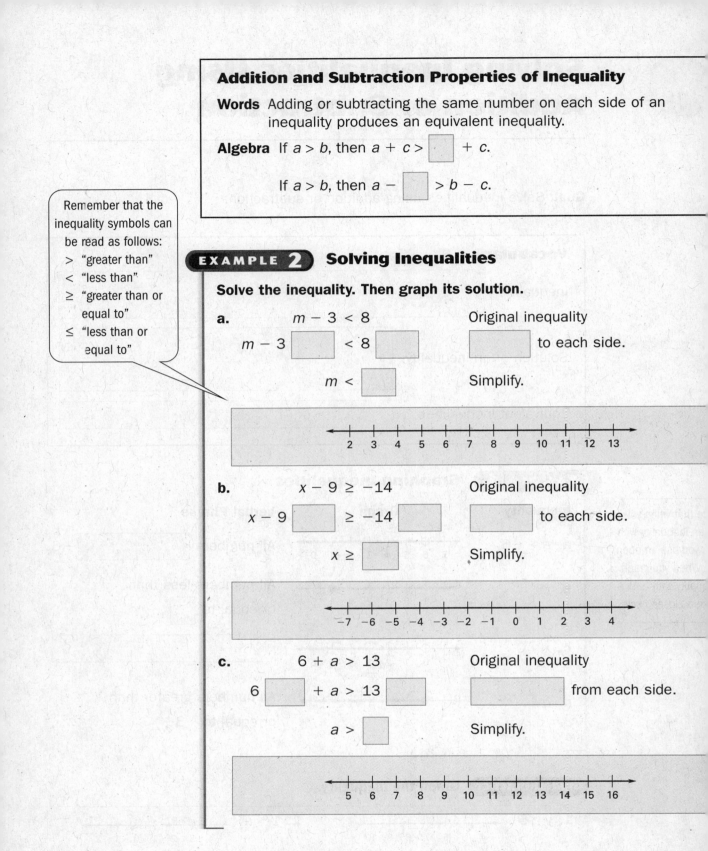

a. $m - 3 < 8$ Original inequality

$m - 3$ ____ < 8 ____ ____ to each side.

$m <$ ____ Simplify.

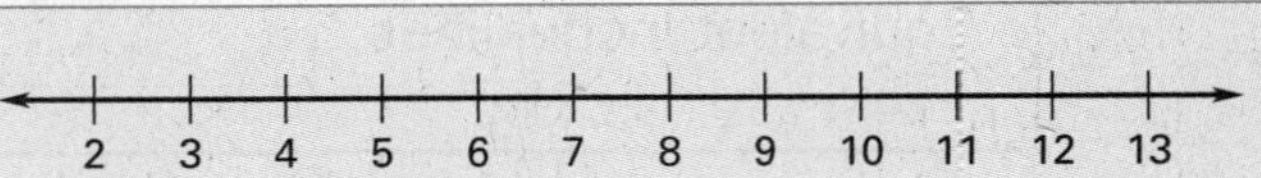

b. $x - 9 \geq -14$ Original inequality

$x - 9$ ____ ≥ -14 ____ ____ to each side.

$x \geq$ ____ Simplify.

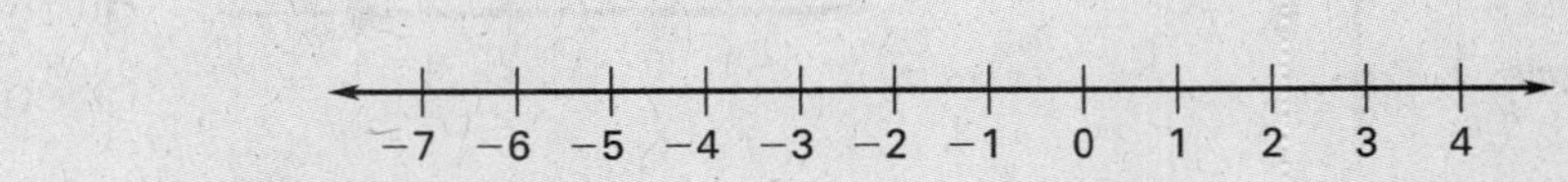

c. $6 + a > 13$ Original inequality

6 ____ $+ a > 13$ ____ ____ from each side.

$a >$ ____ Simplify.

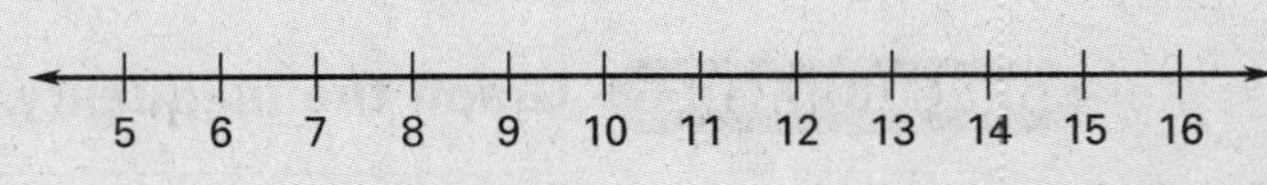

Guided Practice Solve the inequality. Then graph its solution.

5. $y - 7 \le -2$ 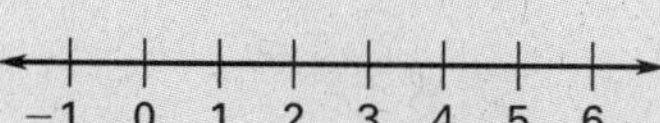	**6.** $4 < t - 10$ 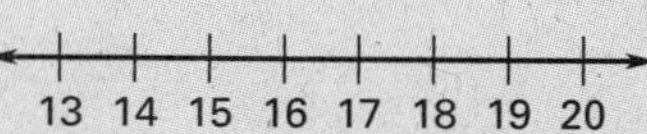
7. $15 \ge z + 18$ 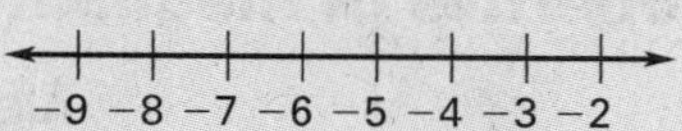	**8.** $7.5 + r > 3$ 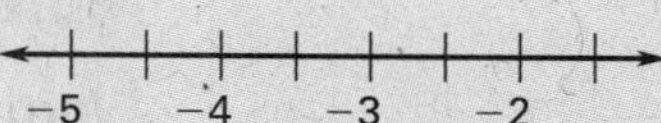

EXAMPLE 3 Writing and Solving an Inequality

Shopping You want to buy a DVD player that costs \$89. You have \$110 to spend. You also want to buy a DVD. What can the cost of the DVD be in order for you to buy both the DVD player and the DVD?

Solution

Let *d* be the cost of the DVD.

Cost of DVD + Cost of DVD player ____ ____

$d + 89$ ____ ____ Write an algebraic model.

$d + 89$ ____ ____ ____ ____ from each side.

d ____ ____ Simplify.

ANSWER The cost of the DVD must be less than or equal to ____.

Solving Inequalities Using Multiplication or Division

Goal: Solve inequalities using multiplication or division.

Multiplication Properties of Inequality

Words	Algebra
Multiplying each side of an inequality by a *positive* number produces an equivalent inequality.	If $6x < 14$, then $\left(\frac{1}{6}\right)(6x)$ ☐ $\left(\frac{1}{6}\right)(14)$.
Multiplying each side of an inequality by a *negative* number and *reversing the direction of the inequality symbol* produces an equivalent inequality.	If $-3x < 15$, then $\left(-\frac{1}{3}\right)(-3x)$ ☐ $\left(-\frac{1}{3}\right)(15)$.

EXAMPLE 1 **Solving an Inequality Using Multiplication**

$-\frac{1}{4}m \geq 6$ Original inequality

☐ $\cdot \left(-\frac{1}{4}\right)m$ ☐ ☐ $\cdot\ 6$ Multiply each side by ☐.

☐ inequality symbol

m ☐ ☐ Simplify.

Division Properties of Inequality

Words	Algebra
Dividing each side of an inequality by a *positive* number produces an equivalent inequality.	If $7x < 14$, then $\frac{7x}{☐}$ ☐ $\frac{14}{☐}$.
Dividing each side of an inequality by a *negative* number and *reversing the direction of the inequality symbol* produces an equivalent inequality.	If $-2x < 8$, then ☐ ☐ $\frac{8}{-2}$.

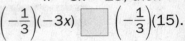

EXAMPLE 2 Solving an Inequality Using Division

$45 > -9x$ Original inequality

$\frac{45}{\square} \square \frac{-9x}{\square}$ Divide each side by ____. ____ inequality symbol.

____ x Simplify.

Guided Practice Solve the inequality.

1. $\frac{n}{7} > 7$	2. $-\frac{1}{5}y \leq 20$	3. $26 < -2x$	4. $8t < 64$

EXAMPLE 3 Using the Division Property of Inequality

en solving real orld problems ving inequalities, for key phrases, ch as *no more n* to determine hat inequality mbol to use.

Stock Market You want to buy shares of stock in a company. Each share of stock costs \$12.50. You can spend no more than \$325. Write and solve an inequality to find how many shares you can buy.

Solution

Let s represent the number of shares you can buy.

____ • Number of shares ____ Amount can spend

____ s ____ 325 Write an algebraic model.

____ Divide each side by ____.

____ Simplify.

ANSWER You can buy no more than ____ shares.

Words to Review

Give an example of the vocabulary word.

Equivalent equations

Inequality

Inverse operation

Solution of an inequality

Base

Equivalent inequalities

Height

Review your notes and Chapter 3 by using the Chapter Review on pages 161–16 your textbook.

Factors and Prime Factorization

Goal: Write the prime factorization of numbers.

Vocabulary

Prime number:

Composite number:

Prime factorization:

Factor tree:

Monomial:

EXAMPLE 1 **Writing Factors**

Band A band with 48 members is arranged into a rectangular formation with the same number of members in each row. There should be at least 2 rows with at least 3 members in each row. Find the number of possible formations by finding the factors of 48.

Solution

1. Write 48 as a product of two numbers in all possible ways.

1×48 ____ $\times 24$ $3 \times$ ____ 4×12 ____

The factors of 48 are 1, ____, 3, 4, ____, ____, 12, ____, 24, and ____.

2. Use these factors to find all the possible formations.

Rows Members	Rows Members	Rows Members
____	6×8	____
____	____	
4×12	12×4	

ANSWER There are ____ possible rectangular formations.

Guided Practice Write all the factors of the number.

1. 30	2. 31	3. 45	4. 51

You can use divisibility tests to help find all the factors of a composite number.

EXAMPLE 2 Identifying Prime and Composite Numbers

Write all the factors of the number and tell whether it is prime or *compos*

	Number	Factors	Prime or Compos
a.	18	1, 2, ___, 6, ___, 18	
b.	49	___	
c.	58	1, ___, ___, 58	
d.	67	1, 67	
e.	131	___	
f.	165	1, 3, ___, ___, 15, ___, 55, 165	

EXAMPLE 3 Writing Prime Factorization

Write the prime factorization of 540.

Two factor trees are shown. Notice that each factor tree produces the s prime factorization, differing only in the order of the factors.

Notice that more than one factor tree can be used to write the prime factorization of some numbers. Another factor tree for the prime factorization of 540 begins with 18 • 30.

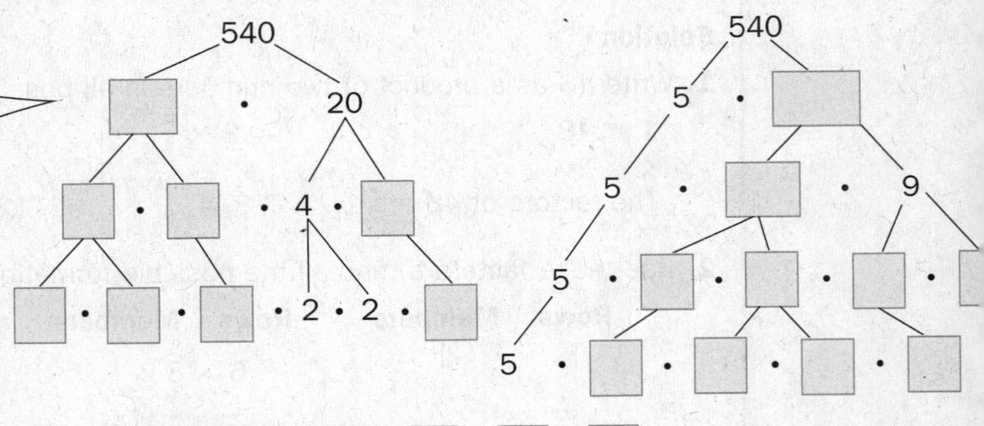

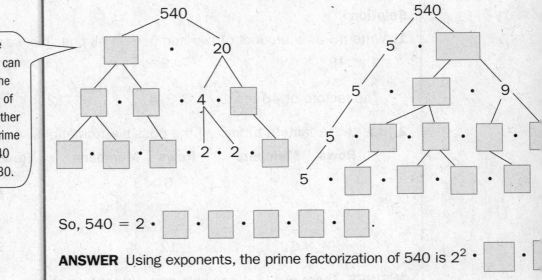

So, 540 = 2 • ___ • ___ • ___ • ___ • ___.

ANSWER Using exponents, the prime factorization of 540 is 2^2 • ___ • ___

Guided Practice **Tell whether the number is prime or composite. If it is composite, write its prime factorization using exponents.**

5. 28	**6.** 61	**7.** 72	**8.** 600

EXAMPLE 4 Factoring a Monomial

Factor the monomial $24xy^3$.

$24xy^3 =$ ______ $\cdot x \cdot y^3$ Factor 24.

$=$ ______ Write y^3 as ______.

Guided Practice **Factor the monomial.**

9. 5ab	**10.** $20t^3$
11. $36x^2y^4$	**12.** $56p^3q$

Greatest Common Factor

Goal: Find the greatest common factor of two or more numbers.

Vocabulary

Common factor:

Greatest common factor (GCF):

Relatively prime :

The GCF is sometimes called the greatest common divisor (GCD) because it is the greatest number that divides the given numbers.

EXAMPLE 1 Finding the Greatest Common Factor

Find the greatest common factor of 45 and 60.

1. Write the prime factorization of each number.

45 = 60 =

2. Find the common prime factors. They are and . The GCF of 45 and 60 is the product of these factors.

ANSWER The GCF of 45 and 60 is • , or .

EXAMPLE 2 Identifying Relatively Prime Numbers

Tell whether the numbers 88 and 63 are relatively prime. If they are not relatively prime, find the greatest common factor.

Write the prime factorization of each number. Then look for all the common prime factors.

88 = 63 =

There are no common prime factors. However, two numbers always have 1 as a common factor. So, the GCF is 1.

ANSWER The numbers 88 and 63 are .

Guided Practice **Find the greatest common factor of the numbers.**

1. 16, 20	**2.** 28, 56	**3.** 36, 63	**4.** 72, 126

Tell whether the numbers are relatively prime. If they are not relatively prime, find the GCF.

5. 24, 64	**6.** 105, 115	**7.** 32, 45	**8.** 140, 81

EXAMPLE 3 Finding the GCF of Monomials

Find the greatest common factor of $15x^3$ and $10x^4$.

1. Write the prime factorization of each expression.

$15x^3 =$ ______ $10x^4 =$ ______

2. Find the common factors, ___ and ___. The GCF is their product.

ANSWER The GCF is ___.

Guided Practice **Find the greatest common factor of the monomials.**

9. 3a, 21a	**10.** $16xy^2$, $12x^2y$	**11.** $20m$, $15m^3n$	**12.** $4pq^4$, $8p^3q^2$

EXAMPLE 4 Solve a Multi-Step Problem

Party Favors You are making favors for a party. You buy 84 pencils, 42 gift certificates, 126 stickers, and 168 pieces of candy. Every favor must have the same contents, and there should be no leftover items. What is the greatest number of favors that you can make? What will eac favor contain?

Solution

1. Find the greatest number of favors by finding the GCF.

$84 = 2^2 \cdot$ ____ $\cdot$ ____ $42 =$ ____ $\cdot\ 3 \cdot$ ____

$126 = 2 \cdot$ ____ $\cdot\ 7$ $168 =$ ____ $\cdot\ 3 \cdot$ ____

The common prime factors are ____, ____, and ____. The GCF is ____, or ____.

2. Divide the number of each item by the greatest number of favors t what each favor will contain.

$84 \div 42 =$ ____ $42 \div 42 =$ ____

$126 \div 42 =$ ____ $168 \div 42 =$ ____

ANSWER The greatest number of favors is ____. Each favor contains ____ pencils, ____ gift certificate, ____ stickers, and ____ pieces of cand

Simplifying Fractions

Goal: Simplify fractions.

Vocabulary

Simplest form: ______

Equivalent fractions: ______

EXAMPLE 1 **Writing a Fraction in Simplest Form**

Farming A farmer has 8 acres of pasture, 48 acres of wheat, 52 acres of hay, and 24 acres of corn. What fraction of the total number of acres is corn?

Solution

Write the fraction of the total number of acres that is corn. Then simplify.

$$\frac{\text{Number of acres of corn}}{\text{Total number of acres}} = \frac{24}{\square}$$

Method 1: Find and use the GCF of 24 and ______.

$24 = \square \cdot 3 \qquad \square = \square \cdot 3 \cdot \square$

The GCF of 24 and ______ is ______.

$$\frac{24}{\square} = \frac{24 \div \square}{\square} = \square$$

Divide numerator and denominator by GCF and simplify.

Method 2: Write the prime factorization of each number.

$$\frac{24}{\square} = \frac{\square \cdot 3}{\square \cdot 3 \cdot \square}$$

Write prime factorizations.

$$= \frac{\square \cdot \cancel{3}^{1}}{\square \cdot \cancel{3}_{1} \cdot \square} = \square$$

Divide out common factors and simplify.

ANSWER The fraction of the farmer's acres that corn is ______.

EXAMPLE 2 Identifying Equivalent Fractions

Tell whether the fractions $\frac{4}{5}$ and $\frac{28}{35}$ are equivalent.

Write each fraction in simplest form.

$\frac{4}{5}$ is in simplest form. $\frac{28}{35} = \frac{28 \div \square}{35 \div \square} = \square$

ANSWER The fractions ______ equivalent.

EXAMPLE 3 Writing Equivalent Fractions

A fraction has many equivalent fractions. There are other correct answers to Example 3.

Write two fractions that are equivalent to $\frac{8}{12}$.

Multiply or divide the numerator and denominator by the same nonzero number.

$\frac{8}{12} = \frac{8 \times 2}{12 \times 2} = \square$ Multiply numerator and denominator by 2.

$\frac{8}{12} = \frac{8 \div 4}{12 \div 4} = \square$ Divide numerator and denominator by 4, a common factor of 8 and 12.

ANSWER The fractions ______ and ______ are equivalent to $\frac{8}{12}$.

Guided Practice **Use the information in Example 1. Write the fraction of total number of acres that are the given crop. Simplify if possible.**

1. pasture	**2.** wheat	**3.** hay

Write two fractions that are equivalent to the given fraction.

4. $\frac{7}{21}$	**5.** $\frac{8}{20}$	**6.** $\frac{18}{24}$	**7.** $\frac{10}{16}$

EXAMPLE 4 Simplifying a Variable Expression

$\frac{6x^2}{12xy} =$ [ ] Factor numerator and denominator.

$= \frac{\not{2}^{1} \cdot [\ ]}{{}_{1}\not{2} \cdot 2 \cdot [\ ]}$ Divide out common factors.

$=$ [ ] Simplify.

EXAMPLE 5 Evaluating a Variable Expression

Evaluate the expression $\frac{-18x}{9x^3}$ when $x = 2$.

$\frac{-18x}{9x^3} = \frac{-1 \cdot [\ ]}{[\ ]}$ Factor numerator and denominator.

$= \frac{-1 \cdot 2 \cdot \not{3}^{1} \cdot [\ ]}{\not{3}_{1} \cdot [\ ]}$ Divide out common factors.

$= \frac{-2}{[\ ]}$ Simplify.

$= \frac{-2}{[\ ]}$ Substitute 2 for x.

$= \frac{-2}{[\ ]} =$ [ ] Evaluate powers and simplify.

Guided Practice **Simplify the variable expression.**

8. $\frac{9a}{12ab}$	**9.** $\frac{35x^2y}{5y}$	**10.** $\frac{2p^4}{10p}$	**11.** $\frac{15mn}{18m^2}$

12. Evaluate the expression $\frac{32t^4}{-8t^2}$ when $t = 4$.

Least Common Multiple

Goal: Find the least common multiple of two numbers.

Vocabulary

Multiple:

Common multiple:

Least common multiple (LCM):

EXAMPLE 1 **Finding the Least Common Multiple**

Inline Skating You and your friend are inline skating around a trail at a park. You both start skating at the same time from the same location. You skate the trail in 8 minutes, while your friend skates the trail in 6 minutes. You both stop skating when you both are at your starting place at the same time again. How long do you and your friend skate?

Method 1: Make a list. List the multiples of each number.

Multiples of 6: 6, 12, ___, ___, ___, ___, 42, 48, 54, ...

Multiples of 8: 8, 16, ___, ___, ___, 48, 56, ...

The LCM of 6 and 8 is ___.

Method 2: Use prime factorization.

Write the prime factorization of each number.

6 = ___ 8 = ___

Write the product of the highest power of each prime number in the p factorizations.

___ = ___

The LCM of 6 and 8 is ___.

ANSWER You and your friend skate for ___ minutes.

EXAMPLE 2 Finding the Least Common Multiple

Find the LCM of 56, 84, and 112 using prime factorization.

1. Write the prime factorization of each number.

$56 = 2^3 \cdot$ ☐ $84 =$ ☐ $\cdot$ ☐ $\cdot 7$ $112 =$ ☐ $\cdot$ ☐

Hint:
…en you are asked to …d the LCM of larger …mbers, it may be …sier to use prime …ctorization than to …t the multiples of each number.

2. Write the product of the highest power of each prime number in the prime factorizations.

☐ $\cdot$ ☐ $\cdot$ ☐ $=$ ☐

ANSWER The LCM of 56, 84, and 112 is ☐.

Guided Practice **Find the least common multiple of the numbers.**

1. 4, 10	**2.** 3, 21	**3.** 20, 28	**4.** 18, 45, 60

EXAMPLE 3 Finding the LCM of Monomials

Find the LCM of $8a^3bc^2$ and $12ac^4$.

1. Factor each expression using exponents.

$8a^3bc^2 =$ ☐ $12ac^4 =$ ☐

2. Find the product of the highest power of each factor, including the variables.

☐ $=$ ☐

ANSWER The LCM of $8a^3bc^2$ and $12ac^4$ is ☐.

Guided Practice **Find the least common multiple of the monomials.**

5. $12x^5$, $16x^8$	**6.** $15t^6$, $75t$	**7.** $9mn^3$, $24m^3n$

LESSON 4.5

Comparing Fractions and Mixed Numbers

Goal: Compare and order fractions and mixed numbers.

Vocabulary

Least common denominator (LCD):

EXAMPLE 1 Comparing Fractions Using the LCD

Compare $\frac{5}{6}$ and $\frac{7}{10}$.

1. Find the least common denominator of the fractions.

The LCM of 6 and 10 is ______, so the least common denominator is ______.

2. Use the least common denominator to write equivalent fractions.

You can write equivalent fractions by multiplying or dividing the numerator and denominator by the same nonzero number.

$\frac{5}{6} = \frac{5 \cdot \square}{6 \cdot \square} = \square \qquad \frac{7}{10} = \frac{7 \cdot \square}{10 \cdot \square} = \square$

3. Compare the numerators: ______, so .

ANSWER Because , you can write $\frac{5}{6}$ ______ $\frac{7}{10}$.

Guided Practice **Copy and complete the statement with <, >, or =.**

1. $\frac{1}{3}$? $\frac{2}{5}$	**2.** $\frac{3}{4}$? $\frac{11}{16}$	**3.** $\frac{7}{12}$? $\frac{7}{15}$	**4.** $\frac{5}{10}$? $\frac{3}{6}$

EXAMPLE 2 Standardized Test Practice

What is the order of $1\frac{1}{6}$, $\frac{19}{16}$, and $\frac{9}{8}$ from least to greatest?

Ⓐ $\frac{9}{8}, 1\frac{1}{6}, \frac{19}{16}$ Ⓑ $1\frac{1}{6}, \frac{9}{8}, \frac{19}{16}$

Ⓒ $\frac{9}{8}, \frac{19}{16}, 1\frac{1}{6}$ Ⓓ $\frac{19}{16}, \frac{9}{8}, 1\frac{1}{6}$

o compare or
rder improper
tions and mixed
ers, first write any
ed numbers as
roper fractions.

1. Find the least common denominator of the fractions.

The LCM of 6, 16, and 8 is ____, so the LCD is .

2. Use the least common denominator to write equivalent fractions.

$$1\frac{1}{6} = \frac{1 \cdot 6 + 1}{6} = \frac{7}{6} = \frac{7 \cdot \square}{6 \cdot \square} = \square$$

$$\frac{19}{16} = \frac{19 \cdot \square}{16 \cdot \square} = \square \qquad \frac{9}{8} = \frac{9 \cdot \square}{8 \cdot \square} = \square$$

3. Compare the numerators: 54 < ____, and ____ < 57, so

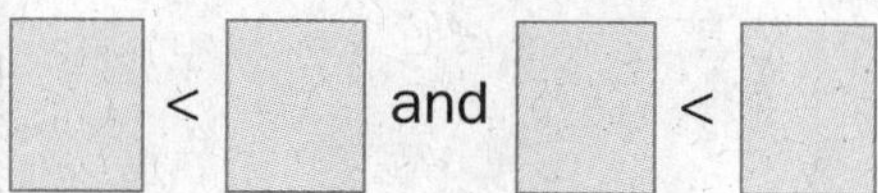

ANSWER From least to greatest, the numbers are ____.

The correct answer is . Ⓐ Ⓑ Ⓒ Ⓓ

EXAMPLE 3 Comparing Mixed Numbers

Long Jump At a track meet, your first jump is $5\frac{3}{5}$ meters, your second ju is $5\frac{3}{4}$ meters, and your third jump is $5\frac{5}{8}$ meters. Which jump is the long

Solution

The LCM of 5, 4, and 8 is ______, so the least common denominator is

Use the least common denominator to write equivalent fractions.

$5\frac{3}{5} = \frac{5 \cdot 5 + 3}{5} =$ ______ $5\frac{3}{4} = \frac{5 \cdot 4 + 3}{4} =$ ______ $5\frac{5}{8} = \frac{5 \cdot 8 + 5}{8} =$

Because ______ > 225 and $225 >$ ______, you can write ______ $>$

and ______ $>$ ______.

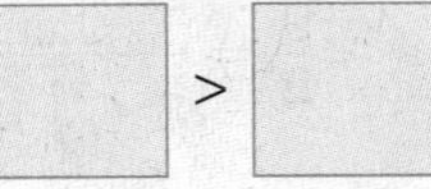

ANSWER Your ______ jump is the longest.

Guided Practice **Copy and complete the statement with $<$, $>$, or $=$.**

5. $2\frac{3}{4}\ \underline{?}\ \frac{14}{5}$

6. $\frac{40}{12}\ \underline{?}\ 3\frac{4}{9}$

7. $-1\frac{3}{8}\ \underline{?}\ -1\frac{1}{2}$

8. Order the numbers $\frac{17}{4}$, $4\frac{3}{18}$, and $4\frac{2}{9}$ from least to greatest.

Rules of Exponents

Goal: Multiply and divide expressions with exponents.

Product of Powers Property

Words To multiply powers with the same ______, ______ their exponents.

Algebra ______ $\cdot a^n = a$______

Numbers $4^5 \cdot 4^3 = 4$______ = ______

EXAMPLE 1 **Using the Product of Powers Property**

$x^2 \cdot x^8 = x$______ Product of powers property

= ______ Add exponents.

EXAMPLE 2 **Using the Product of Powers Property**

TCH OUT!
ember that
bers raised to the
power are usually
en without an
nent. For example,
= 2.

$2^4x^3 \cdot 2x^4 = (2^4 \cdot$ ______ $) \cdot ($ ______ $\cdot x^4)$ Use properties of multiplication.

$= 2$______ $\cdot x$______ Product of powers property

= ______ Add exponents.

= ______ Evaluate the power.

Quotient of Powers Property

Words To divide two powers with the same nonzero ______, ______ the exponent of the denominator from the exponent of the numerator.

Algebra $\frac{a^m}{\text{______}} = a$______

Numbers $\frac{6^8}{6^6} = 6$______ = ______

EXAMPLE 3 Using the Quotient of Powers Property

Simplify the expression. Write your answer as a power.

a. $\frac{x^{11}}{x^3} = x^{\square}$ Quotient of powers property

$= \square$ Subtract exponents.

b. $\frac{7^9}{7^6} = 7^{\square}$ Quotient of powers property

$= \square$ Subtract exponents.

Guided Practice **Simplify the expression. Write your answer as a power.**

1. $m^{10} \cdot m^5$	2. $3^7 \cdot 3^2$	3. $\frac{x^{12}}{x^4}$	4. $\frac{8^9}{8^8}$

EXAMPLE 4 Simplifying Fractions with Powers

a. $\frac{t^6 \cdot t^2}{t} = \frac{\square}{t}$ Simplify numerator using product of powers pro

$= \square$ Quotient of powers property

$= \square$ Subtract exponents.

b. $\frac{m^3 n^5}{n^4} = \square$ Quotient of powers property

$= \square$ Subtract exponents.

WATCH OUT!
The bases of the powers must be the same to use the product or quotient property. In part (b) of Example 4, you cannot simplify the numerator any further because the bases, *m* and *n*, are different.

Guided Practice **Simplify the expression. Write your answer as a power**

5. $\frac{a \cdot a^7}{a^4}$	6. $\frac{5^8 \cdot 5^5}{5^{10}}$	7. $\frac{q^9}{pq^3}$	8. $\frac{x^{12}y^{12}}{y^5}$

Negative and Zero Exponents

Goal: Simplify expressions with negative exponents.

Negative Exponents

Words For any integer n and any number $a \neq 0$, a^{-n} is equal to $\frac{1}{a^n}$.

Algebra $\quad = \frac{1}{a^n}$ **Numbers** $4^{-5} =$

EXAMPLE 1 Using a Negative Exponent

Computers The speed of a computer chip is measured in nanoseconds. One nanosecond is $\frac{1}{1,000,000,000}$ second. Write one nanosecond in seconds as a power of ten.

Solution

$\frac{1}{1,000,000,000} =$ Write 1,000,000,000 as .

$=$ Definition of negative exponent

ANSWER One nanosecond is second.

EXAMPLE 2 Evaluating a Numerical Expression

$6^4 \cdot 6^{-7} = 6$ Product of powers property

$=$ Simplify.

$= \quad =$ Definition of negative exponent

Zero Exponents

Words For any number $a \neq 0$, a^0 is equal to .

Algebra $a^0 = 1$ **Numbers** $5^0 =$

EXAMPLE 3 Simplifying Variable Expressions

Simplify. Write the expression using only positive exponents.

a. $-9x^0 = -9 \cdot$ ___ Zero exponent applies only to x.

$= -9 \cdot$ ___ Definition of zero exponent

$=$ ___ Multiply.

b. $-3a^{-4} = -3 \cdot$ ___ Exponent applies only to a.

$= -3 \cdot$ ___ Definition of negative exponent

$=$ ___ Multiply.

c. $\frac{10t^{-3}}{t^2} = \frac{\_\_\_}{t^2}$ Exponent applies only to t.

$=$ ___ $\cdot\ t^{\_\_\_}$ Quotient of powers property

$=$ ___ $\cdot$ ___ Simplify.

$=$ ___ Definition of negative exponent

WATCH OUT!

In an expression such as $-9x^0$ or $-3a^{-4}$, the exponent is applied only to the variable, not to the coefficient.

Guided Practice **Evaluate the expression.**

1. 8^0	**2.** $(-2)^{-6}$	**3.** $7 \cdot 7^{-2}$	**4.** $12^{-9} \cdot 1$

Simplify. Write the expression using only positive exponents.

5. $5y^{-3}$	**6.** $n^{-11} \cdot n^{-5}$	**7.** $\frac{8p^2}{p^{-4}}$	**8.** $\frac{15x}{3x^{10}}$

Scientific Notation

Goal: Read and write numbers using scientific notation.

Using Scientific Notation

A number is written in scientific notation if it has the form $c \times 10^n$ where $c \geq$ ____, $c <$ ____ and n is an integer.

Standard form	Product form	Scientific notation
289,000	____	____
____	8×0.001	____

EXAMPLE 1 Writing a Number in Scientific Notation

owers of Ten
= 100,000
= 10,000
= 1000
= 100
= 10
= 1
= 0.1
= 0.01
= 0.001
= 0.0001
= 0.00001

Lightning A flash of lightning consists of 3 or 4 strokes. The time between each stroke is about 0.00005 second. Write this number in scientific notation.

Standard form	Product form	Scientific notation
0.00005	$5 \times$ ____	5×10^{____}
Move decimal point ____ places to the right.		Exponent is ____.

ANSWER The number written in scientific notation is ____.

EXAMPLE 2 Standardized Test Practice

Space The maximum distance from Earth to Jupiter is 968,100,000 kilometers. What is the distance written in scientific notation?

(A) 96.81×10^7 km
(B) 0.9681×10^8 km
(C) 9.681×10^8 km
(D) 9.681×10^{-8} km

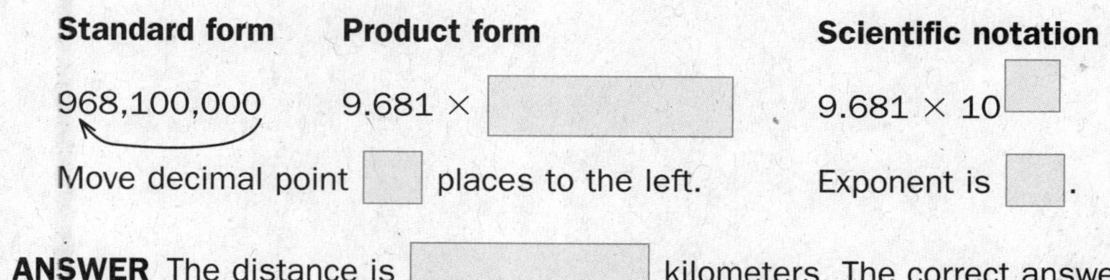

Standard form	Product form	Scientific notation
968,100,000	$9.681 \times$ ____	9.681×10^{____}
Move decimal point ____ places to the left.		Exponent is ____.

ANSWER The distance is ____ kilometers. The correct answer is ____.    (D)

EXAMPLE 3 **Writing Numbers in Standard Form**

	Scientific notation	Product form	Standard form
a.	3.1×10^7	$3.1 \times$ ______	______
	Exponent is ____.		Move decimal point ____ places to the r
b.	9.08×10^{-4}	$9.08 \times$ ______	______
	Exponent is ____.		Move decimal point ____ places to the l

Guided Practice **Write the number in scientific notation.**

1. 9000	**2.** 253,000	**3.** 1,207,000,000

Write the number in standard form.

4. 8.2×10^2	**5.** 5.51×10^{10}	**6.** 6.49×10^{12}

WATCH OUT!
When a number is in scientific notation, the factor c must be greater than or equal to 1 and less than 10.

EXAMPLE 4 Multiplying Numbers in Scientific Notation

Find the product $(6.5 \times 10^4) \times (8.4 \times 10^{10})$.

$(6.5 \times 10^4) \times (8.4 \times 10^{10})$

$= 6.5 \times 8.4 \times 10^4 \times 10^{10}$ Commutative property of multiplication

$= (6.5 \times 8.4) \times (10^4 \times 10^{10})$ Associative property of multiplication

$= \square \times \square$ Product of powers property

$= \square \times \square \times \square$ Write $\square$ in scientific notation.

$= \square \times \square$ Product of powers property

Think: Is this number in scientific notation?

Guided Practice **Write the product in scientific notation.**

7. $(6.75 \times 10^3) \times (9.2 \times 10^8)$	**8.** $(2.35 \times 10^6) \times (4 \times 10^9)$

Words to Review

Give an example of the vocabulary word.

Prime Number

Monomial

Composite Number

Common Factor

Prime Factorization

Greatest Common Factor (GCF)

Factor Tree

Relatively Prime

Simplest Form

Least Common Multiple (LCM)

Equivalent Fractions

Least Common Denominator (LCD)

Multiple

Scientific Notation

Common Multiple

Review your notes and Chapter 4 by using the Chapter Review on pages 220–224 of your textbook.

Fractions with Common Denominators

Goal: Add and subtract fractions with common denominators.

Adding and Subtracting Fractions

Words To add fractions or subtract fractions with a common denominator, write the sum or difference of the ______ over the denominator.

Numbers $\frac{3}{8} + \frac{4}{8} = \frac{7}{\square}$ **Algebra** $\frac{a}{c} + \frac{b}{c} = \frac{a+b}{\square}$ $(c \neq 0)$

$\frac{5}{7} - \frac{2}{7} = \square$ $\frac{a}{c} - \frac{b}{c} = \frac{\square}{c}$ $(c \neq 0)$

Part (b) of Example 1 shows how to operate with negative mixed numbers. Notice that the fraction part of $5\frac{3}{5}$ is greater than the fraction part of $8\frac{2}{5}$. So you need to rename $8\frac{2}{5}$.

EXAMPLE 1 **Fractions and Mixed Numbers**

a. $-\frac{9}{11} + \frac{3}{11} = \frac{-9+3}{\square}$

$= \square$

b. $8\frac{2}{5} - 5\frac{3}{5} = 7\frac{7}{5} - 5\frac{3}{5}$

$= (7 - \square) + \left(\square - \frac{3}{5}\right)$

$= \square$

EXAMPLE 2 Simplifying Fractions with Variables

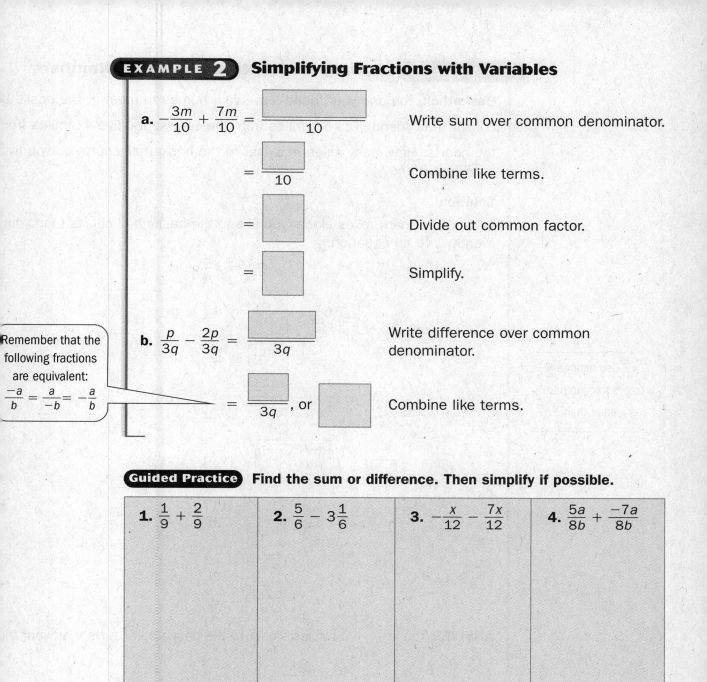

a. $-\frac{3m}{10} + \frac{7m}{10} = \frac{\square}{10}$ Write sum over common denominator.

$= \frac{\square}{10}$ Combine like terms.

$= \square$ Divide out common factor.

$= \square$ Simplify.

Remember that the following fractions are equivalent: $\frac{-a}{b} = \frac{a}{-b} = -\frac{a}{b}$

b. $\frac{p}{3q} - \frac{2p}{3q} = \frac{\square}{3q}$ Write difference over common denominator.

$= \frac{\square}{3q}$, or $\square$ Combine like terms.

Guided Practice **Find the sum or difference. Then simplify if possible.**

1. $\frac{1}{9} + \frac{2}{9}$	**2.** $\frac{5}{6} - 3\frac{1}{6}$	**3.** $-\frac{x}{12} - \frac{7x}{12}$	**4.** $\frac{5a}{8b} + \frac{-7a}{8b}$

EXAMPLE 3 Solving an Equation with Mixed Numbers

Basketball You and your friend leave your homes to meet at the basketb courts. Your friend lives $6\frac{1}{6}$ miles from the courts. You live $4\frac{5}{6}$ miles fron the courts. How many miles *m* closer to the basketball courts do you live than your friend?

Solution

To find how many miles closer you live to the basketball courts than your friend, write an equation.

$$6\frac{1}{6} = 4\frac{5}{6} + m$$

$$6\frac{1}{6} - \square = 4\frac{5}{6} + m - \square$$

$$6\frac{1}{6} - \square = m$$

$\frac{1}{6} < \frac{5}{6}$, so rename $6\frac{1}{6}$ so its fraction part is greater than $\frac{5}{6}$.

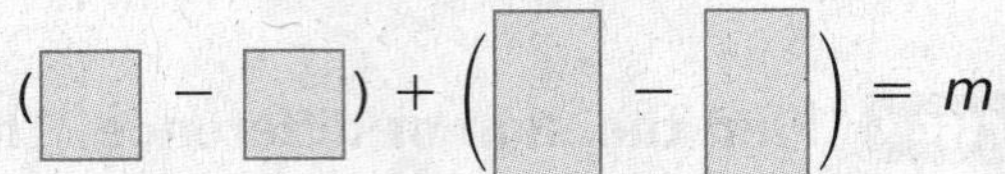

$$\square = m$$

$$\square = m$$

ANSWER You live $\square$ miles closer to the basketball courts than your fri

EXAMPLE 4 Evaluating Longer Expressions

emember to use the order of operations when evaluating longer expressions.

a. $-\frac{4}{5} + \frac{2}{5} - \frac{1}{5} = \frac{\square}{5}$ Write sum over common denominator.

$= \square$ Evaluate numerator from left to right.

b. $3\frac{9}{16} - 4\frac{3}{16} + 2\frac{11}{16}$

$= (\square - \square + 2) + \left(\frac{9}{16} - \square + \square\right)$ Group whole numbers and fractions.

$= \square$ Evaluate inside parentheses.

$= \square$ Rename.

Guided Practice **Evaluate. Then simplify if possible.**

5. $\frac{7}{8} + \frac{3}{8} + \frac{1}{8}$	**6.** $\frac{1}{4} - \frac{7}{4} + \frac{3}{4}$	**7.** $1\frac{4}{9} + 5\frac{1}{9} - \frac{8}{9}$

LESSON 5.2

Fractions with Different Denominators

Goal: Add and subtract with different denominators.

EXAMPLE 1 **Adding and Subtracting Fractions**

Remember that when you add or subtract fractions with different denominators, you first rewrite the fractions so that the denominators are the same.

a. $\frac{3}{4} + \frac{-1}{3} =$ ☐ + ☐ Rewrite fractions using LCD of ☐.

= ☐ Write sum over LCD.

= ☐ Evaluate numerator.

b. $\frac{5}{8} - \frac{11}{12} =$ ☐ − ☐ Rewrite fractions using LCD of ☐

= ☐ Write difference over LCD.

= ☐, or ☐ Evaluate numerator.

Guided Practice **Find the sum or difference. Then simplify if possible.**

1. $\frac{2}{7} + \frac{1}{2}$	**2.** $\frac{7}{9} - \frac{5}{6}$
3. $\frac{2}{5} + \frac{-9}{10}$	**4.** $\frac{11}{12} - \frac{5}{18}$

EXAMPLE 2 Simplifying Variable Expressions

Algebra Simplify the expression.

a. $\frac{x}{4} - \frac{4x}{5} = \square - \square$ Rewrite fractions using LCD of $\square$.

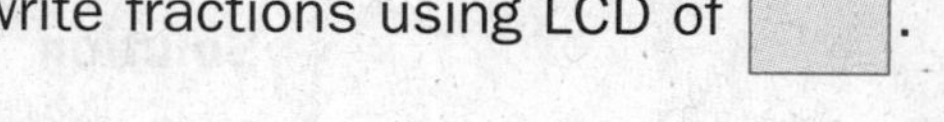

$= \square$ Write difference over LCD.

$= \square$, or $\square$ Combine like terms.

b. $\frac{6}{t} + \frac{7}{9} = \left(\frac{6}{t} \cdot \square\right) + \left(\frac{7}{9} \cdot \square\right)$ Multiply $\frac{6}{t}$ by $\square$ and $\frac{7}{9}$ by $\square$ for LCD of $\square$.

$= \square + \square$ Multiply inside parentheses.

$= \square$ Write sum over LCD.

ATCH OUT!

e expression is
ready in simplest
rm if the terms in
variable expression
e not like terms.

EXAMPLE 3 Modeling with Mixed Numbers

Running You run $8\frac{5}{6}$ miles on Monday and $6\frac{3}{4}$ miles on Wednesday. Your goal is to run 25 miles. How many miles must you run to meet your goal?

Solution

To find the number of miles you must run, write a verbal model.

Think: What mixed number with a denominator of 12 equals 25?

Miles to run, m	=	Goal	− (______ + ______)

$m = \square - \left(8\frac{5}{6} + \square\right)$ Write an algebraic model.

$= \square\frac{12}{12} - \left(8\frac{\square}{12} + \square\right)$ Rewrite fractions using LCD of

$= \square\frac{12}{12} - \square$ Add inside parentheses.

$= \square\frac{12}{12} - \square$ Rename mixed numbers.

$= (\square - \square) + \left(\frac{12}{12} - \square\right)$ Group whole numbers and fractions.

$= \square$ Subtract whole numbers and fractions.

ANSWER You must run ______ miles to meet your goal.

Guided Practice **Find the sum or difference. Then simplify if possible.**

5. $\frac{5x}{9} + \frac{x}{3}$	**6.** $\frac{7}{10} - \frac{4}{y}$
7. $5\frac{1}{12} - 3\frac{3}{4}$	**8.** $2\frac{2}{3} + 6\frac{3}{8}$

Multiplying Fractions

Goal: Multiply fractions and mixed numbers.

Multiplying Fractions

Words The product of two or more fractions is equal to the product of the ______ divided by the product of the ______.

Numbers $\frac{2}{5} \cdot \frac{7}{9} = \frac{2 \cdot 7}{5 \cdot 9} = $ ______

Algebra $\frac{a}{\square} \cdot \frac{c}{d} = \frac{a \cdot \square}{b \cdot d}$ $(b, d \neq 0)$

EXAMPLE 1 **Multiplying Fractions**

...ember that the ...oduct of two ...nbers with the ... sign is positive. ... product of two ...ers with different ...ns is negative.

a. $-\frac{3}{4} \cdot \left(-\frac{5}{8}\right) = \frac{\square \cdot (-5)}{4 \cdot \square}$ Use rule for multiplying fractions.

$= \square$ Evaluate numerator and denominator.

b. $-\frac{2}{3} \cdot \frac{9}{10} = \frac{\square}{3 \cdot \square}$ Use rule for multiplying fractions.

$= \square$ Divide out common factors.

$= \square$ Multiply.

EXAMPLE 2 Multiplying Mixed Numbers

Jigsaw Puzzle A completed puzzle is $31\frac{1}{4}$ inches long and $18\frac{2}{5}$ inches wide. What is the area of the puzzle?

Solution

To find the area of the puzzle, use an area formula.

> Remember that when you multiply mixed numbers, you first write them as improper fractions.

Area = length • ____	Write formula for area of a rectang
= ____ • ____	Substitute values.
$= \frac{\_\_\_\_}{4} \cdot \frac{\_\_\_\_}{5}$	Write as improper fractions.
$= \frac{\_\_\_\_}{4 \cdot 5}$	Use rule for multiplying fractions.
= ____	Divide out common factors.
= 	Multiply.

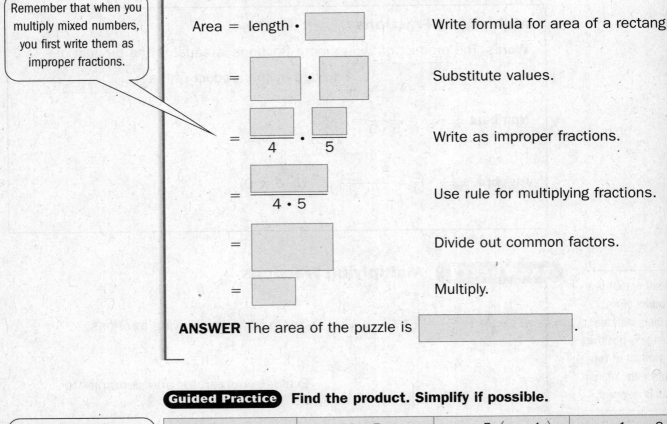

ANSWER The area of the puzzle is ____________.

Guided Practice **Find the product. Simplify if possible.**

> **WATCH OUT!**
> Be careful when you write a negative mixed number as an improper fraction.
>
> $-3\frac{4}{5} = \frac{-3 \cdot 5 + (-4)}{5}$
>
> $-3\frac{4}{5} \neq \frac{-3 \cdot 5 + 4}{5}$

1. $\frac{11}{12} \cdot 18$	**2.** $-\frac{4}{5} \cdot \frac{5}{6}$	**3.** $-\frac{5}{8}\left(-3\frac{1}{10}\right)$	**4.** $1\frac{1}{2} \cdot 1\frac{2}{9}$

EXAMPLE 3 Evaluating a Variable Expression

Algebra Evaluate xy^2 when $x = -\frac{3}{8}$ and $y = -\frac{5}{6}$.

$xy^2 = \square \cdot \left(-\frac{5}{6}\right)^2$ Substitute values.

$= \square \cdot \left(-\frac{5}{6}\right) \cdot \square$ Write $-\frac{5}{6}$ as a factor $\square$ times.

$= \square$ Use rule for multiplying fractions.

$= \square$ Divide out common factor.

$= \square$ Multiply.

Guided Practice **Evaluate the expression when $x = -\frac{1}{2}$ and $y = \frac{2}{5}$. Simplify if possible.**

5. $-\frac{2}{3}x$	**6.** $-7y$	**7.** $\frac{5}{9}xy$	**8.** x^2y

LESSON 5.4

Dividing Fractions

Goal: Divide fractions.

Vocabulary

Reciprocals: ______

Multiplicative inverse: ______

Dividing Fractions

Words To divide by a fraction, multiply by its reciprocal.

Numbers $\frac{3}{8} \div \frac{4}{5} = \frac{3}{8} \cdot \square = \square$

Algebra $\square \div \frac{c}{d} = \frac{a}{b} \cdot \square$ $(b, c, d \neq 0)$

EXAMPLE 1 **Dividing a Fraction by a Fraction**

a. $\frac{9}{10} \div \frac{3}{20} = \frac{9}{10} \cdot \square$

$= \square$

$= \square$

b. $\frac{11}{12} \div \frac{-1}{6} = \square \cdot \square$

$= \square$

$= \square$, or $\square$

Remember that the reciprocal of a negative number is also a negative number.

EXAMPLE 2 Dividing a Fraction by a Whole Number

$\frac{6}{11} \div 4 = \frac{6}{11} \cdot$ ___ $\quad 4 \cdot \frac{1}{4} = 1$, so the reciprocal of 4 is $\frac{1}{4}$.

Remember that $4 = \frac{4}{1}$.

= ___ Multiply fractions. Divide out common factor.

= ___ Multiply.

Guided Practice **Find the quotient. Simplify if possible.**

1. $\frac{4}{9} \div \left(-\frac{5}{6}\right)$	**2.** $\frac{9}{16} \div \frac{3}{10}$	**3.** $-\frac{5}{7} \div \frac{-11}{14}$	**4.** $\frac{3}{8} \div (-6)$

EXAMPLE 3 Dividing Mixed Numbers

$4\frac{1}{2} \div \left(-3\frac{3}{4}\right) =$ ___ $\div$ (___) Write $4\frac{1}{2}$ and $-3\frac{3}{4}$ as improper fractions.

= ___ $\cdot$ (___) Multiply by the reciprocal of ___.

=  Multiply. Divide out common factors.

= ___, or ___ Multiply.

✓ **Check** Use estimation to check your answer. Because $4 \div (-4)$ is equal to ___, you know that  is a reasonable answer.

Guided Practice Find the quotient. Simplify if possible.

5. $8\frac{2}{3} \div 2$	6. $-10\frac{4}{5} \div 18$	7. $8\frac{1}{4} \div 1\frac{5}{6}$	8. $7\frac{5}{7} \div \left(-1\frac{13}{14}\right)$

EXAMPLE 4 Solving an Equation with a Mixed Number

Bake Sale You use 10 cups of flour to make pumpkin bread for a bake s
One loaf of pumpkin bread uses $1\frac{2}{3}$ cups of flour. How many loaves of pumpkin bread did you make for the bake sale?

Solution

Write a verbal model to describe the problem. Let b represent the numb loaves of pumpkin bread.

Number of cups of flour used = [ ] • Number of loaves

$10 = 1\frac{2}{3}b$ Write an algebraic model.

$10 = \square\, b$ Write $1\frac{2}{3}$ as an improper frac

$10 \cdot \square = \square \cdot \square\, b$ The multiplicative inverse is

$\square = b$ Divide out common factor

$\square = b$ Multiply.

ANSWER You made [ ] loaves of pumpkin bread for the bake sale.

Fractions and Decimals

Goal: Write fractions as decimals and decimals as fractions.

Vocabulary

Rational number:

Terminating decimal:

Repeating decimal:

EXAMPLE 1 Writing Fractions as Decimals

To write a fraction as a decimal, divide the numerator by the denominator.

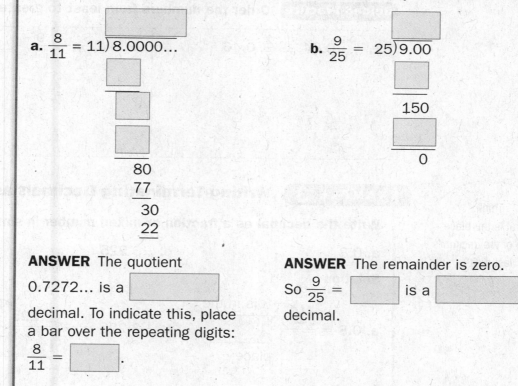

a. $\frac{8}{11} = 11\overline{)8.0000...}$

80
77
30
22

ANSWER The quotient 0.7272... is a ______ decimal. To indicate this, place a bar over the repeating digits: $\frac{8}{11} =$ ______.

b. $\frac{9}{25} = 25\overline{)9.00}$

150

0

ANSWER The remainder is zero. So $\frac{9}{25} =$ ______ is a ______ decimal.

EXAMPLE 2 Ordering Rational Numbers

Bowling The table lists the weights of 5 bowling balls. Order the weights from least to greatest.

Weight
$12\frac{3}{16}$ lb
12.2 lb
$12\frac{2}{11}$ lb
12.12 lb
$12\frac{1}{8}$ lb

Solution

Write mixed numbers as decimals.

$12\frac{3}{16} =$ ______ $12\frac{2}{11} =$ ______ $12\frac{1}{8} =$ ______

Then graph all the weights on a number line.

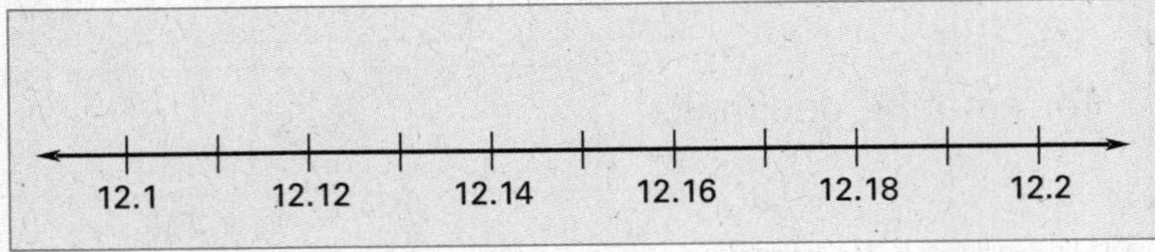

ANSWER From least to greatest:

 lb, 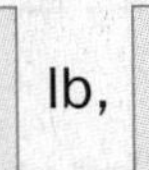 lb, ______ lb, ______ lb, ______ lb.

Guided Practice **Order the numbers from least to greatest.**

1. $\frac{9}{20}$, 0.34, $\frac{1}{3}$, $\frac{2}{5}$, 0.46

2. $-2\frac{3}{4}$, $-2\frac{9}{11}$, -2.8, $-2\frac{7}{8}$, -2.87

EXAMPLE 3 Writing Terminating Decimals as Fractions

Think: What is the place value of the decimal's last digit?

Write the decimal as a fraction or mixed number in simplest form.

a. 0.8 **b.** -3.225

Solution

a. $0.8 = \frac{8}{\square}$ ← 8 is in the ______ place.

$= \square$

b. $-3.225 = -3\frac{225}{\square}$ ← 5 is in the ______ place.

$= \square$

$= \square$

EXAMPLE 4 Writing Repeating Decimals as Fractions

To write $0.\overline{54}$ as a fraction, let $x = 0.\overline{54}$ or 0.545454....

1. The number has ___ repeating digits, so multiply by ___.

   ___ $x =$ ___, or ___.

Think: many repeating digits does the decimal have?

2. Then subtract x from $100x$.

   ___ $x =$ ___

   $-$ $x =$ 0.545454...

   ___ $x =$ ___

3. Solve for x. Simplify. $x =$ ___, or ___

ANSWER The decimal $0.\overline{54}$ is equivalent to the fraction ___.

Guided Practice **Write the decimal as a fraction or mixed number.**

3. 0.9	**4.** 0.76	**5.** −1.15	**6.** −5.25
7. $-0.\overline{4}$	**8.** $-8.\overline{6}$	**9.** $0.\overline{63}$	**10.** $0.9\overline{4}$

Adding and Subtracting Decimals

Goal: Add and subtract decimals.

Vocabulary

Front-end estimation:

EXAMPLE 1 Adding and Subtracting Decimals

Electricity The table shows a household's electricity usage (in kilowatt-hours) for 4 months.

Electricity Usage	
Month	**Kilowatt-h**
September	490.7
October	501.8
November	510.3
December	538.29

a. How many kilowatt-hours were used in September and October?

b. How many more kilowatt-hours were used in December than in November?

Solution

a. To find how many kilowatt-hours were used in September and October, add the values from the table for September and October.

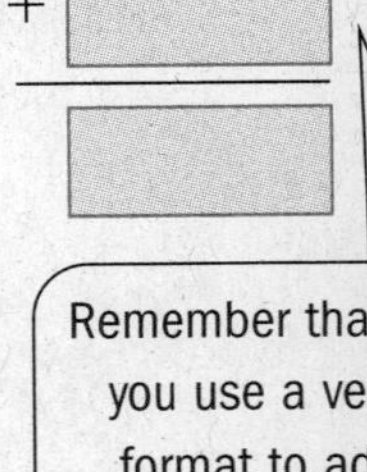

Remember that you use a vertical format to add or subtract decimals, begin by lining up decimal points, then add or subtract as with whole numbers.

ANSWER In September and October, ______ kilowatt-hours were used.

b. To find how many more kilowatt-hours were used in December than in November, subtract the value for November from the value for December.

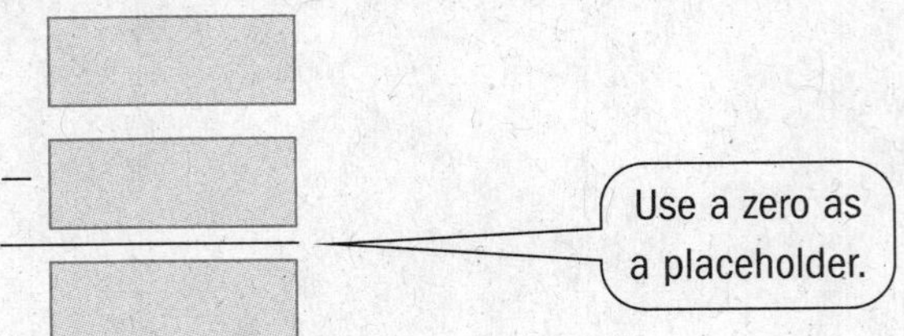

ANSWER In December, ______ more kilowatt-hours were used than in November.

Guided Practice Find the sum or difference.

1. $4.097 + (-1.394)$	2. $-0.48 + 0.6$	3. $-3.25 + (-10.008)$
4. $6.54 - 4.634$	5. $-11.2 - 15.71$	6. $4.265 - (-1.9)$

EXAMPLE 2 Solving an Equation with Decimals

$y - 2.845 = 3.91$ Original equation

$y - 2.845 + \square = 3.91 + \square$ Add $\square$ to each side.

$y = \square$ Simplify.

EXAMPLE 3 Standardized Test Practice

What is the solution of the equation $x - (-2.5) = 7.09$?

(A) $x = 2.59$ (B) $x = 4.59$ (C) $x = 8.09$ (D) $x = 9.59$

Solution

other way to solve the equation in mple 3 is to begin dding the opposite: + 2.5 = 7.09. nen subtract 2.5 rom each side.

$x - (-2.5) = 7.09$ Original equation

$x - (-2.5) + (\square) = 7.09 + (\square)$ Add $\square$ to each side.

$x = \square$ Simplify.

ANSWER The solution is $x = \square$. The correct answer is $\square$.

(A) (B) (C) (D)

EXAMPLE 4 Using Front-End Estimation

School You want to estimate the cost of your school supplies. Is the cost of the items shown (excluding tax) more or less than your $40 budget?

School Supplies	
Notebooks	$8.19
Pencils	$2.79
Pens	$4.39
Backpack	$23.58

Solution

Use front-end estimation.

1. Add the **front-end digits**: the dollars.

$**8**.19
$**2**.79
$**4**.39
$**23**.58
$37

2. Estimate the sum of the **remaining digits**: the cents.

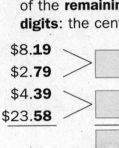

$8.**19**
$2.**79**
$4.**39**
$23.**58**

3. Add your results.

+

ANSWER The cost of the items is ______ than your $40 budget.

Guided Practice **Solve the equation.**

7. $t + (-0.18) = -1.33$	**8.** $z - 9.6 = 24.31$	**9.** $s + 6.58 = -1($

10. Use front-end estimation to estimate the sum $8.99 + $13.72 + $3

Multiplying and Dividing Decimals

Goal: Multiply and divide decimals.

Vocabulary

Leading digit: ______

Multiplying Decimals

Words Multiply decimals as you do whole numbers. Then place the decimal point. The number of decimal places in the product is the total number of decimal places in the ______.

Numbers 3.16 × 8.7 = 27.492
2 places, 1 place, ___ places

EXAMPLE 1 **Multiplying Decimals**

Deli You buy 1.5 pounds of lunchmeat that costs $4.98 per pound. How much do you pay for the lunchmeat?

Solution

To find how much you pay for the lunchmeat, multiply the cost per pound by the number of pounds.

4.98	___ decimal place(s)
× 1.5	+ ___ decimal place(s)
___	
___	
___	___ decimal place(s)

Hint: se unit analysis check the units of your answer.

ANSWER You pay ______ for the lunchmeat.

Remember that you don't need to write the zero in the thousandths' place in your answer.

Guided Practice Multiply. Check that your answer is reasonable.

To check that a product is reasonable, round each factor to its leading digit and multiply.

1. $-8.62 \cdot 2.3$	2. $15.01 \cdot (-4.95)$	3. $1.21 \cdot 0.07$

Dividing Decimals

Words When you divide by a decimal, multiply both the divisor and the dividend by the power of ______ that will make the ______ an integer. Then divide.

Numbers $3.25\overline{)15.925}$ Multiply by ______. $\begin{array}{r} 4.9 \\ 325\overline{)1592.5} \end{array}$

EXAMPLE 2 Dividing Decimals

To find the quotient $27.048 \div 2.8$, multiply the divisor and dividend by ______. Move the decimal points ______ place to the right.

$2.8\overline{)27.048}$ Move decimal points. $28\overline{)270.48}$

Then divide.

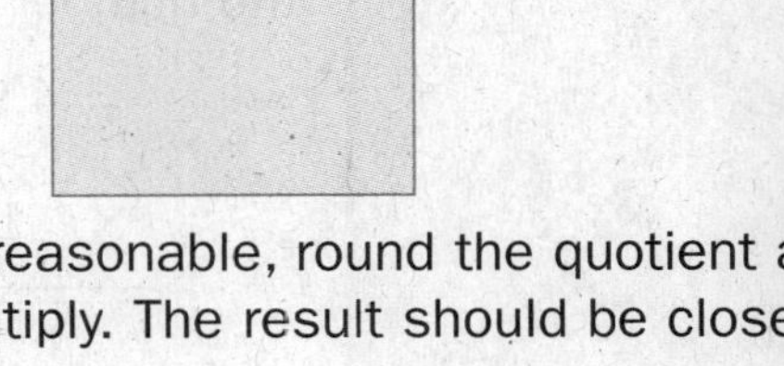

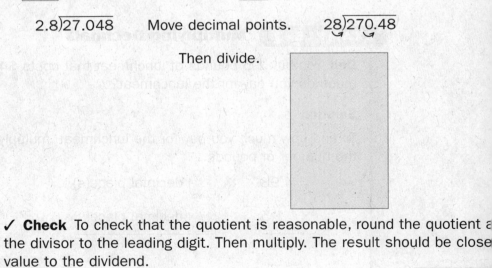

✓ **Check** To check that the quotient is reasonable, round the quotient a the divisor to the leading digit. Then multiply. The result should be close value to the dividend.

______ $\cdot$ 2.8 Round. ______ $\cdot$ ______ = ______ ✓

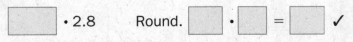

EXAMPLE 3 Using Zeros as Placeholders

To find some quotients, you may need to use zeros as placeholders.

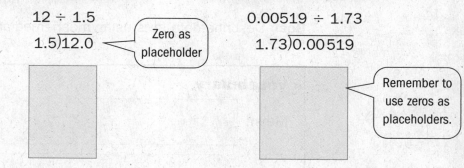

Placeholder in Dividend	Placeholder in Quotient
$12 \div 1.5$	$0.00519 \div 1.73$
$1.5\overline{)12.0}$ (Zero as placeholder)	$1.73\overline{)0.00519}$
	Remember to use zeros as placeholders.

Guided Practice **Find the quotient. Check that your answer is reasonable.**

4. $5.6 \div 0.07$	**5.** $0.792 \div 0.88$	**6.** $-15 \div (-0.25)$
7. $-2.496 \div (-6.4)$	**8.** $1.5759 \div (-3.09)$	**9.** $-0.0188 \div 9.4$

Mean, Median, and Mode

Goal: Describe data sets using mean, median, mode, and range.

Vocabulary

Mean:

Median:

Mode:

Range:

You can use the mean, median, or mode to represent the average of a data set.

EXAMPLE 1 Finding a Mean

Geology A geologist records the locations of five underground rivers in relation to sea level. The rivers are found at −227 meters, −180 meter −238 meters, −214 meters, and −221 meters. What is the mean loca of the underground rivers?

Solution

To find the mean of the 5 locations of the underground rivers, divide the of the locations by 5.

$$\text{Mean} = \frac{\qquad}{5}$$

=

=

ANSWER The mean location in relation to sea level is ______ meters.

Guided Practice **Find the mean of the data.**

1. 12°F, −4°F, 0°F, −6°F, 7°F, −3°F	2. 24.8 m, 31.6 m, 27.4 m, 25.2 m

EXAMPLE 2 Finding Median, Mode, and Range

CDs Find the median, mode(s), and range of the CD prices.

$9.80, $10.24, $11.49, $11.49, $12.63, $12.99, $13.50, $17.22

Solution

Median: The data set has an even number of prices, so the median is the mean of the two middle values, ______ and ______.

Median = ______ = ______ = ______

Mode: The price that occurs most often is ______. This is the mode.

Range: Find the difference of the greatest and the least values.

Range = ______ − ______ = ______

Guided Practice **Find the median, mode(s), and range of the data.**

3. 36, 28, 31, 33, 27, 40, 37, 24, 30, 34

4. 5, 12, 7, 7, 6, 9, 10, 6, 14

TCH OUT!
e data are not
red, you need to
r the data so you
find the median.

EXAMPLE 3 Standardized Test Practice

Video Games Ten people try a new video game and rate it on a scale of 1 to 10. The ratings are shown below. Which average best represents the data?

1, 2, 2, 3, 4, 4, 4, 5, 9, 10

Ⓐ mean　　Ⓑ median

Ⓒ mode　　Ⓓ Each average is a fair representat

Solution

Mean = ____ = ____

Median = ____ = ____

Mode: ____

ANSWER The mean, median, and mode are close. So, each average is a fair representation of the data. The correct answer is ____.

Guided Practice **Use the information at the top of the page.**

5. Ten more people try the new video game and rate it on a scale of 1 to 10. The ratings are shown below. Which average best represents the data?

1, 1, 2, 7, 7, 8, 9, 10, 10

Words to Review

Give an example of the vocabulary word.

Reciprocals

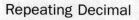

Repeating Decimal

Multiplicative Inverses

Front-end Estimation

Rational Number

Leading Digit

Terminating Decimal

Mean

Median

Range

Mode

Review your notes and Chapter 5 by using the Chapter Review on pages 280–28
of your textbook.

Solving Multi-Step Equations

Goal: Solve equations that require using two or more steps.

EXAMPLE 1 Writing and Solving a Multi-Step Equation

Fundraising You are participating in a 15 mile walk-a-thon. You walk and run for the same amount of time. You walk at a rate of 4 miles per hour, and you run at a rate of 6 miles per hour. How many hours will it take you to complete the walk-a-thon?

Solution

To find the number of hours it will take you to complete the walk-a-thon, first write a verbal model. Let h = the number of hours you walk or run.

Think: Can I simplify one or both sides of the equation?

Walk ______ • Number of hours

+ **Run** Miles per hour • ______

Total ______

______ $+ 6h =$ ______ Write algebraic model.

______ $=$ ______ Combine like terms.

______ $=$ ______ Divide each side by ______.

$h =$ ______ or ______ Simplify.

ANSWER It takes you ______ = ______ hours to complete the walk-a-thon.

✓ **Check** Substitute ______ for h in original equation.

______(______) + 6(______) $\stackrel{?}{=}$ ______

______ + ______ $\stackrel{?}{=}$ ______

______ = ______ ✓

EXAMPLE 2 Combining Like Terms

$5x - 16 - 8x = 23$		Original equation
____ $- 16 = 23$		Combine like terms.
____ $- 16$ ____ $= 23$ ____	____ to each side.	
____ = ____		Simplify.
____ = ____		Divide each side by ____.
$x =$ ____		Simplify.

Guided Practice **Solve the equation. Then check your solution.**

1. $-7 = 9a - 2a$	**2.** $m + 15 - 2m = 6$	**3.** $6y - 4 + 3y =$

EXAMPLE 3 Using the Distributive Property

When distributing a negative number, remember to distribute the negative sign to *each* term inside the parentheses.

$10n - 3(n + 1) = -24$	Original equation
$10n$ ____ $= -24$	Distributive property
____ $= -24$	Combine like terms.
____ $= -24$ ____	Add ____ to each side.
____ = ____	Simplify.
____ = ____	Divide each side by ____.
$n =$ ____	Simplify.

Guided Practice **Solve the equation. Then check your solution.**

4. $4(x - 7) = -36$	**5.** $a + 5(3 - a) = 11$	**6.** $26 = -8(t + 2) - 6t$

EXAMPLE 4 Standardized Test Practice

When solving the equation $\frac{6x - 17}{11} = 5$, what could the first step be to produce a simpler, equivalent equation?

Ⓐ Add 17. Ⓑ Divide by 6.

Ⓒ Multiply by 11. Ⓓ Multiply by 5.

Solution

Think:
ıat must I do to
e the equation into
ıuivalent equation
does not have a
fraction?

$\frac{6x - 17}{11} = 5$ Original equation

$\frac{6x - 17}{11}$ ____ $= 5$ ____ Multiply each side by ____.

$6x - 17 =$ ____ Simplify.

$6x - 17$ ____ $=$ ____ ____ to each side.

$6x =$ ____ Simplify.

____ $=$ ____ Divide each side by ____.

$x =$ ____ Simplify.

ANSWER The first step is to ____ each side by ____. The correct answer is ____.  Ⓐ Ⓑ Ⓒ Ⓓ

Solving Equations with Variables on Both Sides

Goal: Solve equations that have variables on both sides.

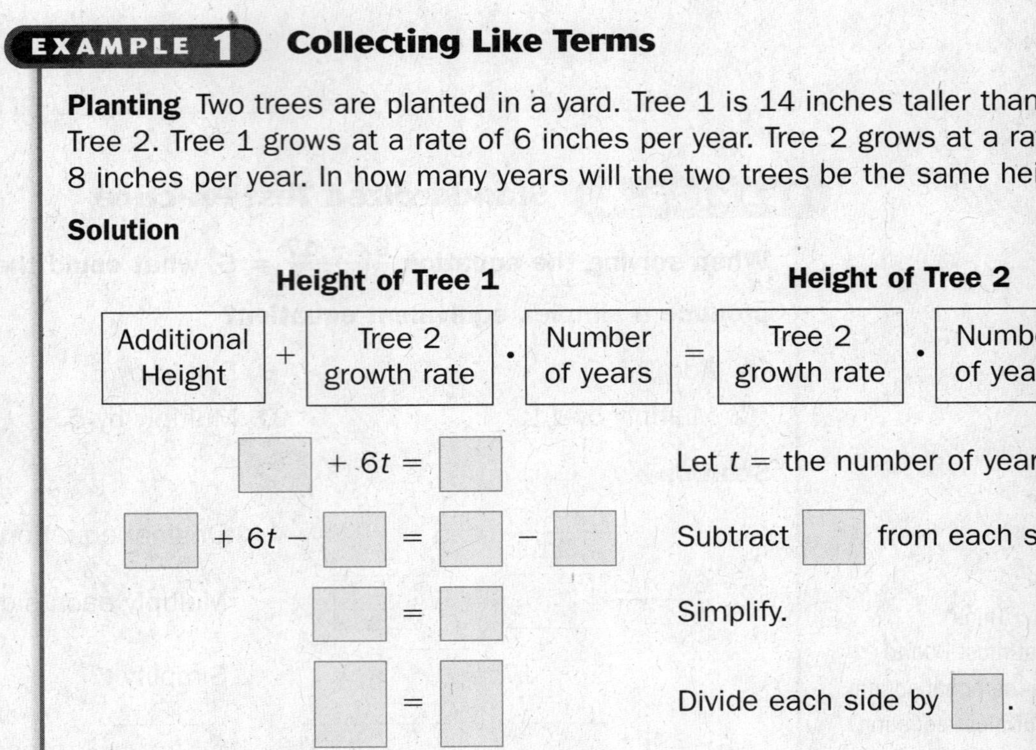

EXAMPLE 1 **Collecting Like Terms**

Planting Two trees are planted in a yard. Tree 1 is 14 inches taller than Tree 2. Tree 1 grows at a rate of 6 inches per year. Tree 2 grows at a rat[e of] 8 inches per year. In how many years will the two trees be the same hei[ght?]

Solution

Height of Tree 1 — **Height of Tree 2**

Additional Height + Tree 2 growth rate • Number of years = Tree 2 growth rate • Numbe[r] of year[s]

☐ + 6t = ☐ — Let t = the number of year[s].

☐ + 6t − ☐ = ☐ − ☐ — Subtract ☐ from each si[de].

☐ = ☐ — Simplify.

☐ = ☐ — Divide each side by ☐.

☐ = t — Simplify.

ANSWER The trees will be the same height in ☐.

EXAMPLE 2 Solve a Multi-Step Problem

Each side of the triangle has the same length. What is the perimeter of the triangle?

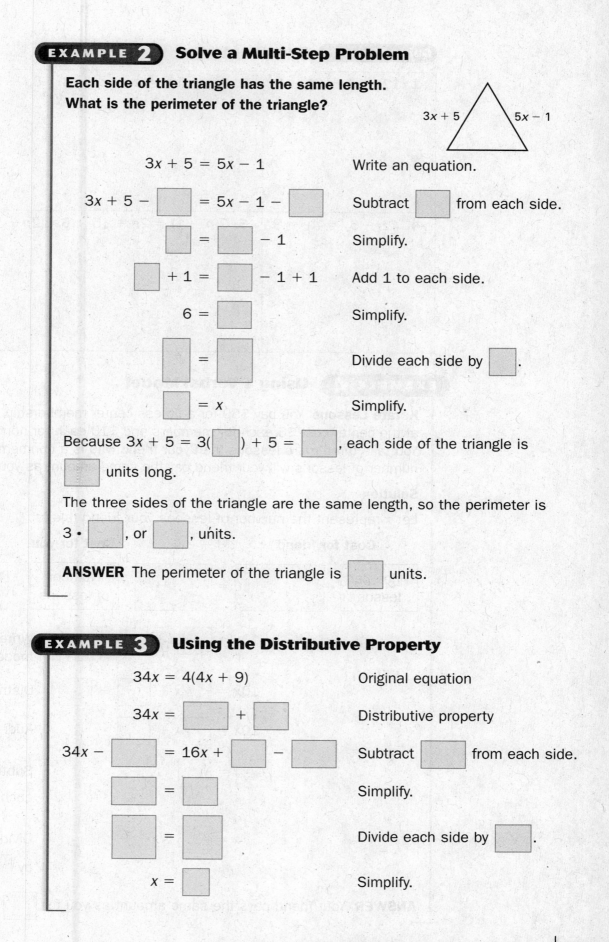

$3x + 5 = 5x - 1$	Write an equation.
$3x + 5 - \square = 5x - 1 - \square$	Subtract $\square$ from each side.
$\square = \square - 1$	Simplify.
$\square + 1 = \square - 1 + 1$	Add 1 to each side.
$6 = \square$	Simplify.
$\square = \square$	Divide each side by $\square$.
$\square = x$	Simplify.

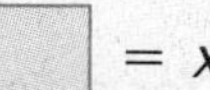

Because $3x + 5 = 3(\square) + 5 = \square$, each side of the triangle is $\square$ units long.

The three sides of the triangle are the same length, so the perimeter is $3 \cdot \square$, or $\square$, units.

ANSWER The perimeter of the triangle is $\square$ units.

EXAMPLE 3 Using the Distributive Property

$34x = 4(4x + 9)$	Original equation
$34x = \square + \square$	Distributive property
$34x - \square = 16x + \square - \square$	Subtract $\square$ from each side.
$\square = \square$	Simplify.
$\square = \square$	Divide each side by $\square$.
$x = \square$	Simplify.

Guided Practice Solve the equation.

1. $12t + 7 = 6t + 11$	2. $4m - 13 = m + 8$	3. $-8a + 5 = -3a -$
4. $42 - 5y = 4y - 3$	5. $3(n - 1) = 2n + 15$	6. $5(2p + 9) = -6p -$

EXAMPLE 4 Using a Verbal Model

Karate Lessons You pay $50 for a fitness center membership. Karate les at the center cost $6 each for members and $10 each for nonmembers. You take three more lessons than your friend who is a nonmember. For wh number of lessons will your friend pay the same amount as you?

Solution

Let x represent the number of lessons your friend takes.

Cost for friend **Cost for you**

Price per lesson • ____ = ____ • Number of lessons + Membershi fee

$10x =$ ____ $(x + 3) +$ ____ Write algebraic model.

$10x =$ ____ $x +$ ____ $+$ ____ Distributive prop

$10x =$ ____ $x +$ ____ Add.

____ $=$ ____ Subtract ____ f each side.

$x =$ ____ Divide each side by ____.

ANSWER Your friend pays the same amount as you for ____ lessons.

Solving Equations Involving Fractions and Decimals

Goal: Solve equations with fractions and decimals.

EXAMPLE 1 Solving an Equation Involving Decimals

Pizza You and your friend each order a pizza. You order a medium pizza with 3 toppings. Your friend orders a large pizza with 1 topping. A medium pizza with no toppings costs $5.45 and a large pizza with no toppings costs $7.95. You each pay the same amount. What is the price of one topping?

Solution

To solve the problem, you need to solve an equation involving decimals. First write a verbal model. Let t represent the price of one topping.

xample 1, some of steps are not shown. lake sure you can entify these steps.

Medium Pizza **Large Pizza**

[ ] + Number of toppings • Price of topping = Pizza Cost + Number of toppings • [ ]

$5.45 + 3t =$ [ ] $+ t$ Write algebraic model.

$5.45 +$ [ ] $=$ [ ] Subtract [ ] from each side.

[ ] $=$ [ ] Subtract [ ] from each side.

[ ] $=$ [ ] Divide each side by [ ].

$t =$ [ ] Simplify.

ANSWER The price of one topping is [ ].

Guided Practice **Write a verbal model. Then solve.**

1. Dawn and Jenna are growing their hair. Dawn's hair is 10 inches long and grows at a rate of 0.46 inch per month. Jenna's hair is 8 inches long and grows at a rate of 0.54 inch per month. In how many months will Dawn's hair and Jenna's hair be the same length?

EXAMPLE 2 Solving an Equation Involving Decimals

To eliminate decimals, multiply each side of the equation by a power of ten that will make all the coefficients integers.

$2.3x + 3.9 - 6.62x = 0.12$	Original equation
$(2.3x + 3.9 - 6.62x)\_\_\_ = (0.12)\_\_\_$	Multiply to clear decima
$\_\_\_ + 390 - \_\_\_ = \_\_\_$	Simplify.
$\_\_\_ + 390 = \_\_\_$	Combine like terms.
$\_\_\_ = \_\_\_$	Subtract ___ from each side.
$\_\_\_ = \_\_\_$	Divide each side by ___.
$x = \_\_\_$	Simplify.

EXAMPLE 3 Solving an Equation Involving Fractions

$-\frac{2}{3} = \frac{1}{6}x + \frac{5}{8}$	Original equation
$\left(-\frac{2}{3}x\right)\_\_\_ = \left(\frac{1}{6}x + \frac{5}{8}\right)\_\_\_$	Multiply each side by the LCD
$\left(-\frac{2}{3}x\right)\_\_\_ = \left(\frac{1}{6}x\right)\_\_\_ + \left(\frac{5}{8}\right)\_\_\_$	___ property
$\_\_\_ = 4x + 15$	Simplify.
$\_\_\_ = 15$	Subtract ___ from each sid
$\_\_\_ = \_\_\_$	Divide each side by ___.
$x = \_\_\_ = \_\_\_$	Simplify.

Guided Practice Solve the equation. Then check your solution.

2. $-4.1a + 8.9a = 14.4$	**3.** $1.05t + 0.63 = -0.07t$	**4.** $\frac{3}{4}p - \frac{5}{6} = \frac{1}{6}p$

Solving Equations Involving Circumference

Goal: Solve equations involving the circumference of a circle.

Vocabulary

Circle:

Center:

Radius:

Diameter:

Circumference:

Pi (π):

can approximate using 3.14, $\frac{22}{7}$, the π key on a calculator.

Circumference of a Circle

Words The circumference of a circle is the product of π and the ______.

Algebra $C = \pi$ ______ or $C =$ ______

EXAMPLE 1 Using Radius to Find Circumference

Find the circumference of a circle with a radius of 15 feet.

$C = 2\pi r$ Circumference formula

$\approx 2(\quad)(\quad)$ Substitute ______ for π and ______ for r.

$=$ ______ Multiply.

ANSWER The circumference is about ______.

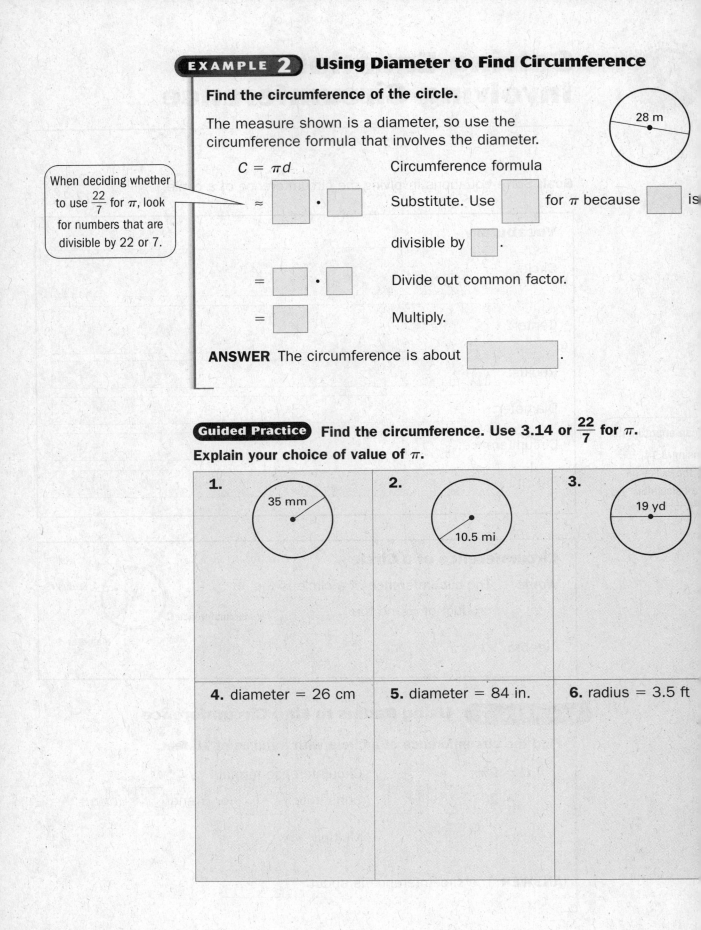

EXAMPLE 2 Using Diameter to Find Circumference

Find the circumference of the circle.

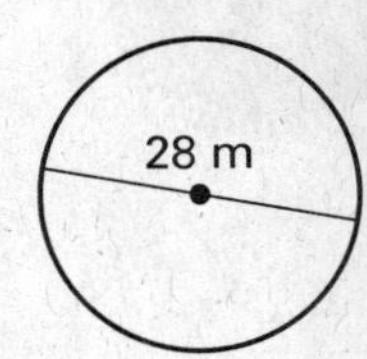

The measure shown is a diameter, so use the circumference formula that involves the diameter.

When deciding whether to use $\frac{22}{7}$ for π, look for numbers that are divisible by 22 or 7.

$C = \pi d$	Circumference formula
$\approx$ ____ • ____	Substitute. Use ____ for π because ____ is divisible by ____.
$=$ ____ • ____	Divide out common factor.
$=$ ____	Multiply.

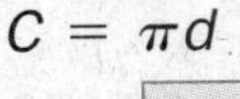

ANSWER The circumference is about ____.

Guided Practice **Find the circumference. Use 3.14 or $\frac{22}{7}$ for π. Explain your choice of value of π.**

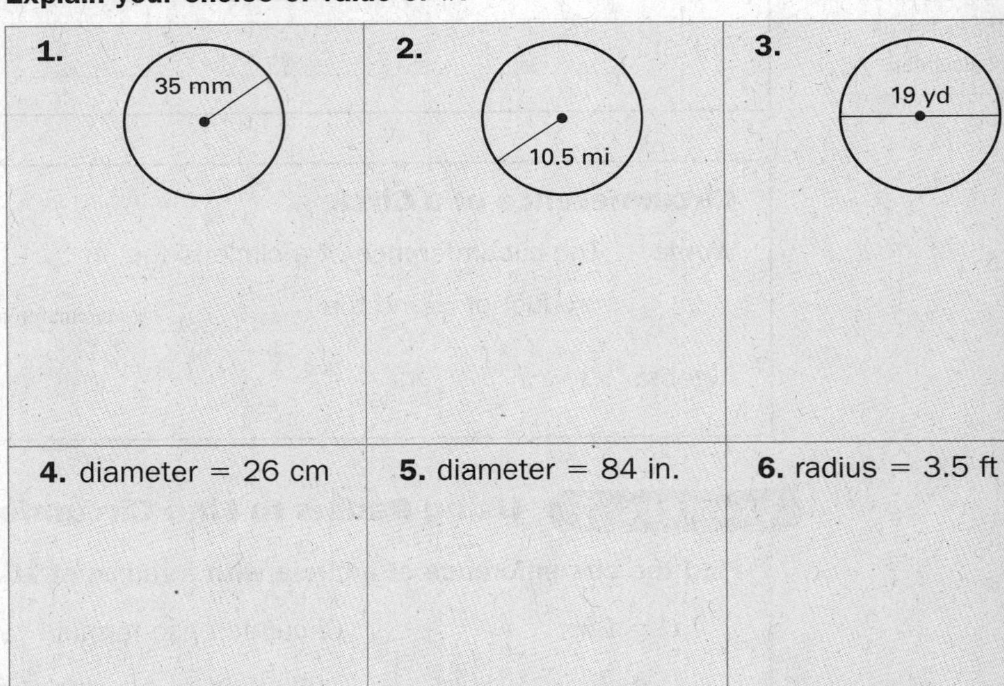

1. 35 mm	**2.** 10.5 mi	**3.** 19 yd
4. diameter = 26 cm	**5.** diameter = 84 in.	**6.** radius = 3.5 ft

EXAMPLE 3 Standardized Test Practice

Basketball A basketball rim has a circumference of about 56.5 inches. What is its diameter? Use 3.14 for π.

Ⓐ 9 inches Ⓑ 18 inches Ⓒ 24 inches Ⓓ 26 inches

Solution

$C = \pi d$	Circumference formula
____ $\approx$ (____)d	Substitute ____ for C and ____ for π.
____ $\approx$ ____	Divide each side by .
____ $\approx d$	Simplify.

ANSWER The diameter of a basketball rim is about ____.

The correct answer is ____. Ⓐ Ⓑ  Ⓓ

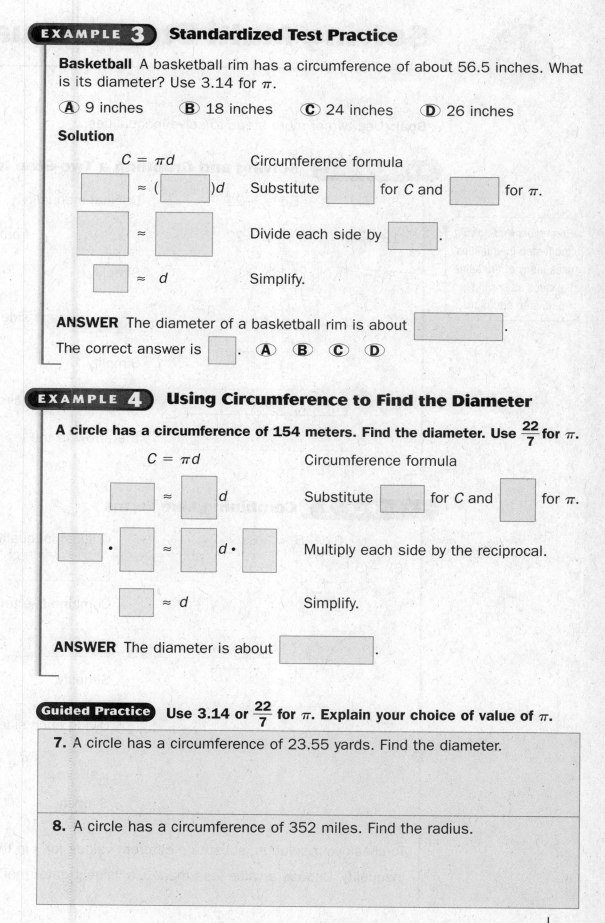

EXAMPLE 4 Using Circumference to Find the Diameter

A circle has a circumference of 154 meters. Find the diameter. Use $\frac{22}{7}$ for π.

$C = \pi d$	Circumference formula
____ $\approx$ ____ d	Substitute ____ for C and ____ for π.
____ • ____ $\approx$ ____ d • ____	Multiply each side by the reciprocal.
____ $\approx d$	Simplify.

ANSWER The diameter is about ____.

Guided Practice **Use 3.14 or $\frac{22}{7}$ for π. Explain your choice of value of π.**

7. A circle has a circumference of 23.55 yards. Find the diameter.

8. A circle has a circumference of 352 miles. Find the radius.

Solving Multi-Step Inequalities

Goal: Use two or more steps to solve inequalities.

EXAMPLE 1 Solving and Graphing a Two-Step Inequality

> Remember that solving multi-step inequalities uses many of the same steps as solving multi-step equations.

$13 + 5n \geq -22$ Original inequality

$13 + 5n$ ______ ≥ -22 ______ ______ from each side.

______ $\geq$ ______ Simplify.

______ $\geq$ ______ ______ each side by 5.

______ $\geq$ ______ Simplify.

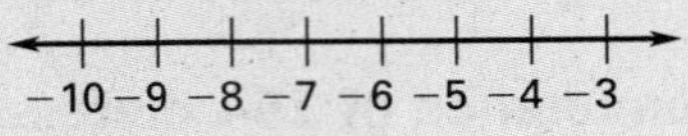

−10 −9 −8 −7 −6 −5 −4 −3

Use a ______ circle and draw the arrow to the ______.

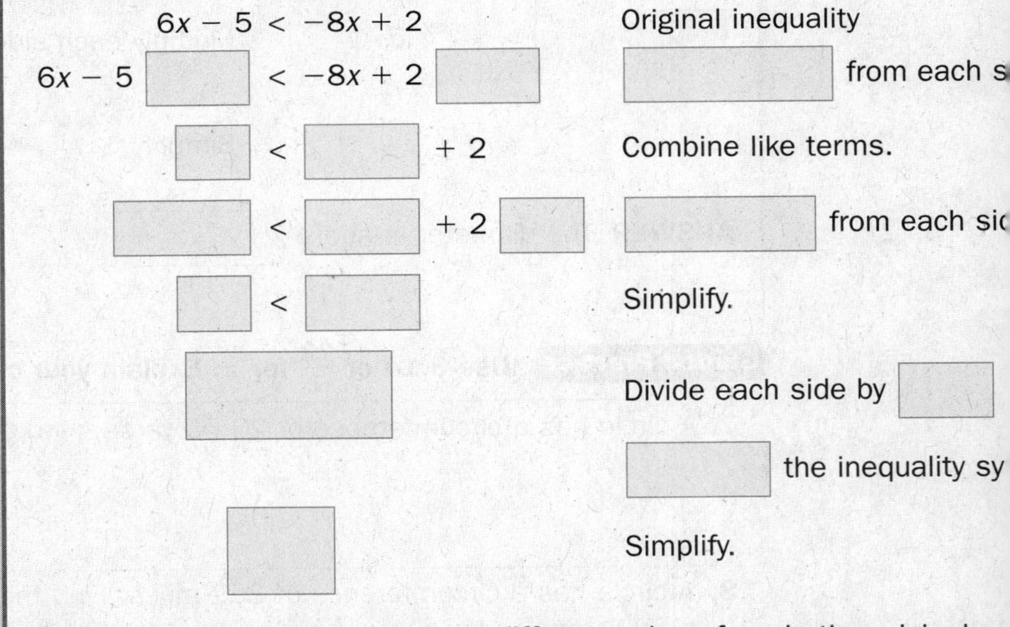

EXAMPLE 2 Combining Like Terms

$6x - 5 < -8x + 2$ Original inequality

$6x - 5$ ______ $< -8x + 2$ ______ ______ from each s

______ $<$ ______ $+ 2$ Combine like terms.

______ $<$ ______ $+ 2$ ______ ______ from each sic

______ $<$ ______ Simplify.

______ Divide each side by ______

______ the inequality sy

______ Simplify.

To check your solution, substitute different values for x in the original inequality. Choose a value less than $\frac{1}{2}$, a value greater than $\frac{1}{2}$, and $\frac{1}{2}$.

Guided Practice **Solve the inequality. Then graph the solution.**

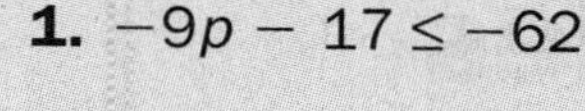

1. $-9p - 17 \le -62$

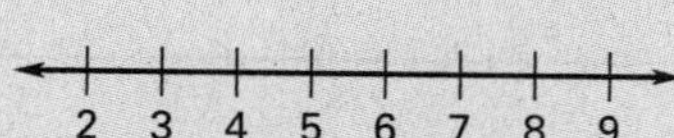

2. $10a - 21 > 4a + 15$

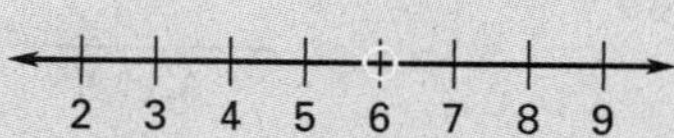

EXAMPLE 3 Writing and Solving a Multi-Step Inequality

Video Games You are saving money to buy a video game system. You have saved \$30. You earn \$32 each week babysitting. You pay \$7 each week for piano lessons. For how many weeks must you save your money to have at least \$205?

Solution

To find the number of weeks you must save your money to have at least \$205, subtract your expenses from your earnings. Let *w* represent the number of weeks.

Earnings

Money saved + Babysitting earnings per week • ____

Lesson Expenses **Savings**

− ____ • Number of Weeks ____ Savings

30 + ____ − ____ ____ 205 Write an inequality.

30 + ____ ____ 205. Combine like terms.

____ ____ ____ ____ from each side.

____ Divide each side by ____.

ANSWER You must save your money for at least ____ weeks.

Problem Solving and Inequalities

Goal: Write and solve multi-step inequalities to solve real-world problems.

EXAMPLE 1 Writing and Solving an Inequality

Go-Karts At a go-kart park, you can pay $6 for admission and $4 for eac ride, or you can buy an all-day pass for $25, which includes admission a unlimited rides. How many times would you have to ride the go-karts so buying an all-day pass is a better value than paying for each ride?

Solution

To decide how many times you would have to ride the go-karts so that buying an all-day pass is a better value, write and solve an inequality. Let *x* represent the number of go-kart rides.

Price of go-kart ride	·	Number of rides	+	______	______	Cost of all-day pass

______ + ______ ______ ______ Write an inequality.

______ ______ ______ ______ from each side.

______ ______ ______ Divide each side by ______.

ANSWER It doesn't make sense to ride the go-karts ______ times.

So you would have to ride the go-karts ______ or more times to make buying an all-day pass a better value than paying for each ride.

Guided Practice **Write an inequality. Then solve the following problem.**

1. At a miniature golf course, you can pay $5 for admission and $2 for round, or you can buy an all-day pass for $17, which includes admiss and unlimited rounds. How many rounds would you have to play so tl buying an all-day pass is a better value than paying for each round?

EXAMPLE 2 Translating Verbal Sentences

Write the sentence as an inequality.

a. 3 times the sum of a number and 2 is less than 36.

b. 6 times a number, minus 8 is no more than twice the number.

Solution

First decide which inequality symbol to use. Then substitute numbers, variables, and operation symbols.

a. The phrase "is less than" means ______.

3 times the sum of a number and 2 is less than 36.

ANSWER The inequality is ______.

b. The phrase "is no more than" means ______.

6 times a number, minus 8 is no more than twice the number.

ANSWER The inequality is ______.

Guided Practice **Write the sentence as an inequality. Let *x* represent the unknown number.**

2. 8 times the difference of a number and 2 is at least 30.

3. The sum of a number and 5 is more than 4 times the difference of the number and 4.

EXAMPLE 3 Writing and Solving an Inequality

Cell Phone Plans A cell phone company offers two calling plans.

Plan A: no monthly fee, \$.14 per minute

Plan B: \$5 monthly fee, \$.04 per minute

How many minutes do you need to use each month so that Plan B is the better value?

Solution

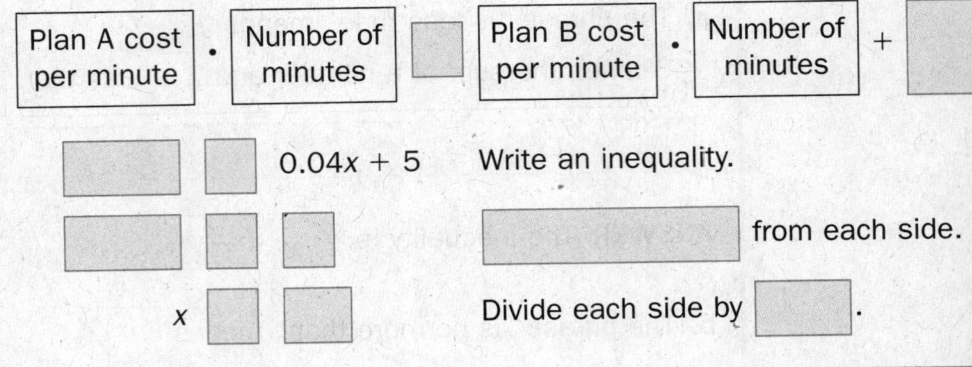

Plan A cost per minute
•
Number of minutes
Plan B cost per minute
•
Number of minutes
+
$0.04x + 5$
Write an inequality.
from each side.
x
Divide each side by .

ANSWER Plan B is the better value if you use more than ______ each month.

Words to Review

Give an example of the vocabulary word.

Circle

Diameter

Center

Circumference

Radius

Pi (π)

Review your notes and Chapter 6 by using the Chapter Review on pages 331–334 of your textbook.

Ratios and Rates

Goal: Find ratios and unit rates.

Vocabulary

Ratio:

Equivalent ratios:

Rate:

Unit rate:

EXAMPLE 1 **Writing a Ratio**

Shopping An outlet mall has 36 clothing stores, 6 footwear stores, 4 cr stores, and 20 specialty shops. Write the ratio of clothing stores to spe shops in three ways.

Solution

$\frac{\text{clothing stores}}{\text{specialty shops}} = \square = \square$ Write as a fraction and simpl

ANSWER The ratio can be written as $\square$, $\square$, or $\square$.

Guided Practice **Use the information in Example 1 to write the ratio in simplest form and two other ways.**

1. craft stores to footwear stores	**2.** specialty shops to craft store

EXAMPLE 2 Finding an Equivalent Rate

Population About 245 babies are born every minute around the world. About how many babies are born per hour around the world?

Solution

Use the fact that ______ = 1 h. So, ______ is equivalent to 1.

Notice that equivalent rates have the same value.

$\frac{245 \text{ births}}{1 \text{ min}} = \frac{245 \text{ births}}{1 \text{ min}} \cdot$ ______ Multiply by a fraction that is equivalent to 1.

= ______ Simplify.

ANSWER About ______ babies are born per hour around the world.

EXAMPLE 3 Finding a Unit Rate

Write −33 gallons per 8 minutes as a unit rate.

$-\frac{33 \text{ gal}}{8 \text{ min}} =$ ______ Divide numerator and denominator by ______ to get a denominator of 1 unit.

= ______ Simplify.

…ce that a unit rate …equivalent rate with …ominator of 1 unit.

ANSWER The unit rate is ______ gallons per minute.

✓ **Check** Round ______ gal/min to ______ gal/min. The product ______ • ______ = −32 which is about −33, so your answer is reasonable.

Guided Practice **Write your answer as a rate.**

3. You rollerblade 0.3 mile per minute. How many miles per hour do you rollerblade?

Write the rate as a unit rate.

4. $\frac{168 \text{ students}}{7 \text{ classes}}$	5. $-\frac{252 \text{ ft}}{3 \text{ sec}}$	6. $\frac{57 \text{ h}}{38 \text{ days}}$	7. $\frac{\$430}{40 \text{ h}}$

Writing and Solving Proportions

Goal: Write and solve proportions.

Vocabulary

Proportion:

Cross products:

Scale model:

Scale:

EXAMPLE 1 Writing and Solving a Proportion

Renting Movies On Tuesday, you paid \$7.47 to rent movies. On Friday, y rent 5 movies for a total of \$12.45. Each movie costs the same amoun rent. How many movies did you rent on Tuesday?

Solution

To find how many movies you rented on Tuesday, write and solve a proport

	Cost	Number
Tuesday	\$7.47	x
Friday	\$12.45	5

Use a table to set up a proportion

In Example 1, the ratios in the proportion use the following units: $\frac{\text{dollars}}{\text{dollars}}$ and $\frac{\text{number of movies}}{\text{number of movies}}$.

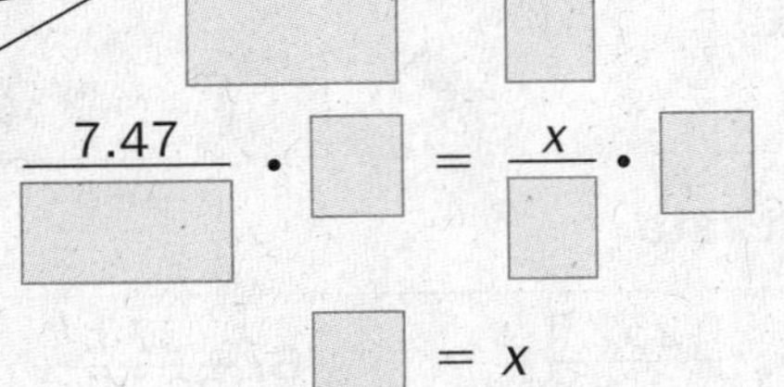

$\frac{7.47}{\square} = \frac{x}{\square}$ Write a proportion.

$\frac{7.47}{\square} \cdot \square = \frac{x}{\square} \cdot \square$ Multiply each side by the same nu

$\square = x$ Simplify.

ANSWER You rented $\square$ movies on Tuesday.

Guided Practice Solve the proportion.

1. $\frac{a}{15} = \frac{2}{3}$	2. $\frac{28}{16} = \frac{m}{24}$	3. $\frac{45}{117} = \frac{x}{52}$

Cross Products Property

Words The cross products of a proportion are ______.

Algebra If $\frac{a}{b} = \frac{c}{d}$, where b and d are nonzero numbers, then ______ $= bc$.

Numbers Because $\frac{4}{5} = \frac{8}{10}$, you know that ______ = ______.

EXAMPLE 2 **Using the Cross Products Property**

$\frac{10.4}{22.1} = \frac{41.6}{n}$ Original proportion

______ = ______ Cross products property

______ = ______ Multiply.

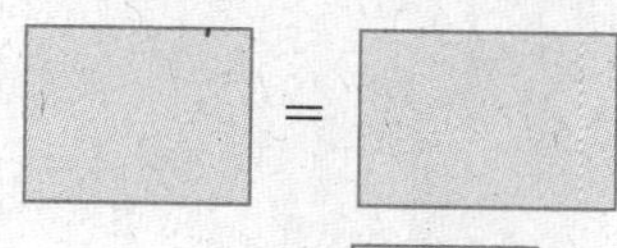

______ = ______ Divide each side by the same number.

$n =$ ______ Simplify.

ember that
an use cross
cts to solve
portion and
ck whether
atios form
oportion.

✓ **Check** You can check your answer by finding the cross products of the proportion. If the cross products are equal, the ratios form a proportion.

$\frac{10.4}{22.1} \stackrel{?}{=} \frac{41.6}{\_\_\_\_}$ Substitute for n in original proportion.

______ $\stackrel{?}{=}$ ______ Cross products property

______ = ______ ✓

Guided Practice Solve the proportion. Then check your solution.

4. $\frac{5}{t} = \frac{20}{32}$	**5.** $\frac{7}{15} = \frac{q}{90}$	**6.** $\frac{2.6}{0.5} = \frac{31.2}{b}$

EXAMPLE 3 Standardized Test Practice

Model Car You are building a model car that has a total length of 6 inc
If the scale of this model is 1 inch to 1.5 feet, how long is the actual ca

Ⓐ 6.5 inches Ⓑ 9 inches Ⓒ 6.5 feet Ⓓ 9 feet

You can also solve Example 3 by using an equivalent scale without units: 1 inch to 18 inches, or 1:18. Notice that your answer will be in inches.

Solution

$\text{Scale} = \frac{\text{Length of model car}}{\text{Length of actual car}}$ Write a verbal model.

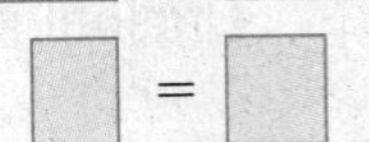

___ = ___ Write a proportion.

 =  Cross products property

ANSWER The length of the actual car is 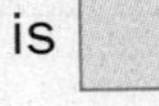. The correct answer is ___. Ⓐ Ⓑ Ⓒ Ⓓ

Solving Percent Problems

Goal: Solve percent problems using proportions.

Vocabulary

Percent: ______

Solving Percent Problems

To represent "*a* is *p* percent of *b*," use the proportion

$$\frac{a}{\square} = \frac{\square}{100}$$

where *a* is part of the base *b* and *p*%, or $\frac{p}{100}$ is the ______.

EXAMPLE 1 **Finding a Percent**

Books A library receives a donation of books. Out of 360 books, 45 are science fiction. What percent of the books donated are science fiction?

Solution

To find the percent of books that are science fiction, use a percent proportion.

$\frac{a}{b} = \frac{p}{100}$	Write a percent proportion.
$\square = \frac{p}{100}$	Substitute values.
$\square \cdot 100 = \frac{p}{100} \cdot 100$	Multiply each side by 100.
$\square = p$	Simplify.

ANSWER Of the books, ______ are science fiction.

Guided Practice **Use a percent proportion.**

1. 136 is what percent of 160?	**2.** 78 is what percent of 60?

EXAMPLE 2 Finding Part of a Base

Mowing Lawns This year from mowing lawns you earned 125% of last ye earnings, which were $484. What are this year's earnings?

Solution

$\frac{a}{b} = \frac{p}{100}$ Write a percent proportion.

$\square = \frac{\square}{100}$ Substitute values.

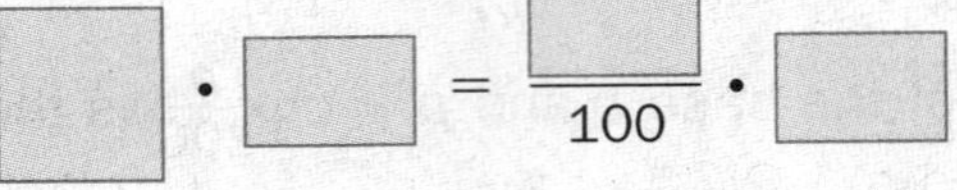

$\square \cdot \square = \frac{\square}{100} \cdot \square$ Multiply each side by the same num

$\square = \square$ Simplify.

ANSWER This year's earnings are ______.

EXAMPLE 3 Finding a Base

27 is 6% of what number?

$\frac{a}{b} = \frac{p}{100}$ Write a percent proportion.

$\square = \frac{\square}{100}$ Substitute values.

$\square \cdot 100 = \square$ Cross products property.

$\square = \square$ Simplify.

ANSWER 27 is 6% of ______.

Summary of Percent Problems

Question	Method	Proportion
a is what percent of b?	Solve for $\square$.	$\frac{a}{b} = \frac{\square}{100}$
What number is $p\%$ of b?	Solve for $\square$.	$\frac{\square}{b} = \frac{p}{100}$
a is $p\%$ of what number?	Solve for $\square$.	$\frac{a}{\square} = \frac{p}{100}$

Guided Practice **Use a percent proportion.**

3. What is 0.2% of 98?	**4.** 234 is 104% of what number?

LESSON 7.4

Fractions, Decimals, and Percents

Goal: Rewrite fractions, decimals, and percents.

Vocabulary

Circle graph:

EXAMPLE 1 Writing a Percent as a Decimal

Remember that dividing by 100 is the same as moving the decimal point two places to the left.

a. 0.48% = 0.48 ÷ 100 = .0048 =

b. 175% = 175 ÷ 100 = 1.75 =

c. 3.6% = 3.6 ÷ 100 = .036 =

EXAMPLE 2 Writing a Decimal as a Percent

a. 1.09 = 1.09

=

b. 0.3 = 0.30

=

You can also write a decimal as percent by writing the decimal a fraction with a denominator of 100 percent is the numerator. For exar

$0.3 = \frac{3}{10} = \frac{30}{100} = 30\%$

Guided Practice Write the decimal as a percent.

1. 0.78	**2.** 0.5	**3.** 9.2	**4.** 0.401

Write the percent as a decimal and as a fraction in simplest form.

5. 92%	**6.** 206%	**7.** 47.5%	**8.** 0.8%

EXAMPLE 3 Writing a Percent as a Fraction

a. $0.48\% = \frac{\square}{100} = \frac{\square \times \square}{100 \times \square} = \square = \square$

b. $175\% = \frac{\square}{100} = \frac{\square \div \square}{100 \div \square} = \square = \square$

c. $3.6\% = \frac{\square}{100} = \frac{\square \times \square}{100 \times \square} = \square = \square$

EXAMPLE 4 Writing a Fraction as a Percent

Survey The circle graph at the right shows the results of a survey of what 400 students prefer to order for breakfast at a restaurant. What percent of students prefer to order pancakes?

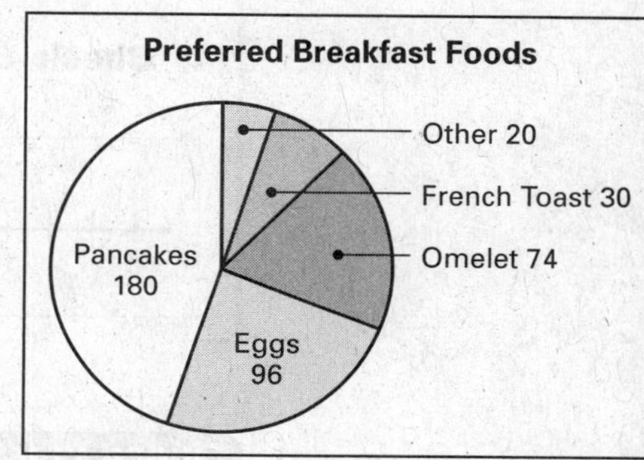

Solution

To write the fraction of students who prefer to order pancakes as a percent, write a percent proportion with $\square$ and solve for p.

$\square = \frac{p}{100}$ Write a percent proportion.

$\square \cdot 100 = \frac{p}{100} \cdot 100$ Multiply each side by 100.

$\square = p$ Simplify.

ANSWER $\square$ of the students prefer to order pancakes.

...member that each ... of a circle graph is ...ercent of the data. ...sum of the percents ...equal 100% because ...rcle graph represents ...all of the data.

Guided Practice **Write the fraction as a percent.**

9. $\frac{7}{10}$	**10.** $\frac{11}{25}$	**11.** $\frac{3}{50}$	**12.** $\frac{7}{8}$

EXAMPLE 5 Ordering Fractions, Decimals, and Percents

Order the numbers from least to greatest: $\frac{7}{20}$, 3.5, and 3.5%.

1. Write the numbers as decimals with the same number of decimal places.

   $\frac{7}{20} =$ ______ 3.5 = ______ 3.5% = ______

2. Compare the decimals.

   ______ < ______ and ______ < 3.500

ANSWER The numbers ordered from least to greatest are

, ______, and 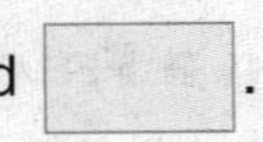.

✓ **Check** Use a number line to order the decimals.

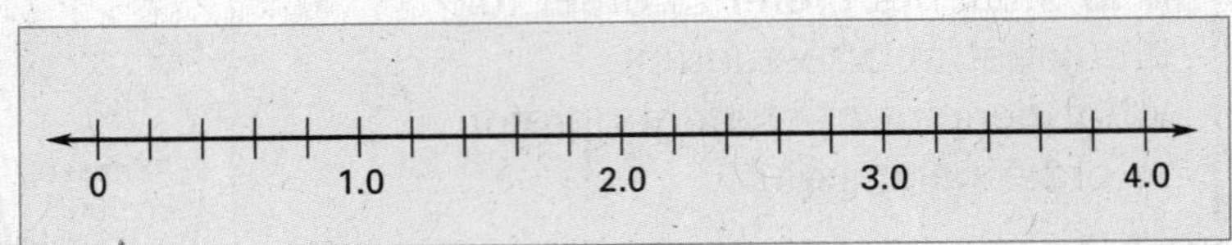

Guided Practice **Order the numbers from least to greatest.**

13. 0.165, $\frac{4}{25}$, 1.5%	**14.** 25%, 0.02, $\frac{1}{5}$	**15.** $\frac{11}{8}$, 0.13, 13.75%

Percent of Change

Goal: Solve problems with percent of increase or decrease.

Vocabulary

Percent of change:

Percent of increase:

Percent of decrease:

Percent of Change

Use the following equation to find the percent of change.

Percent of change, $p\% = \dfrac{\text{Amount of } \_\_\_ \text{ or } \_\_\_}{\_\_\_}$

EXAMPLE 1 Finding a Percent of Decrease

Population In 2000, a town's population was 1260. In 2006, the population was 1050. What is the percent of decrease in the town's population?

Solution

To find the percent of decrease, use the percent of change equation.

$p\% = \dfrac{\_\_\_ - \_\_\_}{\_\_\_}$ Write amount of decrease and divide by original amount.

$= \_\_\_$ Subtract.

$= \_\_\_ = \_\_\_$ Simplify. Write fraction as a percent.

te the fraction percent, begin ing the fraction a decimal.

ANSWER The percent of decrease is about ___.

EXAMPLE 2 Finding a Percent of Increase

WATCH OUT! Make sure you use the original amount, not the new amount, in the denominator when finding a percent of change.

Sales A real estate agent sells 32 properties one year. The next year, the agent sells 54 properties. Find the percent of increase.

Solution

$p\% = \frac{\square - \square}{\square}$ Write amount of increase and divide by original amount.

$= \square$ Subtract.

$= \square = \square$ Simplify. Write fraction as a percent.

ANSWER The percent of increase is ______.

Guided Practice **Tell whether the change is an *increase* or *decrease*. Then find the percent of change.**

1. Original amount: 80 New amount: 60	**2.** Original amount: 25 New amount: 40	**3.** Original amount: New amount: 64

EXAMPLE 3 Using Percent of Increase

Banking Two years ago, your savings account balance was $492.19. Since then, the balance has increased 32.6%. What is the current balan

Solution

A shortcut to finding a percent of a number is to write the percent as a decimal and then find the product of the decimal and the number.

1. Find the increase.

Increase = 32.6% of 492.19

= ______ (______) Write 32.6% as a decimal.

≈ ______ Multiply.

2. Add the increase to the original amount.

New amount ≈ ______ + ______ = ______

ANSWER The current balance in your savings account is ______.

Percent Applications

Goal: Solve percent application problems.

Vocabulary

Markup:

Discount:

EXAMPLE 1 **Finding a Sale Price**

Bicycles You are shopping for a bicycle and find one with an original price of $240. The store is offering a 35% discount on all bicycles. What is the sale price of the bicycle?

Solution

Remember that the discount must be subtracted from the original price to find the sale price.

1. Find the amount of the discount.

Discount = 35% of $240

= ______ Write 35% as a decimal.

=  Multiply.

2. Subtract the discount from the original price.

______ − ______ = ______

ANSWER The sale price of the bicycle is ______.

Guided Practice **Find the sale price.**

1. Original price: $56 Percent discount: 15%	**2.** Original price: $70.95 Percent discount: 40%

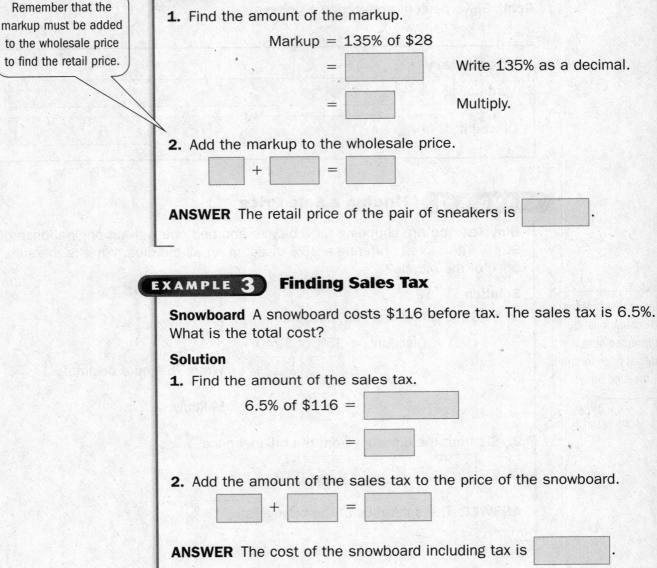

EXAMPLE 2 Finding a Retail Price

Sneakers A pair of sneakers has a wholesale price of $28. The percent markup is 135%. What is the retail price?

Remember that the markup must be added to the wholesale price to find the retail price.

Solution

1. Find the amount of the markup.

Markup = 135% of $28

= ______ Write 135% as a decimal.

= ______ Multiply.

2. Add the markup to the wholesale price.

______ + ______ = ______

ANSWER The retail price of the pair of sneakers is ______.

EXAMPLE 3 Finding Sales Tax

Snowboard A snowboard costs $116 before tax. The sales tax is 6.5%. What is the total cost?

Solution

1. Find the amount of the sales tax.

6.5% of $116 = ______

= ______

2. Add the amount of the sales tax to the price of the snowboard.

______ + ______ = ______

ANSWER The cost of the snowboard including tax is ______.

Guided Practice **Find the retail price.**

3. Wholesale price: \$71 Percent markup: 90%	**4.** Wholesale price: \$29 Percent markup: 105%

Find the total cost.

5. Price: \$33 Sales tax: 7%	**6.** Price: \$104.96 Sales tax: 5.5%

EXAMPLE 4 Solve a Multi-Step Problem

Pizza Delivery You order pizza to be delivered. The bill is \$16. You give the delivery person a 15% tip. The sales tax is 5%. What is the total cost of the pizza?

Solution

1. Find the tip.

15% of \$16 = ______

= ______

2. Find the amount of the sales tax.

5% of \$16 = ______

= ______

3. Add the pizza bill, the tip, and the amount of the sales tax.

______ + ______ + ______ = ______

ANSWER The total cost of the pizza is ______.

Guided Practice **Find the total cost.**

7. You order pizza to be delivered. The bill is \$12.50. You give the delivery person a 10% tip. The sales tax is 6%. What is the total cost of the pizza?

Using the Percent Equation

Goal: Solve percent problems using the percent equation.

Vocabulary

Interest:

Principal:

Annual interest rate:

The Percent Equation

To represent the statement "*a* is *p* percent of *b*" use the equation:

$\square = \square \cdot b$ Part of the base = $\square \cdot \square$

EXAMPLE 1 **Finding Part of a Base**

Pets In a survey of 1500 people, 82.6% said that they have at least one pet. Find the number of people who said they have at least one pet.

Solution

To find the number of people, use the percent equation.

$a = p\% \cdot b$ Write percent equation.

$= \square \cdot \square$ Substitute values.

$= \square \cdot \square$ Write percent as a decimal.

$= \square$ Multiply.

ANSWER The number of people is $\square$.

Think: Does the number 1500 represent *a* or *b* in the percent equation? Notice that 1500 represents all of the people surveyed. Therefore, 1500 represents *b*.

Guided Practice **Use the percent equation.**

1. Find 24% of 950.	2. Find 70.4% of 500.

EXAMPLE 2 Finding a Base

Math Test You receive a score of 152 points, or 95%, on your math test. How many points is the test worth?

Solution

$a = p\% \cdot b$	Write percent equation.
$\_\_\_ = \_\_\_ \cdot b$	Substitute values.
$\_\_\_ = \_\_\_ \cdot b$	Write 95% as a decimal.
$\_\_\_ = b$	Divide each side by the same number.

ANSWER The test is worth ______ points.

Think:
oes the number
2 represent *a* or
in the percent
equation?
nember that 152
epresents your
re, only a part of
e points of the
t. Therefore, 152
represents *a*.

Guided Practice **Solve using the percent equation.**

3. 5.46 is 37.5% of what number?	**4.** 32 is what percent of 250?

Simple Interest

Words To find ______ *I*, find the product of the ______ *P*, the ______ *r* written as a decimal, and the ______ *t* in years.

Algebra $I =$ ______

ien you borrow
ey from a bank,
u pay the bank
est as well as the
int you borrowed.

EXAMPLE 3 Finding Simple Interest

Loans You borrow $2500 and pay a simple interest rate of 3.5% per year. How much interest will you pay after 30 months?

Solution

$I = Prt$	Write formula for simple interest.
$= (\_\_\_)(\_\_\_)(\_\_\_)$	Substitute values.
$= \_\_\_$	Multiply.

Think:
How can 30
nths be written
in years?

ANSWER You will pay ______ in interest.

Simple Probability

Goal: Find the probabilities of events.

Vocabulary

Outcome:

Event:

Favorable outcome:

Probability of an event:

Theoretical probability:

Experimental probability:

Probability of an Event

The theoretical probability of an event when all outcomes are equally likely is:

$$P(\text{event}) = \frac{\text{Number of } \underline{\qquad} \text{ outcomes}}{\text{Number of } \underline{\qquad} \text{ outcomes}}$$

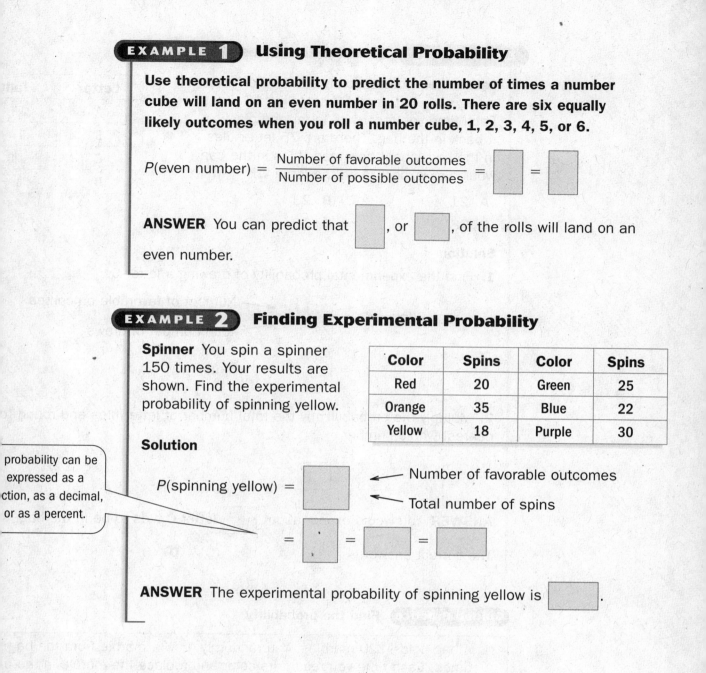

EXAMPLE 1 Using Theoretical Probability

Use theoretical probability to predict the number of times a number cube will land on an even number in 20 rolls. There are six equally likely outcomes when you roll a number cube, 1, 2, 3, 4, 5, or 6.

$$P(\text{even number}) = \frac{\text{Number of favorable outcomes}}{\text{Number of possible outcomes}} = \square = \square$$

ANSWER You can predict that ☐, or ☐, of the rolls will land on an even number.

EXAMPLE 2 Finding Experimental Probability

Spinner You spin a spinner 150 times. Your results are shown. Find the experimental probability of spinning yellow.

Color	Spins	Color	Spins
Red	20	Green	25
Orange	35	Blue	22
Yellow	18	Purple	30

Solution

probability can be expressed as a ction, as a decimal, or as a percent.

$P(\text{spinning yellow}) = \square$ ← Number of favorable outcomes ← Total number of spins

$= \square = \square = \square$

ANSWER The experimental probability of spinning yellow is ☐.

EXAMPLE 3 Standardized Test Practice

Letter tiles You randomly draw a tile from a bag of A, B, C, and D letter tiles 16 times. Each time you record its letter and place it back in the bag. There are 75 letter tiles in the bag. About how many tiles in the bag would you expect to be the letter C?

Letter	Tally
A	𝍸
B	II
C	𝍸
D	III

Ⓐ 21 Ⓑ 23

Ⓒ 28 Ⓓ 30

Solution

1. Find the experimental probability of drawing a letter C.

P(letter C) = ☐ ← Number of favorable outcomes / ← Total number of draws

= ☐ Simplify.

2. Multiply the probability by the total number of letter tiles and round to nearest whole number.

☐ • ☐ ≈ ☐

ANSWER You would expect about ☐ letter C tiles to be in the bag.

The correct answer is ☐. Ⓐ Ⓑ Ⓒ Ⓓ

Guided Practice **Find the probability.**

1. A bag holds 120 marbles. You randomly draw a marble from the bag times. Each time you record its color and replace the marble in the ba You draw 6 blue marbles. What is the experimental probability of draw a blue marble? How many blue marbles do you predict are in the bag

Words to Review

Give an example of the vocabulary word.

Ratio

Proportion

Equivalent ratios

Cross products

Rate

Scale model

Unit rate

Scale

Percent

Markup

Circle graph

Discount

Percent of change

Interest

Percent of increase

Principal

Percent of decrease

Annual interest rate

Favorable outcome

Probability of an event

Outcome

Event

Theoretical probability

Experimental probability

Review your notes and Chapter 7 by using the Chapter Review on pages 388–392 of your textbook.

Angle Pairs

Goal: Solve equations to find angle measures.

Vocabulary

Straight angle:

Right angle:

Supplementary angles:

Complementary angles:

Vertical angles:

Perpendicular lines:

Parallel lines:

EXAMPLE 1 **Finding an Angle Measure**

∠1 and ∠2 are complementary, and $m\angle 2 = 24°$. Find $m\angle 1$.

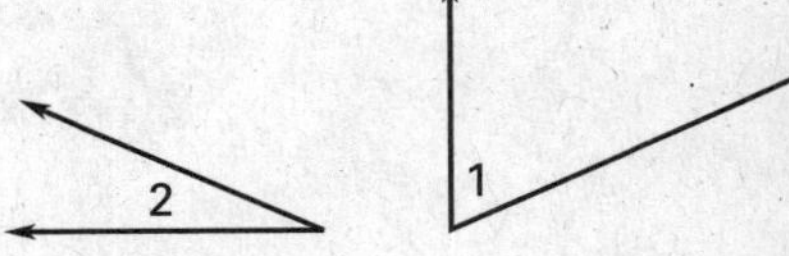

Solution

$m\angle 1 + m\angle 2 = 90°$ Definition of complementary angles

$m\angle 1 +$ ____ $= 90°$ Substitute ____ for $m\angle 2$.

$m\angle 1 =$ ____ Subtract ____ from each side.

Guided Practice **Tell whether ∠1 and ∠2 are *complementary, supplementary,* or *neither.***

1. $m\angle 1 = 168°$ $m\angle 2 = 12°$	**2.** $m\angle 1 = 27°$ $m\angle 2 = 73°$	**3.** $m\angle 1 = 48°$ $m\angle 2 = 42°$
4. $m\angle 1 = 19°$ $m\angle 2 = 71°$	**5.** $m\angle 1 = 92°$ $m\angle 2 = 94°$	**6.** $m\angle 1 = 83°$ $m\angle 2 = 97°$

EXAMPLE 2 Solve a Multi-Step Problem

$m\angle 1 = 133°$. Find $m\angle 2$, $m\angle 3$, and $m\angle 4$.

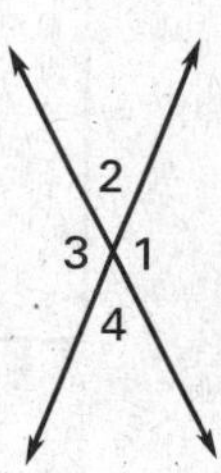

Solution

$m\angle 1 =$ ______.

1. ∠1 and ∠3 are ______. Their measures are equal,

so $m\angle 3 =$ ______.

2. ∠1 and ∠2 are ______.

$m\angle 1 + m\angle 2 =$ ______ Definition of ______

______ $+ m\angle 2 =$ ______ Substitute ______ for $m\angle 1$.

$m\angle 2 =$ ______ Subtract ______ from each side.

3. ∠2 and ∠4 are ______. Their measures are equal,

so $m\angle 4 =$ ______.

ANSWER $m\angle 3 = m\angle 1 =$ ______, 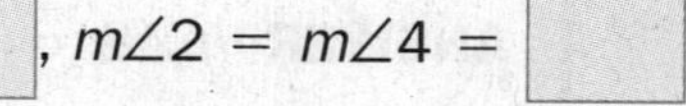 $m\angle 2 = m\angle 4 =$ ______

Guided Practice Find the measures of the numbered angles.

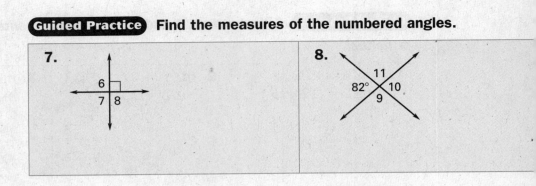

7. 6, 7, 8

8. 82°, 9, 10, 11

Angles and Parallel Lines

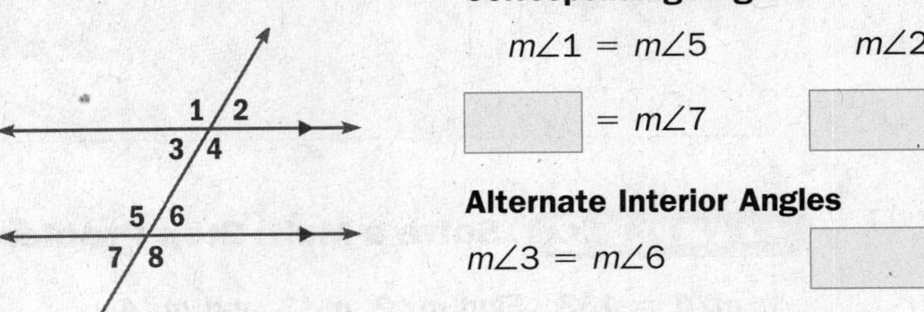

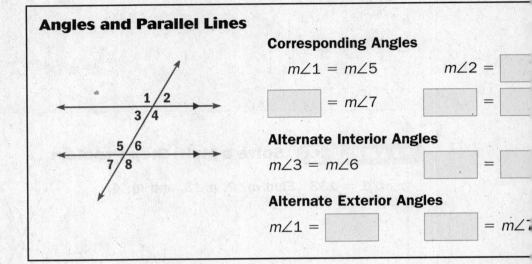

Corresponding Angles

$m\angle 1 = m\angle 5$ $m\angle 2 =$ ____

____ $= m\angle 7$ ____ $=$ ____

Alternate Interior Angles

$m\angle 3 = m\angle 6$ ____ $=$ ____

Alternate Exterior Angles

$m\angle 1 =$ ____ ____ $= m\angle 7$

EXAMPLE 3 Using Parallel Lines

Use the diagram to find $m\angle 8$.

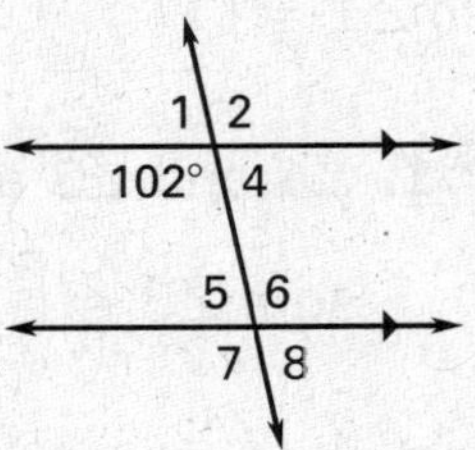

You can find $m\angle 8$ in more than one way. Another way is to find $m\angle 1$ using the fact that $\angle 1$ and the angle with measure 102° are supplementary. Then find $m\angle 8$ using the fact that $\angle 1$ and $\angle 8$ are alternate exterior angles.

Solution

The angle with measure 102° and $\angle 6$ are ____

so they have equal measures. $m\angle 6 =$ ____.

$\angle 6$ and $\angle 8$ are ____.

$m\angle 8 +$ ____ $= 180°$ Definition of ____

$m\angle 8 =$ ____ Subtract ____ from each side.

ANSWER $m\angle 8 =$ ____

Guided Practice **Find the angle measure.**

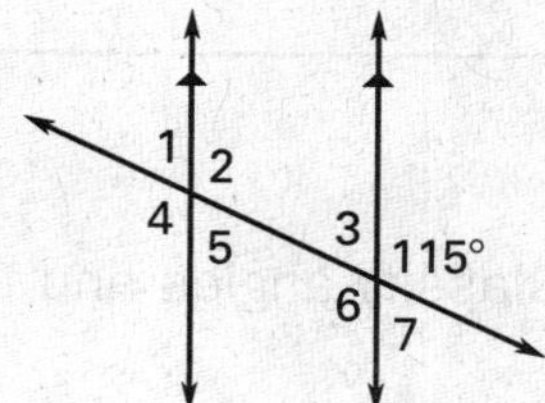

9. $m\angle 2$	**10.** $m\angle 3$	**11.** $m\angle 4$	**12.** $m\angle 6$

Angles and Triangles

Goal: Classify angles and triangles.

Vocabulary

Acute angle:

Right angle:

Obtuse angle:

Acute triangle:

Right triangle:

Obtuse triangle:

Equilateral triangle:

Isosceles triangle:

Scalene triangle:

Classifying Triangles

By Angles

An acute triangle has three ____ angles.

A ____ has ____ right angle.

An ____ has ____ obtuse angle.

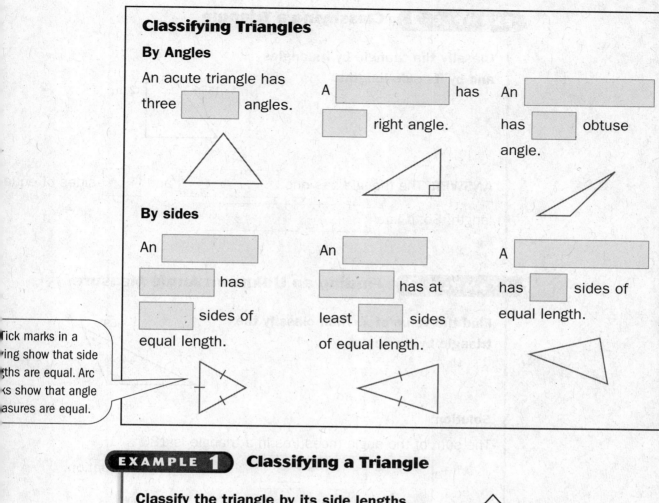

By sides

An ____ ____ has ____ sides of equal length.

An ____ ____ has at least ____ sides of equal length.

A ____ has ____ sides of equal length.

Tick marks in a
ing show that side
gths are equal. Arc
ks show that angle
asures are equal.

EXAMPLE 1 **Classifying a Triangle**

Classify the triangle by its side lengths.

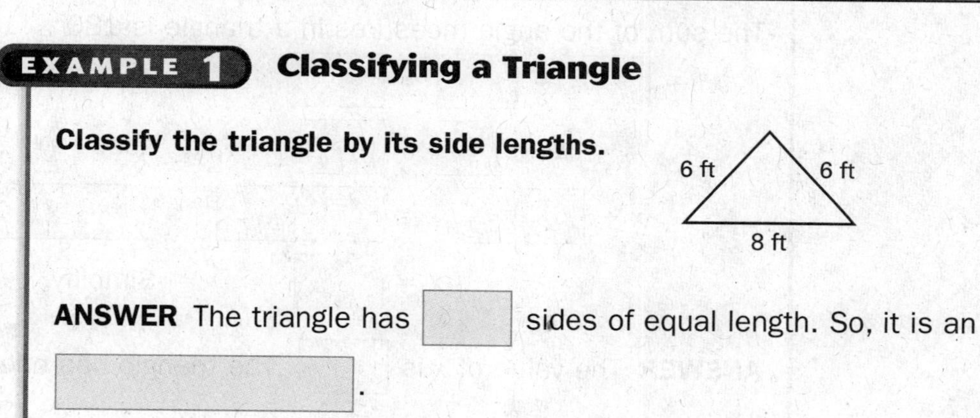

ANSWER The triangle has ____ sides of equal length. So, it is an ____.

EXAMPLE 2 Classifying a Triangle

Classify the triangle by its angles and by its side lengths.

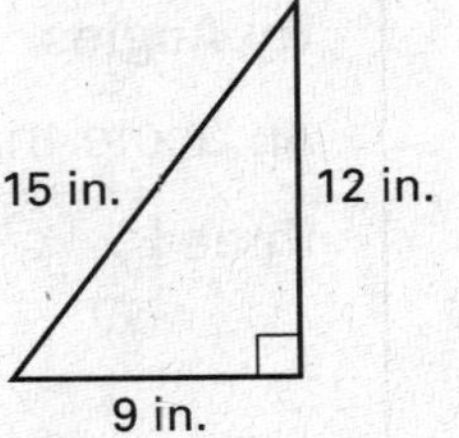

ANSWER The triangle has one ______ and ______ sides of equa

length. So, it is a ______.

EXAMPLE 3 Finding an Unknown Angle Measure

Find the value of *x*. Then classify the triangle by its angles.

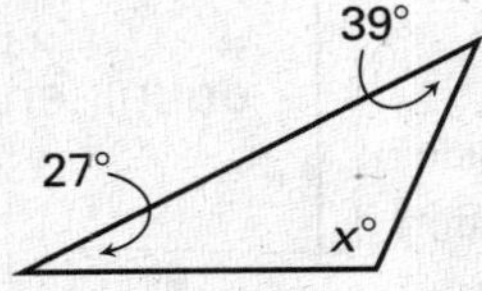

Solution

The sum of the angle measures in a triangle is 180°.

$x° +$ ______ $+$ ______ $=$ ______ Write an equation.

$x +$ ______ $=$ ______ Add.

$x +$ ______ $=$ ______ ______ from each

$x =$ ______ Simplify.

ANSWER The value of *x* is ______. The triangle has one ______ ang

so it is an ______.

Guided Practice **Find the value of *x*. Then classify the triangle by its a**

1.	2.
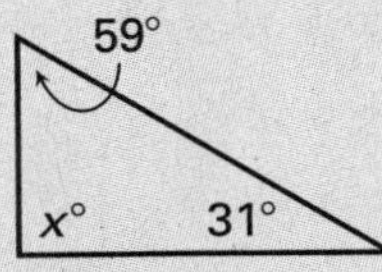	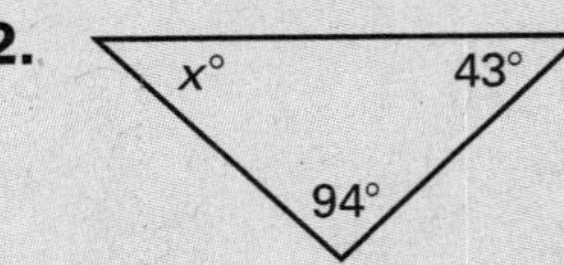

Quadrilaterals

Goal: Classify quadrilaterals.

Vocabulary

Quadrilateral:

Trapezoid:

Parallelogram:

Rhombus:

EXAMPLE 1 Classifying a Quadrilateral

Classify the quadrilateral.

Both pairs of opposite sides of the quadrilateral are ______. So, the quadrilateral is a ______.

3 mm

5 mm 5 mm

3 mm

Remember that a quadrilateral that does not have 4 sides of equal length or 4 right angles cannot be a rhombus, a rectangle, or a square.

Guided Practice **Classify the quadrilateral.**

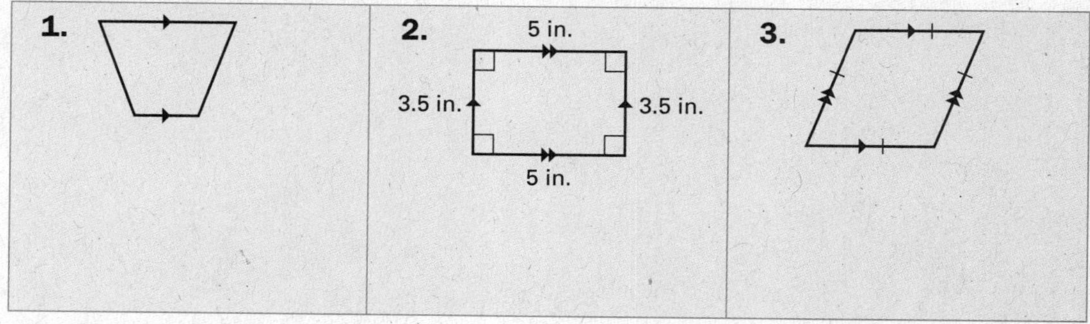

EXAMPLE 2 Finding an Unknown Angle Measure

Find the value of *x*.

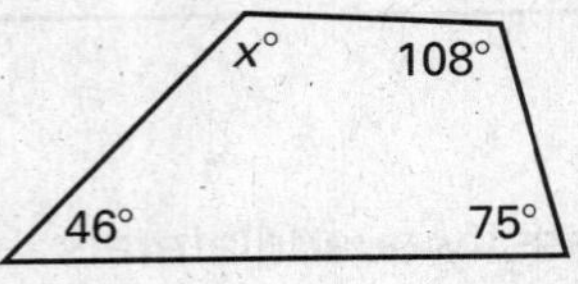

Solution

The sum of the angle measures in a quadrilateral is ______.

$x° +$ ______ $+$ ______ $+$ ______ $=$ ______ Write an equation.

$x +$ ______ $=$ ______ Add.

$x =$ ______ Subtract ______ from each side.

Polygons and Angles

Goal: Find angle measures in polygons.

Vocabulary

Polygon:

Regular polygon:

Pentagon:

Hexagon:

Heptagon:

Octagon:

EXAMPLE 1 **Identifying Figures**

Is the figure a *polygon, a regular polygon,* or *not a polygon*? Explain.

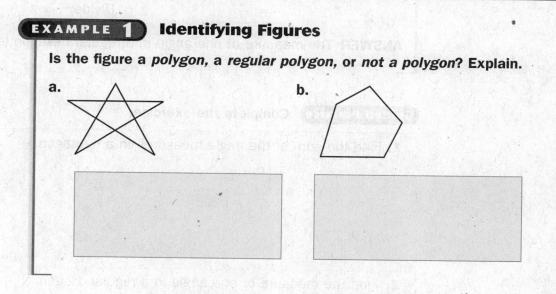

a.

b.

You can use n-gon, where n is the number of sides, to identify any polygon if you haven't learned its name. A 13-gon is a 13-sided polygon.

Angle Measures in a Polygon

Sum of angle measures in an n-gon: $(n - 2) \cdot$ ______

Measure of one angle in a *regular* n-gon: $\frac{(n - 2) \cdot \_\_\_\_}{\_\_\_\_}$

EXAMPLE 2 **Finding an Angle Measure**

Find the measure of one angle in a regular hexagon.

A regular hexagon has ______ sides,

so $n =$ ______.

$\frac{(n - 2) \cdot \_\_\_\_}{\_\_\_\_} =$ ______ Substitute.

$=$ ______ Simplify numerator.

$=$ ______ Divide.

ANSWER The measure of one angle in a regular hexagon is ______.

Guided Practice **Complete the exercise.**

1. Find the sum of the angle measures in a heptagon.

2. Find the measure of one angle in a regular 12-gon.

Congruent Polygons

Goal: Identify and name congruent polygons.

Vocabulary

Congruent segments:

Congruent angles:

Corresponding parts:

EXAMPLE 1 **Naming Congruent Polygons**

member that
hen naming
ruent polygons,
corresponding
es are listed in
same order.

Quadrilateral *ABCD* ≅ quadrilateral *MLKJ*. in the flag at the right. Name all pairs of congruent angles and sides.

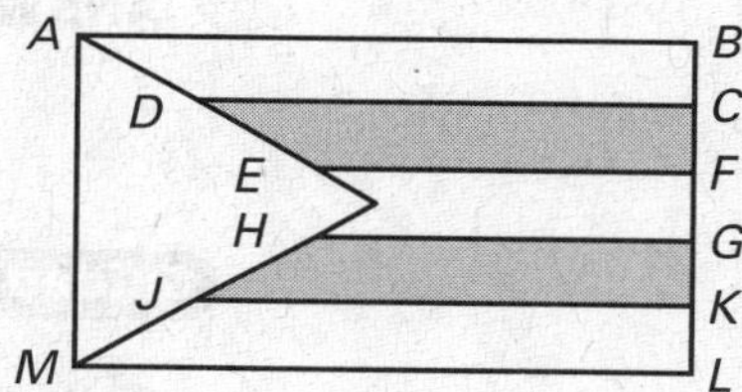

Solution

Corresponding ______ are congruent.

$\angle A \cong$ ______   ______ $\cong \angle L$

______ $\cong \angle K$ ______ $\cong$ ______

Corresponding ______ are congruent.

______ $\cong \overline{ML}$ ______ $\cong \overline{LK}$

$\overline{CD} \cong$ ______   ______ $\cong$ ______

Guided Practice **Use the flag above.**

1. Name all pairs of congruent angles and sides of two different congruent quadrilaterals.

EXAMPLE 2 Using Congruent Polygons

> $\triangle MNO$ is read "triangle MNO" and refers to the triangle with vertices M, N, and O.

$\triangle MNO \cong \triangle PQR$

Find $m\angle P$.

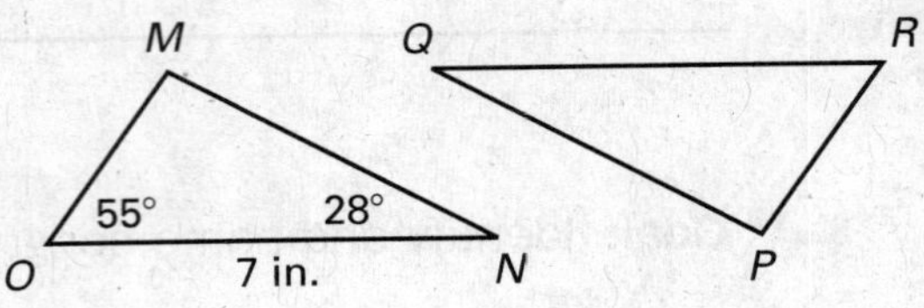

Solution

$\angle M$ and ______ are corresponding angles, so they have the same meas

Find $m\angle M$.

$m\angle M +$ ______ $+$ ______ $= 180°$ Sum of angle measures is 1

$m\angle M +$ ______ $+$ ______ $= 180°$ Substitute values.

$m\angle M +$ ______ $= 180°$ Add.

$m\angle M =$ ______ ______ from each

ANSWER Because $m\angle M = m\angle P$, $m\angle P =$ ______.

Guided Practice **Find the measure using the triangles in Example 2.**

2. length of $\overline{QR}$	**3.** $m\angle Q$	**4.** $m\angle R$

The angle
een two sides
ometimes called
included angle.
side between
wo angles is
netimes called
included side.

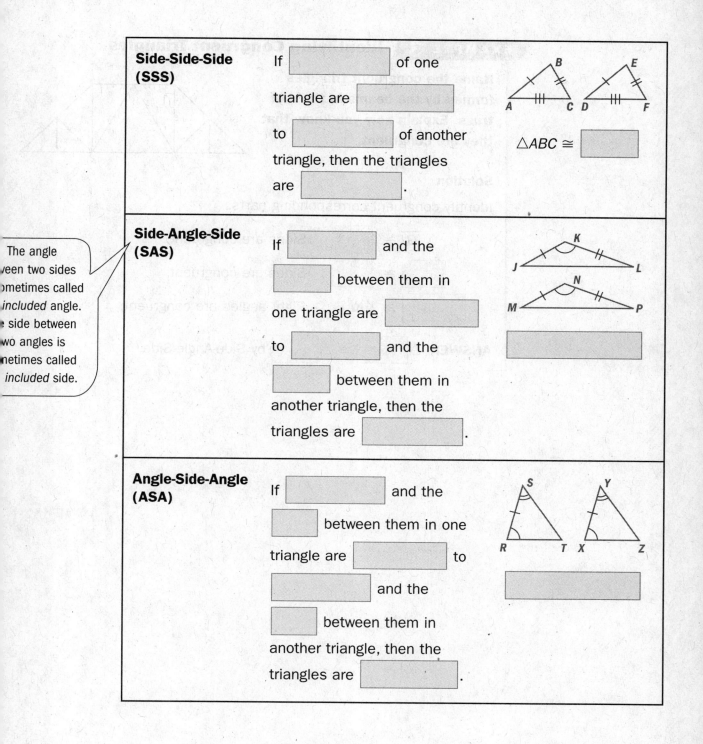

Side-Side-Side (SSS)	If ____ of one triangle are ____ to ____ of another triangle, then the triangles are ____.	$\triangle ABC \cong$ ____
Side-Angle-Side (SAS)	If ____ and the ____ between them in one triangle are ____ to ____ and the ____ between them in another triangle, then the triangles are ____.	____
Angle-Side-Angle (ASA)	If ____ and the ____ between them in one triangle are ____ to ____ and the ____ between them in another triangle, then the triangles are ____.	____

EXAMPLE 3 Identifying Congruent Triangles

Name the congruent triangles formed by the beams in the roof truss. Explain how you know that they are congruent.

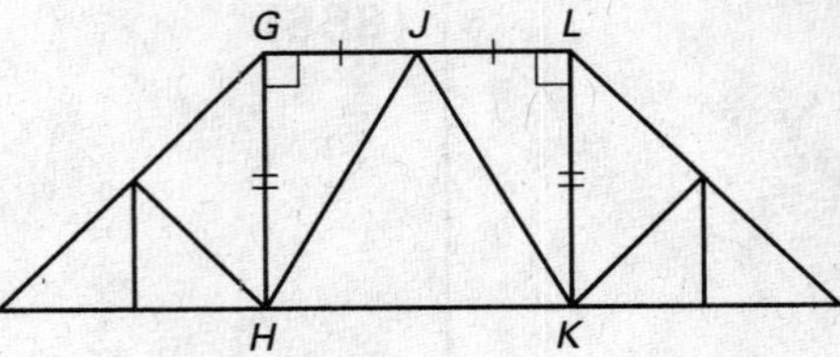

Solution

Identify congruent corresponding parts.

$\overline{GJ} \cong$ ______ Sides are congruent.

______ $\cong$ ______ Sides are congruent.

______ $\cong \angle KLJ$ Right angles are congruent.

ANSWER $\triangle$ ______ $\cong \triangle$ ______ by Side-Angle-Side.

Reflections and Symmetry

Goal: Reflect figures and identify lines of symmetry.

Vocabulary

Reflection:

Transformation:

Image:

Line symmetry:

EXAMPLE 1 Identifying a Reflection

Tell whether the shaded figure is a reflection of the figure on the left.

a.

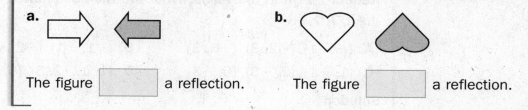

The figure ______ a reflection.

b.

The figure ______ a reflection.

EXAMPLE 2 Reflecting in the *x*-Axis

Quadrilateral *ABCD* has been reflected in the *x*-axis. Write the coordinates of each vertex of quadrilateral *ABCD* and its image, quadrilateral *A′B′C′D′*.

Solution

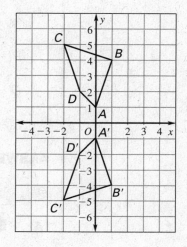

Original			**Image**	
A		⟶	*A′*	
B		⟶	*B′*	
C		⟶	*C′*	
D		⟶	*D′*	

Reflections

Reflections in the *x*-axis

Words To reflect a point in the *x*-axis, multiply its ______-coordinate by ______

	Original	Image
Numbers	(5, −7)	
Algebra	(*x*, *y*)	

Reflections in the *y*-axis

Words To reflect a point in the *y*-axis, multiply its ______-coordinate by ______

	Original	Image
Numbers	(5, −7)	
Algebra	(*x*, *y*)	

EXAMPLE 3 **Standardized Test Practice**

Reflect △*PQR* in the *y*-axis. What are the coordinates of the vertices of △*P′Q′R′*?

Ⓐ (−1, 1), (−2, 3), (−6, 3) Ⓑ (−1, −1), (−2, −3), (−6, −3)

Ⓒ (1, −1), (2, −3), (6, −3) Ⓓ (1, 1), (2, 3), (6, 3)

Solution

Multiply each *x*-coordinate by −1.

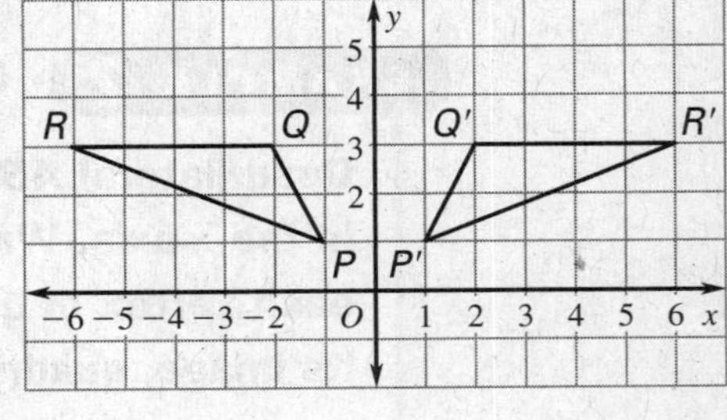

Original		**Image**
(*x*, *y*)	→	
P(−1, 1)	→	*P′*
Q(−2, 3)	→	*Q′*
R(−6, 3)	→	*R′*

ANSWER The coordinates of the vertices of △*P′Q′R′* are *P′* ______, *Q′* ______, and *R′* ______. The correct answer is ______.

   Ⓓ

Guided Practice **Graph the polygon and its image.**

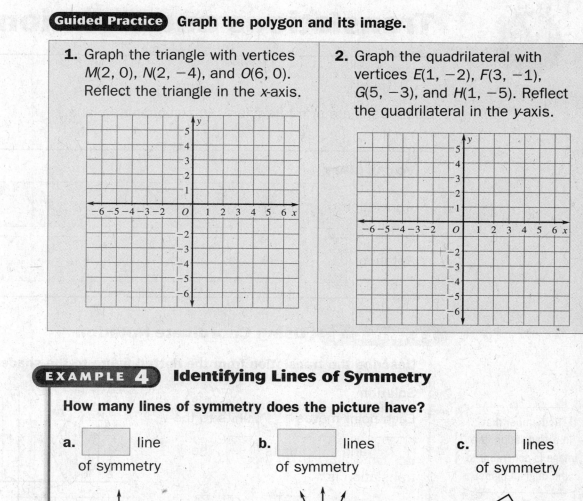

1. Graph the triangle with vertices $M(2, 0)$, $N(2, -4)$, and $O(6, 0)$. Reflect the triangle in the x-axis.

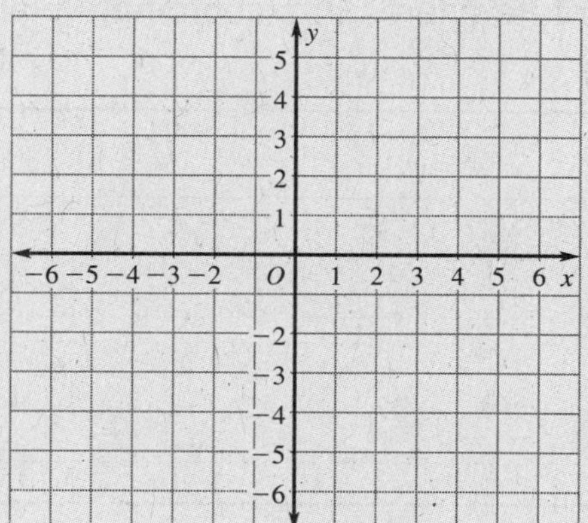

2. Graph the quadrilateral with vertices $E(1, -2)$, $F(3, -1)$, $G(5, -3)$, and $H(1, -5)$. Reflect the quadrilateral in the y-axis.

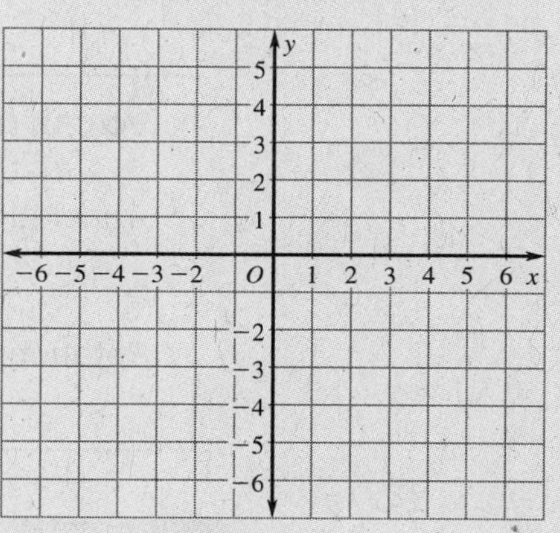

EXAMPLE 4 Identifying Lines of Symmetry

How many lines of symmetry does the picture have?

a. ☐ line of symmetry

b. ☐ lines of symmetry

c. ☐ lines of symmetry

Notice that a
e of symmetry
es the figure into
congruent parts.

Translations and Rotations

Goal: Translate or rotate figures in a coordinate plane.

Vocabulary

Translation:

Rotation:

EXAMPLE 1 **Using Coordinate Notation**

Describe the translation from the dotted figure to the shaded figure.

Remember that in a translation, the image is congruent to the original figure.

Solution

Each point moves ___ units to the ___ and ___ units ___. The translation is

$(x, y) \longrightarrow (x$ ___ $, y$ ___ $)$.

90° Rotations

Clockwise is the direction the hands on a clock turn. Counterclockwise is the opposite direction.

90° Clockwise Rotation

Words To rotate a point 90° *clockwise,* switch the coordinates, then multiply the new *y*-coordinate by −1.

Numbers $P(5, 1) \longrightarrow P'($ ___ , ___ $)$ **Algebra** $P(x, y) \longrightarrow P'($ ___ , ___ $)$

90° Counterclockwise Rotation

Words To rotate a point 90° *counterclockwise,* switch the coordinates, then multiply the new *x*-coordinate by −1.

Numbers $P(3, 4) \longrightarrow P'($ ___ , ___ $)$ **Algebra** $P(x, y) \longrightarrow P'($ ___ , ___ $)$

EXAMPLE 2 Rotating 90° Clockwise

If you draw a … from a vertex of … original figure to … origin and then … the origin to the … responding vertex … he image, you will … that a 90° angle is formed.

Rotate $\triangle XYZ$ 90° clockwise.

Solution

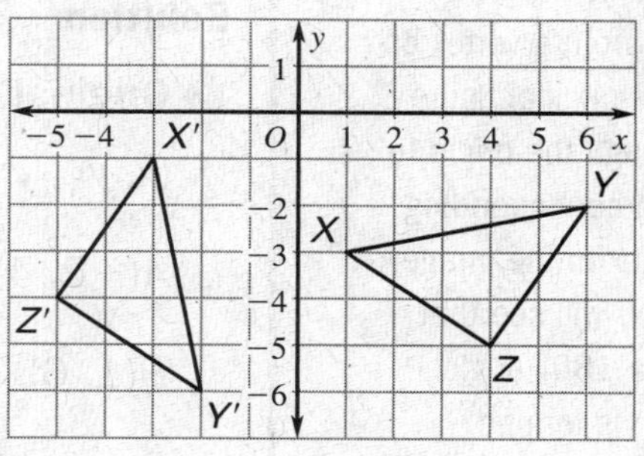

Original		**Image**
(x, y)	→	
$X(1, -3)$	→	X'
$Y(6, -2)$	→	Y'
$Z(4, -5)$	→	Z'

Guided Practice **Graph the figure with the given vertices and its image after the rotation.**

1. $P(-4, 4)$, $Q(-3, 3)$, $R(-3, 1)$, and $S(-5, 1)$; 90° clockwise

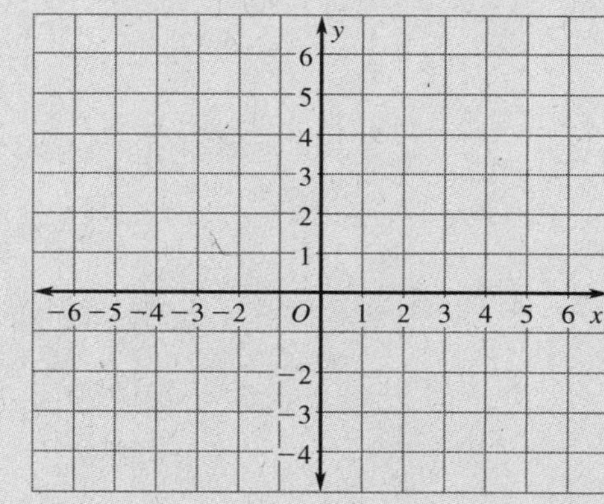

2. $D(0, 2)$, $E(6, 4)$, and $F(2, 1)$; 90° counterclockwise

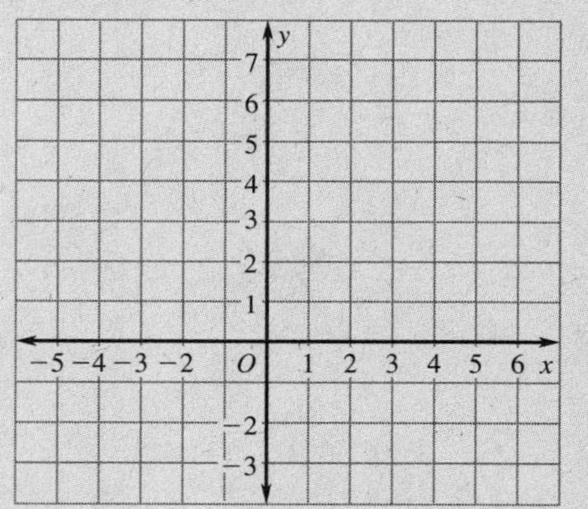

180° Rotation

Words To rotate a point 180°, multiply its coordinates by −1.

Numbers $P(1, 2) \rightarrow P'($ ___ , ___ $)$ **Algebra** $P(x, y) \rightarrow P'($ ___ , ___ $)$

EXAMPLE 3 Rotating 180°

If you draw a line from a vertex of the original figure through the origin to the corresponding vertex of the image, you will see that a 180° angle is formed.

Rotate quadrilateral *ABCD* 180°.

Solution

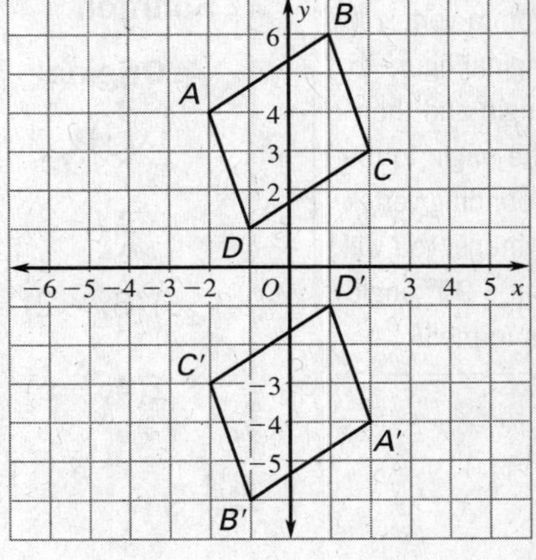

Original		Image
(x, y)	$\longrightarrow$	
$A(-2, 4)$	$\longrightarrow$	A'
$B(1, 6)$	$\longrightarrow$	B'
$C(2, 3)$	$\longrightarrow$	C'
$D(-1, 1)$	$\longrightarrow$	D'

Similarity and Dilations

Goal: Use similar polygons to find missing measures.

Vocabulary

Similar polygons:

Dilation:

Scale factor:

Similar Polygons

$\triangle ABC \sim \triangle XYZ$

Corresponding angles are ______.

$\angle A \cong$ ______ ______ $\cong \angle Y$ ______

Corresponding side lengths are ______.

$\frac{AB}{\_\_\_} = \frac{BC}{YZ}$ $\frac{BC}{YZ} = \frac{\_\_\_}{XZ}$ $\_\_\_ = \frac{AB}{XY}$

B
8 cm
6 cm
A
10 cm
C

Y
4 cm
3 cm
X
5 cm
Z

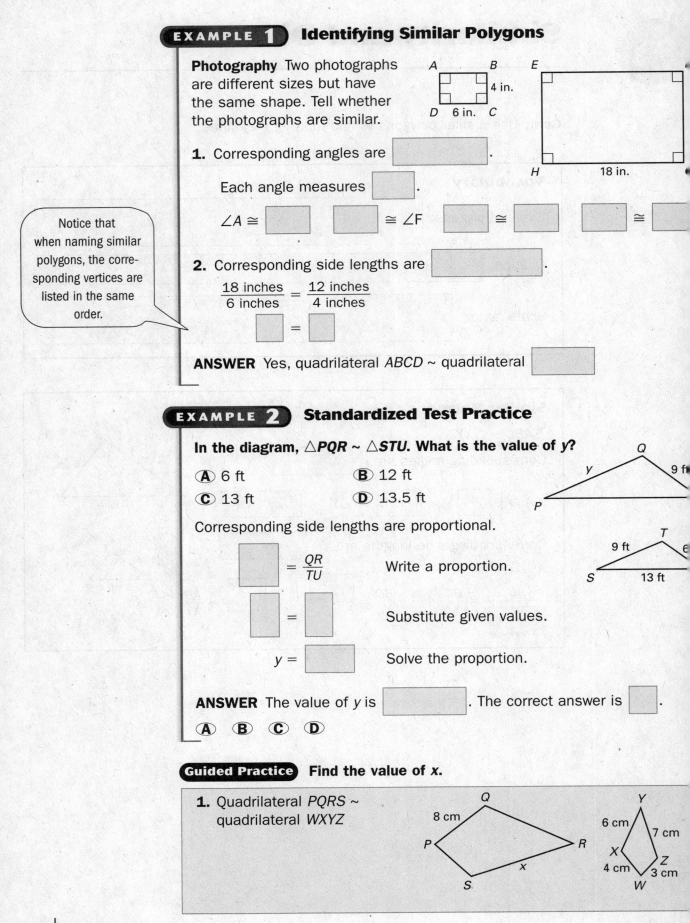

EXAMPLE 1 Identifying Similar Polygons

Photography Two photographs are different sizes but have the same shape. Tell whether the photographs are similar.

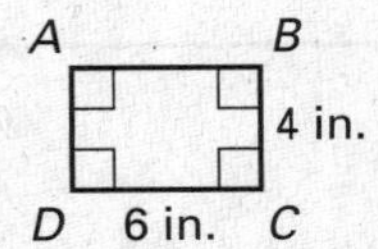

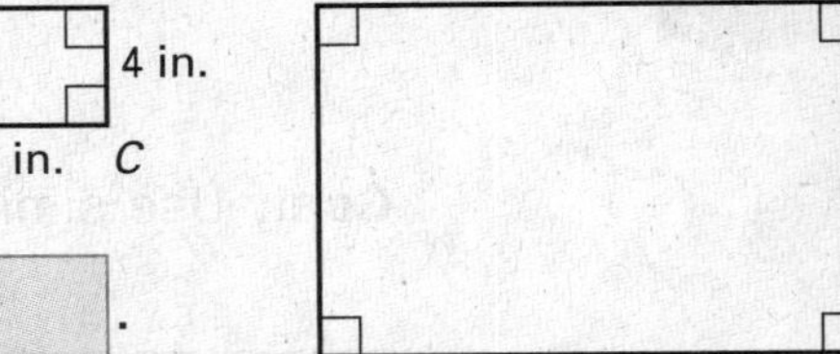

1. Corresponding angles are ______.

   Each angle measures ______.

$\angle A \cong$ ______ ______ $\cong \angle F$ ______ $\cong$ ______ ______ $\cong$ ______

Notice that when naming similar polygons, the corresponding vertices are listed in the same order.

2. Corresponding side lengths are ______.

$$\frac{18 \text{ inches}}{6 \text{ inches}} = \frac{12 \text{ inches}}{4 \text{ inches}}$$

______ = ______

ANSWER Yes, quadrilateral *ABCD* ~ quadrilateral ______

EXAMPLE 2 Standardized Test Practice

In the diagram, $\triangle PQR \sim \triangle STU$. What is the value of *y*?

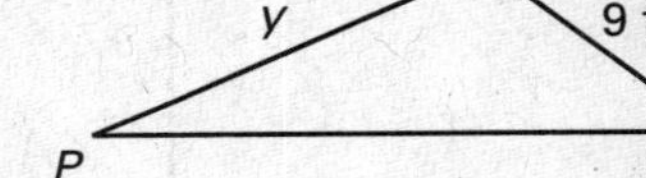

Ⓐ 6 ft Ⓑ 12 ft

Ⓒ 13 ft Ⓓ 13.5 ft

Corresponding side lengths are proportional.

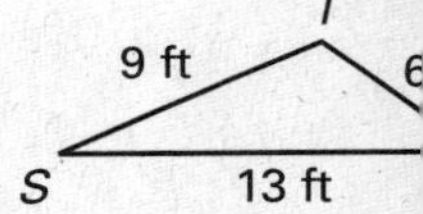

______ $= \frac{QR}{TU}$ Write a proportion.

______ = ______ Substitute given values.

$y =$ ______ Solve the proportion.

ANSWER The value of *y* is ______. The correct answer is ______.

Guided Practice **Find the value of *x*.**

1. Quadrilateral *PQRS* ~ quadrilateral *WXYZ*

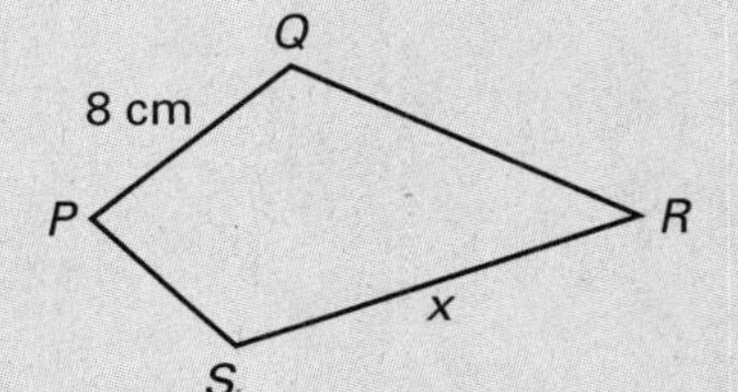

EXAMPLE 3 Using Indirect Measurement

Height A building is 25 feet tall and casts a 10 foot shadow. At the same time, a fence casts a 6 foot shadow. The triangles formed are similar. Find the height of the fence.

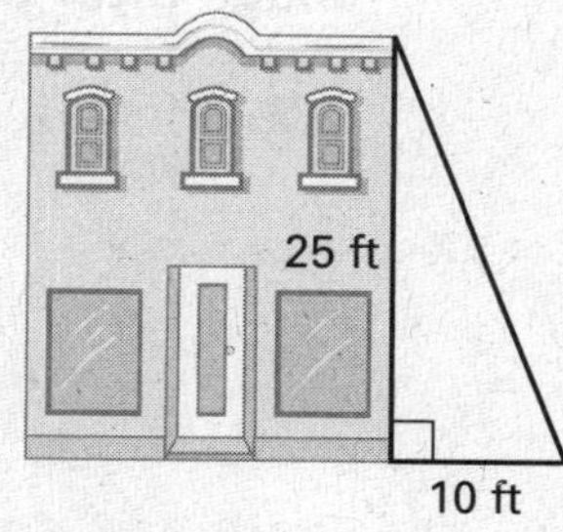

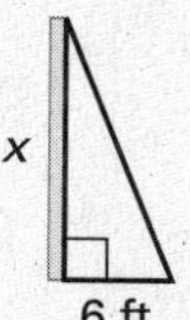

Solution

You can use a proportion to find the height of the fence.

$\frac{\text{Fence's height}}{\boxed{}} = \frac{\text{Length of fence's shadow}}{\boxed{}}$ Write a proportion.

$\boxed{} = \boxed{}$ Substitute given values.

$x = \boxed{}$ Solve the proportion.

ANSWER The fence is ______ tall.

Dilation

Words To dilate a polygon, ______ the coordinates of each vertex by the ______ k and connect the vertices.

Numbers $P(3, 2) \longrightarrow P'(6, \boxed{})$ **Algebra** $P(x, y) \longrightarrow P'(\boxed{}, ky)$

EXAMPLE 4 Dilating a Polygon

TCH OUT!
cale factor is the of corresponding engths:
$\frac{\text{after dilation}}{\text{before dilation}}$

Quadrilateral *ABCD* has vertices *A*(−3, 0), *B*(−2, 3), *C*(1, 1), and *D*(0, −1). Dilate using a scale factor of 2. Then graph its image.

Original		Image
(x, y)	$\longrightarrow$	$(2x, 2y)$
$A(-3, 0)$	$\longrightarrow$	A' ______
B ______	$\longrightarrow$	$B'(-4, 6)$
C ______	$\longrightarrow$	C' ______
$D(0, -1)$	$\longrightarrow$	D' ______

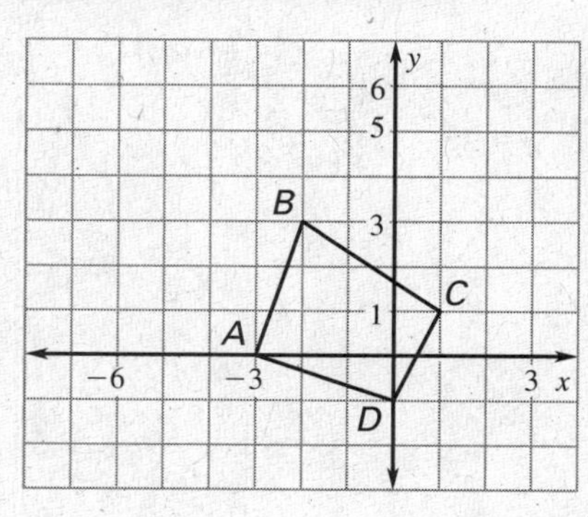

Guided Practice **Graph the polygon with the given vertices. Then graph image after dilation by the scale factor k.**

2. Triangle LMN has vertices $L(2, -1)$, $M(3, 2)$, and $N(4, 1)$; $k = 4$.

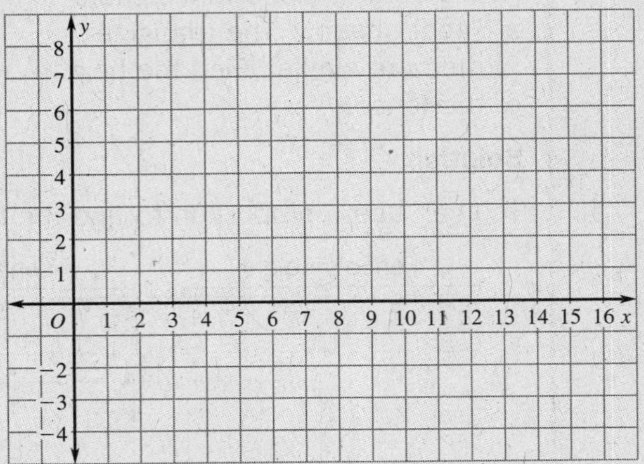

3. Quadrilateral $RSTU$ has vertices $R(-10, -4)$, $S(-6, 4)$, $T(-2, -2)$, $U(-8, -6)$; $k = \frac{1}{2}$.

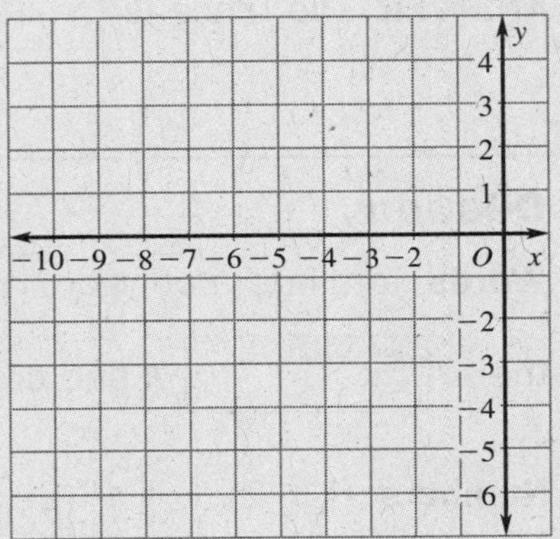

4. Triangle DEF has vertices $D(-3, 6)$, $E(3, 12)$, and $F(6, 0)$; $k = \frac{1}{3}$.

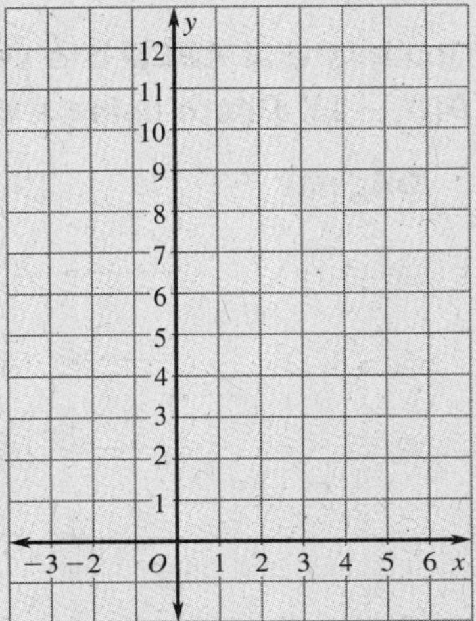

Words to Review

Give an example of the vocabulary word.

Straight angle

Perpendicular lines

Right angle

Parallel lines

Supplementary angles

Acute angle

Complementary angles

Obtuse angle

Vertical angles

Acute triangle

Right triangle

Quadrilateral

Obtuse triangle

Trapezoid

Equilateral triangle

Parallelogram

Isosceles triangle

Rhombus

Scalene triangle

Polygon

Regular polygon

Congruent segments

Pentagon

Congruent angles

Hexagon

Corresponding parts

Heptagon

Reflection

Octagon

Transformation

Image

Similar polygons

Line symmetry

Dilation

Translation

Scale factor

Rotation

Review your notes and Chapter 8 by using the Chapter Review on pages 456–46 of your textbook.

Square Roots

Goal: Find and approximate square roots of numbers.

Vocabulary

Square root:

Radical sign:

Radical expression:

Perfect square:

EXAMPLE 1 **Evaluating Square Roots**

a. $\sqrt{25}$ = ___ because ___^{2} = 25.

b. $-\sqrt{49}$ = ___ because ___^{2} = 49 and ___ is the opposite of ___.

Guided Practice **Find the square root.**

1. $\sqrt{9}$	**2.** $\sqrt{1}$	**3.** $-\sqrt{64}$	**4.** $-\sqrt{100}$

EXAMPLE 2 Standardized Test Practice

Round $\sqrt{70}$ to the nearest whole number.

Ⓐ 7 Ⓑ 8 Ⓒ 9 Ⓓ 10

Solution

You can use a number line to approximate $\sqrt{70}$ to the nearest whole number. Because $\sqrt{70}$ is between ___ and 9, you need to decide whether $\sqrt{70}$ is closer to ___ or 9. Find ___^{2}.

You can calculate that ___^{2} = ___ and $(\sqrt{70})^2$ = ___.

$\sqrt{64}$

8.5

9

$8^2 = 64$ ___^{2} = ___ ___ = ___

As shown on the number line, $\sqrt{70}$ is between $\sqrt{64}$ and ___, so it has a value between ___ and ___. Therefore, $\sqrt{70}$ is closer to ___ than it is to ___.

ANSWER To the nearest whole number, $\sqrt{70} \approx$ ___. The correct answer is ___. Ⓐ Ⓑ Ⓒ Ⓓ

EXAMPLE 3 Using a Calculator

Evaluate the square root. Round to the nearest tenth, if necessary.

a. $\sqrt{361}$ **b.** $-\sqrt{30.25}$ **c.** $\sqrt{12}$ **d.** $-\sqrt{1528}$

Solution

Keystrokes	**Display**	**Answer**
a. 2nd [$\sqrt{\ }$]361 =		
b. [(−)] 2nd [$\sqrt{\ }$]30.25 =		
c. 2nd [$\sqrt{\ }$]12 =		
d. [(−)] 2nd [$\sqrt{\ }$]1528 =		

Guided Practice **Approximate to the nearest whole number.**

5. $\sqrt{19}$	6. $\sqrt{40}$	7. $\sqrt{75}$	8. $\sqrt{138}$

Use a calculator to evaluate. Round to the nearest tenth.

9. $\sqrt{248}$	10. $\sqrt{10}$	11. $-\sqrt{25.25}$	12. $-\sqrt{3965}$

EXAMPLE 4 Using a Square Root Equation

Science The equation $t = \sqrt{\frac{h}{16}}$ gives the time in seconds that it takes an object to fall h feet. An eagle flying at a height of 100 feet drops a fish. How long will it take the fish to reach the ground?

Solution

$t = \sqrt{\frac{h}{16}}$ Write equation for falling object.

$= \sqrt{\frac{\square}{16}}$ Substitute for h.

$= \sqrt{\square}$ Divide.

$= \square$ Find square root.

ANSWER It will take ______ for the fish to reach the ground.

EXAMPLE 5 Solving Equations Using Square Roots

> The symbol $\pm$ is read plus or minus. The statement $x = \pm 6$ means that 6 and -6 are solutions of $x^2 = 36$.

a. $x^2 = 36$ Original equation

$x =$ ______ Definition of square root

$x = \pm 6$ Evaluate square roots.

ANSWER The solutions are 6 and -6.

b. $a^2 - 18 = 6$ Original equation

$a^2 - 18$ ______ $= 6$ ______ Add the same number to each si

$a^2 =$ ______ Simplify.

$a =$ ______ Definition of square root

$a \approx$ ______ Approximate square roots.

ANSWER The solutions are about ______ and about ______.

Guided Practice **Approximate the square root. Round to the nearest te**

13. $\sqrt{3}$	**14.** $\sqrt{21}$	**15.** $\sqrt{30}$	**16.** $\sqrt{55}$

Solve the equation. Check your solutions.

17. $n^2 = 121$	**18.** $p^2 - 23 = -7$	**19.** $y^2 + 11 = 15$

Rational and Irrational Numbers

Goal: Work with irrational numbers.

Vocabulary

Irrational number:

Real number:

EXAMPLE 1 **Classifying Real Numbers**

Number	Type	Decimal Form	Type of Decimal
a. $\frac{4}{5}$		$\frac{4}{5} =$	
b. $\frac{7}{22}$		$\frac{7}{22} =$	
		$=$	
c. $\sqrt{2}$		$\sqrt{2} =$	and

ce that if n is a ve integer and is a perfect square, $\sqrt{n}$ and $-\sqrt{n}$ rational numbers.

Guided Practice **Tell whether the number is *rational* or *irrational*. Explain your reasoning.**

1. $\frac{9}{20}$	**2.** $\sqrt{13}$	**3.** $\frac{5}{6}$	**4.** $\sqrt{81}$

EXAMPLE 2 Comparing Real Numbers

Graph the pair of numbers on a number line. Then copy and complete the statement with < or >.

a. $\sqrt{3}$ __?__ 3

b. $\sqrt{\frac{2}{3}}$ __?__ $\frac{2}{3}$

> **WATCH OUT!**
> You may need to use parenthesis when using a calculator to approximate a square root.

Solution

Use a calculator to approximate the square root and write any fractions as decimals. Then graph the numbers on a number line and compare.

a.

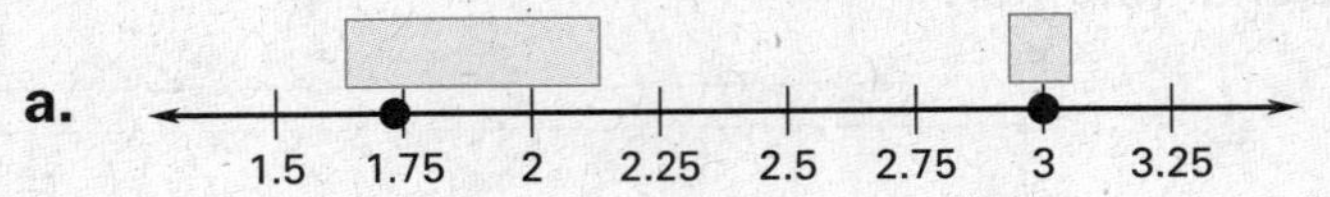

So, $\sqrt{3}$ ☐ 3

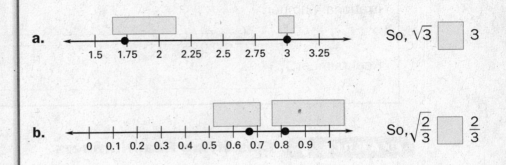

b.

0 0.1 0.2 0.3 0.4 0.5 0.6 0.7 0.8 0.9 1

So, $\sqrt{\frac{2}{3}}$ ☐ $\frac{2}{3}$

Guided Practice **Graph the pair of numbers on a number line. Then copy and complete the statement with <, >, or =.**

5. $\sqrt{6}$ __?__ 3

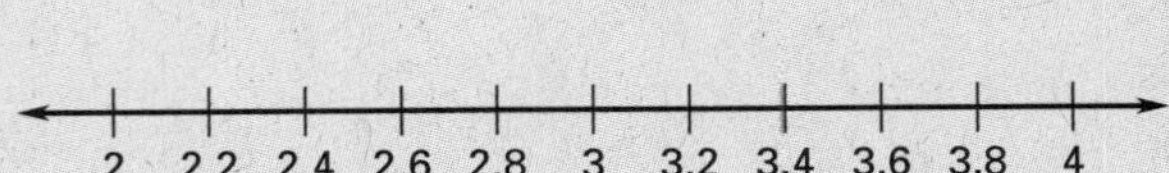

6. $\sqrt{49}$ __?__ 7

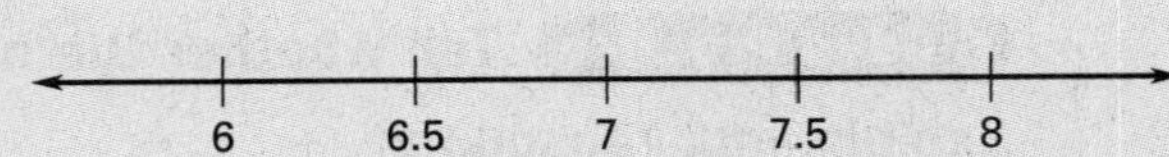

7. $\sqrt{\frac{1}{9}}$ __?__ $\frac{1}{9}$

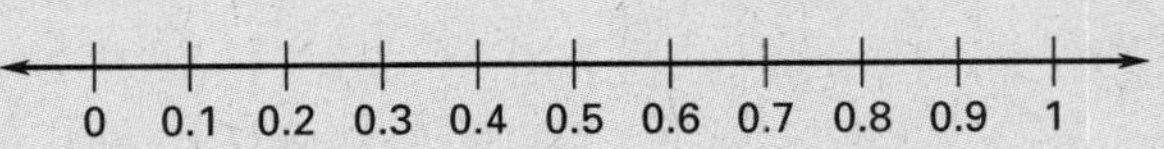

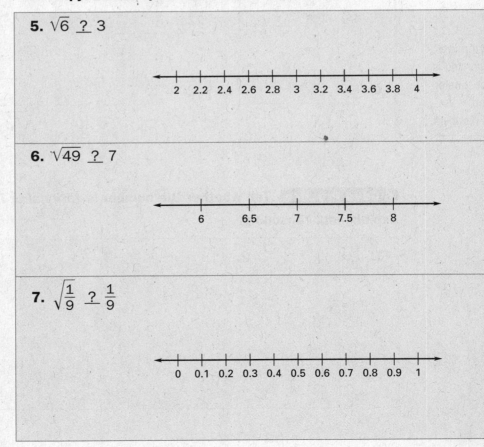

EXAMPLE 3 Ordering Decimals

Order the decimals $0.\overline{63}$, 0.633, $0.6\overline{3}$, and $0.\overline{636}$ from least to greatest.

e that the first two
after the decimal
are the same for
number. Use the
nd pair of digits to
er the decimals.

1. Write each decimal out to six decimal places.

$0.\overline{63} =$ ____ $0.633 =$ ____

$0.6\overline{3} =$ ____ $0.\overline{636} =$ ____

2. Write the decimals in order from least to greatest,

____, ____, ____, ____

ANSWER From least to greatest, the order is ____, ____, ____, and ____.

EXAMPLE 4 Using an Irrational Number

Stopping Distance The equation $s = \sqrt{27d}$ gives the minimum distance that it takes a car to stop on dry pavement after applying the brakes. In the equation, d represents the stopping distance in feet of a car that is traveling at a speed of s miles per hour. A car's stopping distance is 138 feet. How fast was the car traveling?

Solution

$s = \sqrt{27d}$	Write original equation.
$= \sqrt{27(\quad)}$	Substitute for d.
$=$ ____	Multiply.
$\approx$ ____	Approximate square root.

ANSWER The car was traveling about ____ miles per hour.

Guided Practice **Use the equation in Example 4.**

8. A car's stopping distance is 200 feet. How fast was the car traveling?

The Pythagorean Theorem

Goal: Use the Pythagorean theorem to solve problems.

Vocabulary

Leg: ______

Hypotenuse: ______

Converse: ______

Pythagorean Theorem

Words For any ______ triangle, the sum of the ______ of the length of the ______ equals the ______ of the length of the ______.

$a = 3$, $c = 5$, $b = 4$

Algebra $a^2 +$ ______ $=$ ______ **Numbers** $3^2 +$ ______ $=$ ______

EXAMPLE 1 Finding the Length of a Hypotenuse

Find the length of the hypotenuse of a right triangle with leg lengths of 15 feet and 36 feet.

$a^2 + b^2 = c^2$ Pythagorean theorem

$\_\_\_^2 + \_\_\_^2 = c^2$ Substitute values.

$\_\_\_ + \_\_\_ = c^2$ Evaluate powers.

$\_\_\_ = c^2$ Add.

$\_\_\_ = c$ Take positive square root of each side.

$\_\_\_ = c$ Evaluate square root.

ANSWER The length of the hypotenuse is ______.

Guided Practice **Complete the exercise.**

1. Find the length of the hypotenuse of a right triangle with leg lengths of 21 meters and 28 meters.

EXAMPLE 2 Standardized Test Practice

Cable A cable attaches to a utility pole b feet above the ground as shown. To the nearest foot, how high above the ground does the cable attach to the pole?

Ⓐ 68 ft Ⓑ 70 ft

Ⓒ 72 ft Ⓓ 75 ft

b

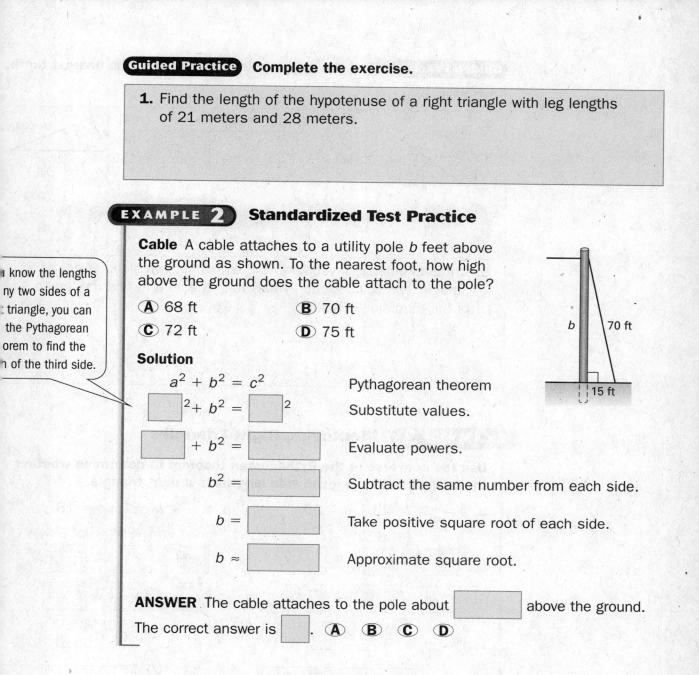

70 ft

15 ft

...u know the lengths ...ny two sides of a ...t triangle, you can ... the Pythagorean ...orem to find the ...h of the third side.

Solution

$a^2 + b^2 = c^2$ Pythagorean theorem

$\square^2 + b^2 = \square^2$ Substitute values.

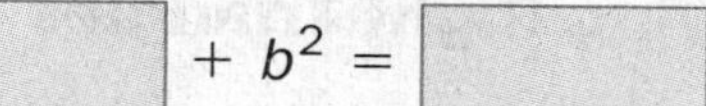

$\square + b^2 = \square$ Evaluate powers.

$b^2 = \square$ Subtract the same number from each side.

$b = \square$ Take positive square root of each side.

$b \approx \square$ Approximate square root.

ANSWER The cable attaches to the pole about ______ above the ground.

The correct answer is ___. Ⓐ Ⓑ Ⓒ Ⓓ

Guided Practice **Find the unknown length. Round to the nearest tenth, if necessary.**

2. 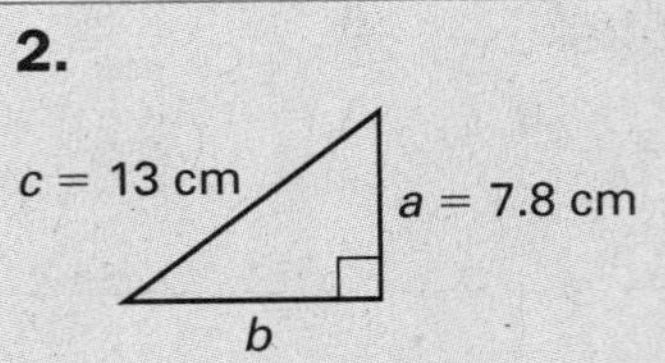	**3.** 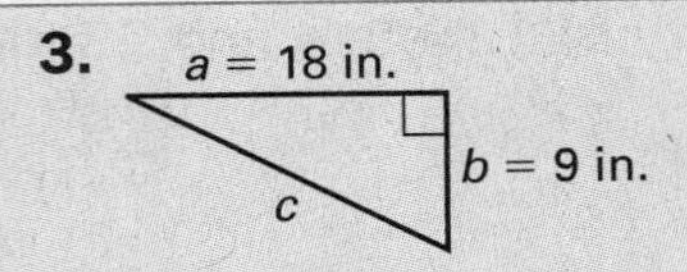	**4.** 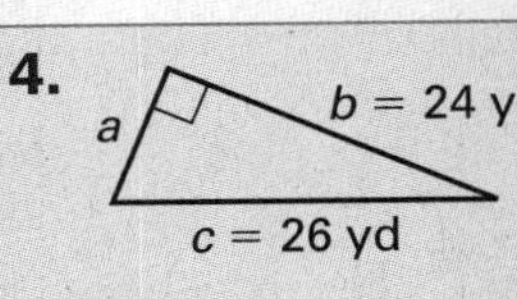

5. Critical Thinking If you know the lengths of two sides of any triangle, can you use the Pythagorean theorem to find the length of the third side? Explain.

EXAMPLE 3 Identifying Right Triangles

Use the converse of the Pythagorean theorem to determine whether the triangle with the given side lengths is a right triangle.

a. $a = 12$, $b = 16$, $c = 20$

$$a^2 + b^2 = c^2$$

$$\square^2 + \square^2 \stackrel{?}{=} \square^2$$

$$\square + \square \stackrel{?}{=} \square$$

$$\square$$

ANSWER $\square$

b. $a = 9$, $b = 15$, $c = 18$

$$a^2 + b^2 = c^2$$

$$\square^2 + \square^2 \stackrel{?}{=} \square^2$$

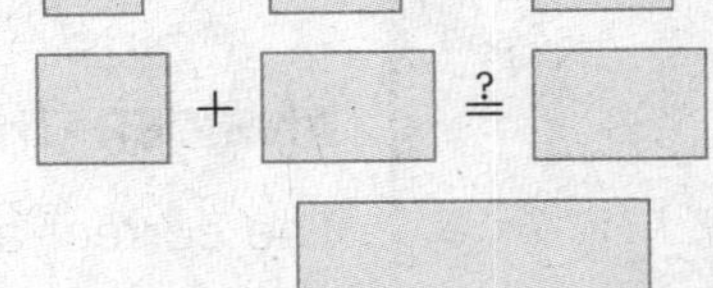

$$\square + \square \stackrel{?}{=} \square$$

$$\square$$

ANSWER $\square$

Using the Pythagorean Theorem

Goal: Solve real-life problems using the Pythagorean theorem.

Vocabulary

Pythagorean triple: ______

EXAMPLE 1 Using Indirect Measurement

Air Travel A pilot flies 150 miles due south of an airport. He then changes his course and flies 325 miles due east. How far is the pilot from the airport?

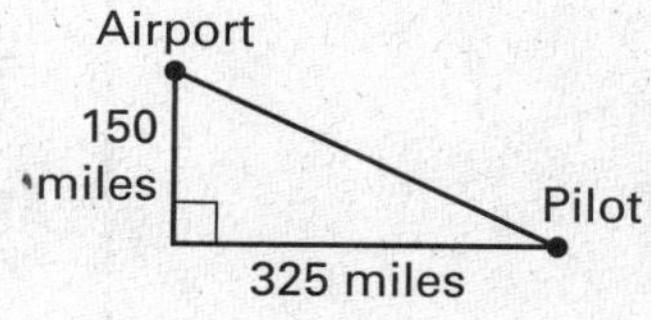

Solution

Let *a* and *b* represent the lengths of the legs (flight paths) of the right triangle. Let *d* represent the length of the hypotenuse (distance from airport).

$a^2 + b^2 = d^2$ Pythagorean theorem

$\_\_\_^2 + \_\_\_^2 = d^2$ Substitute for a and b.

$\_\_\_ + \_\_\_ = d^2$ Evaluate powers.

$\_\_\_ = d^2$ Add.

$\_\_\_ \approx d$ Take positive square root of each side.

ANSWER The pilot is about ______ from the airport.

Guided Practice **Use the information in the map.**

1. A pilot flies 200 miles due north of an airport. He then changes his course and flies 450 miles due west. How far is the pilot from the airport?

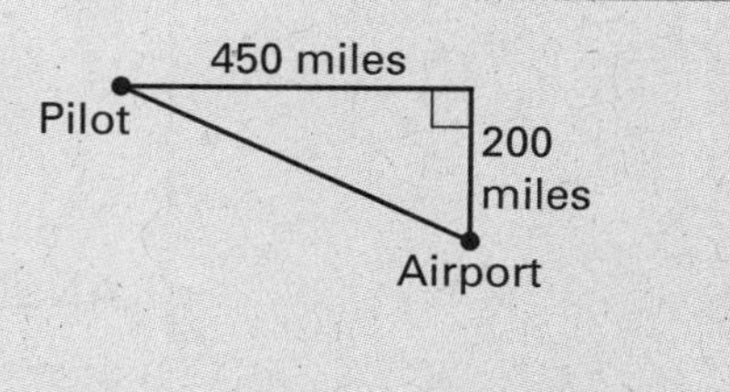

EXAMPLE 2 Finding Perimeter and Area

Find the perimeter and area of the triangle.

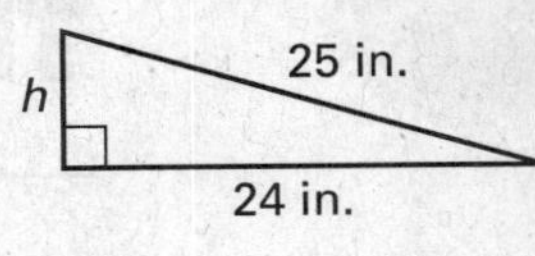

1. Find the height of the triangle.

Think: Do I have all of the values I need to find the perimeter and area of the triangle?

$h^2 + \square^2 = \square^2$ Pythagorean theorem

$h^2 + \square = \square$ Evaluate powers.

$h^2 = \square$ Subtract the same number from each side.

$h = \square$ Take positive square root of each side.

2. Use the height to find the perimeter and area.

Perimeter $= \square + \square + \square = \square$

Area $= \frac{1}{2}bh = \frac{1}{2}(\square)(\square) = \square$

ANSWER The perimeter is ______ and the area is ______.

Guided Practice Complete the exercise.

2. Find the perimeter and area of the triangle.

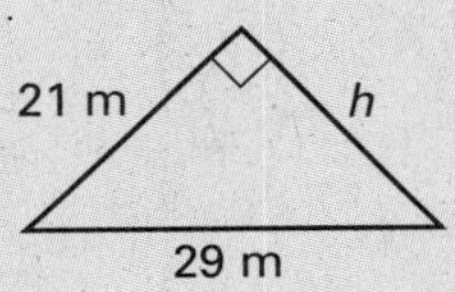

EXAMPLE 3 Identifying a Pythagorean Triple

Determine whether the side lengths of the triangle form a Pythagorean triple.

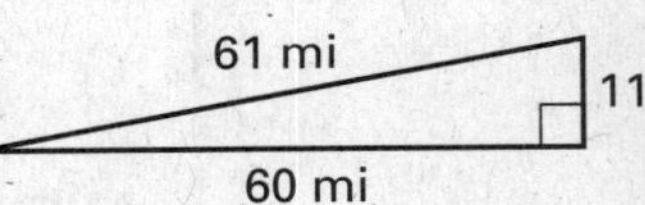

$a^2 + b^2 = c^2$ Definition of Pythagorean triple

$11^2 + \square^2 \stackrel{?}{=} \square^2$ Substitute values.

$\square + \square \stackrel{?}{=} \square$ Evaluate powers.

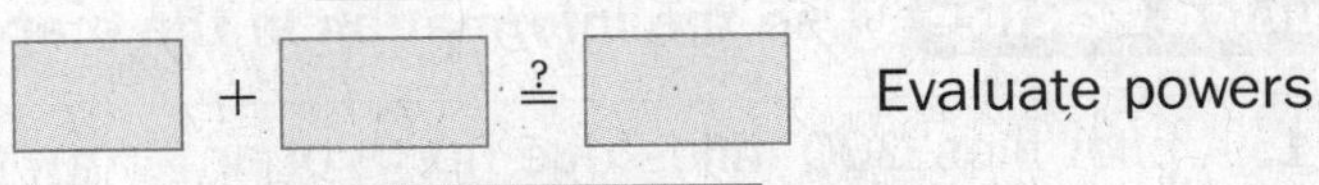 Add.

ANSWER Because $\square^2 + \square^2 \; \square \; \square^2$, the side lengths ______ a Pythagorean triple.

Special Right Triangles

Goal: Use special right triangles to solve real-life problems.

45°-45°-90° Triangle

Words In a 45°-45°-90° isosceles triangle, the length of the hypotenuse is the ______ of the length of a leg and ______.

Diagram

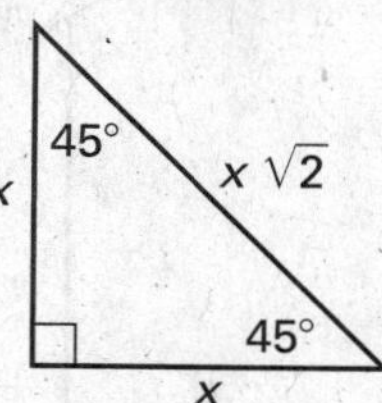

Algebra hypotenuse = ______

= ______

EXAMPLE 1 Using a 45°-45°-90° Triangle

Baseball The infield of a baseball field is a square with a side length of 90 feet. A player throws the ball from third base to first base. How far does the player have to throw the ball?

Solution

To find the distance from third base to first base, first draw a diagram. Then use the rule for a 45°-45°-90° triangle.

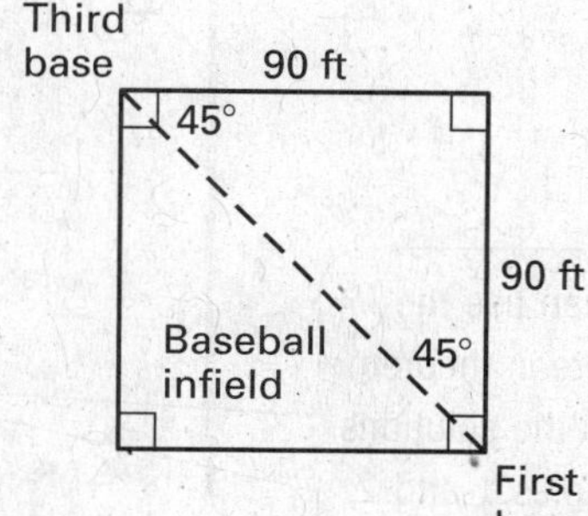

hypotenuse = leg • ______

= ______ • ______

≈ ______ (______)

= ______

ANSWER The player has to throw the ball about ______ feet.

30°-60°-90° Triangle

Words In a 30°-60°-90° triangle, the hypotenuse is twice as long as the ______. The length of the longer leg is the ______ of the length of the ______ and $\sqrt{3}$.

In a 30°-60°-90° triangle, the shorter leg is opposite the 30° angle, and the longer leg is opposite the 60° angle.

Diagram

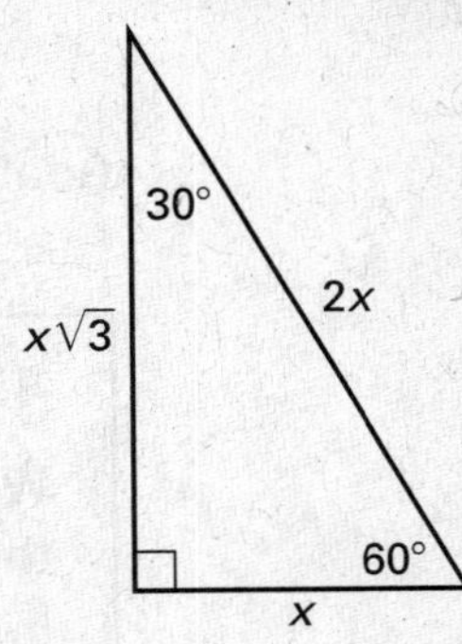

Algebra hypotenuse = ______

= ______

longer leg = ______

= ______

EXAMPLE 2 **Using a 30°-60°-90° Triangle**

Find the value of each variable in the triangle.

You need to find the length of the shorter leg first in order to find the length of the longer leg.

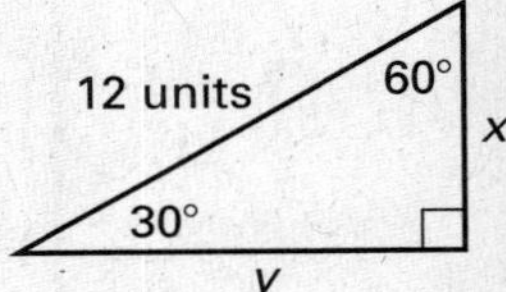

1. Find the length of the shorter leg.

______ = ______ • ______ Rule for 30°-60°-90° tria

______ = ______ • ______ Substitute.

______ = ______ Divide each side by the s number.

You can use the Pythagorean theorem to check the solutions in Examples 1 and 2.

2. Find the length of the longer leg.

______ = ______ • ______ Rule for 30°-60°-90° tria

______ = ______ Substitute.

ANSWER The length of the shorter leg is ______ units. The length of the longer leg is ______ units.

Guided Practice **Find the value of each variable. Give the exact answer.**

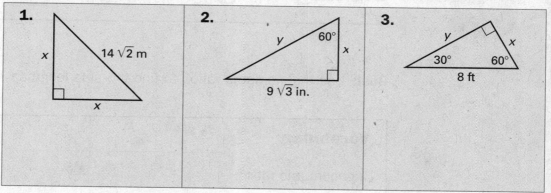

1.

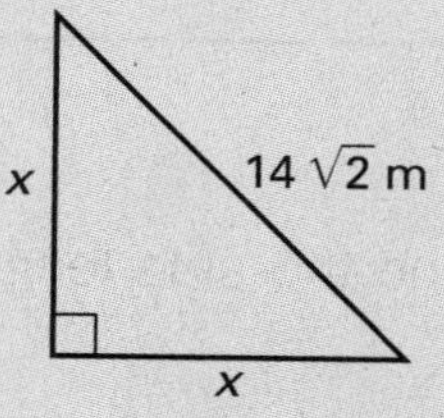

2.

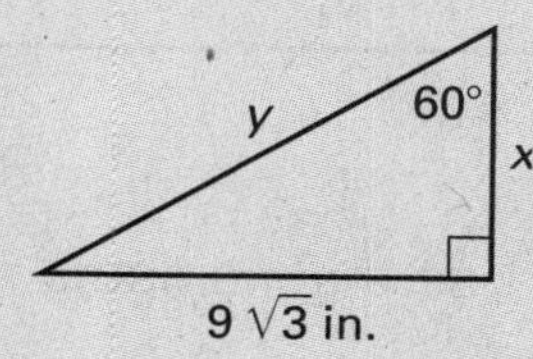

3.

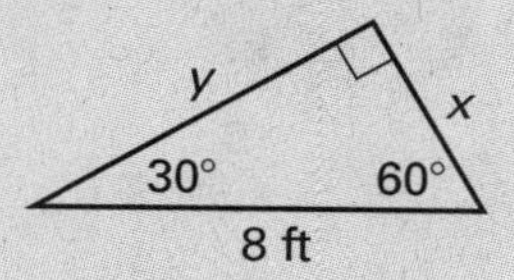

EXAMPLE 3 Using a Special Right Triangle

Flying a Kite Find the length of the kite string.

Solution

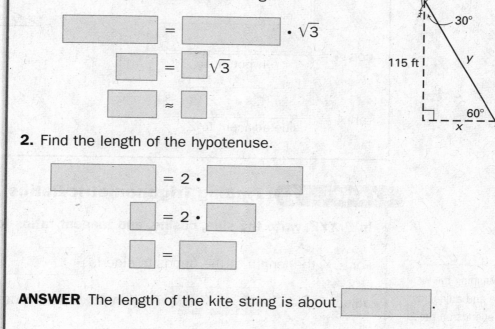

1. Find the length of the shorter leg.

$$\_\_\_\_ = \_\_\_\_ \cdot \sqrt{3}$$

$$\_\_\_\_ = \_\_\_\_\sqrt{3}$$

$$\_\_\_\_ \approx \_\_\_\_$$

2. Find the length of the hypotenuse.

$$\_\_\_\_ = 2 \cdot \_\_\_\_$$

$$\_\_\_\_ = 2 \cdot \_\_\_\_$$

$$\_\_\_\_ = \_\_\_\_$$

ANSWER The length of the kite string is about ____.

Using Trigonometric Ratios

Goal: Use trigonometric ratios to find the side lengths.

Vocabulary

Trigonometric ratio:

Trigonometric Ratios

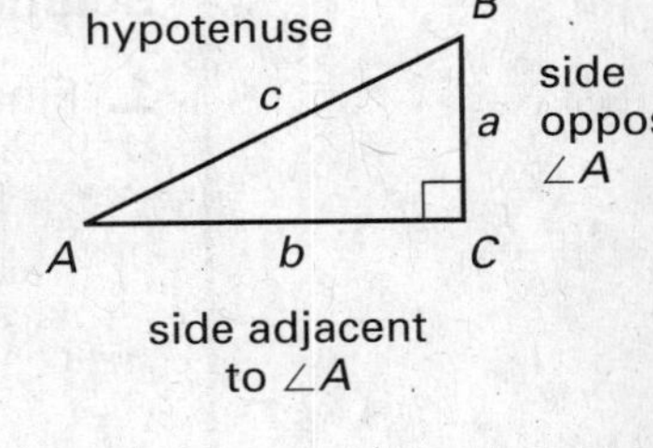

$\sin A = \dfrac{\text{side opposite } \angle A}{\quad} = \quad$

$\cos A = \dfrac{\quad}{\text{hypotenuse}} = \quad$

$\tan A = \dfrac{\quad}{\text{side adjacent to } \angle A} = \quad$

EXAMPLE 1 Finding Trigonometric Ratios

In △*XYZ*, write the sine, cosine, and tangent ratios for ∠*X*.

For ∠*X*, the length of the opposite side is ______, and the length o

adjacent side is ______. The length of the hypotenuse is ______

Determining the opposite and adjacent sides depends on the angle that is being used. For ∠*Y*, the length of the opposite side is 15 inches, and the length of the adjacent side is 8 inches.

$\sin X = \dfrac{\text{opposite}}{\quad} = \quad$

$\cos X = \dfrac{\quad}{\text{hypotenuse}} = \quad$

$\tan X = \dfrac{\quad}{\text{adjacent}} = \quad$

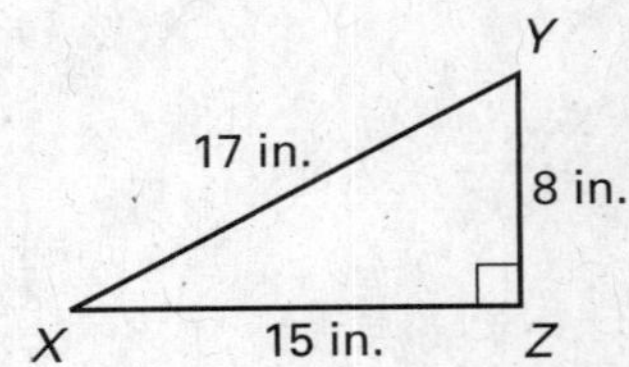

EXAMPLE 2 Using a Calculator

/hen using a culator to find nometric ratios ıgles measured egrees, be sure calculator is in e mode. You can his by checking tan 45° = 1.

Use a calculator to find sine, cosine, and tangent of 60°.

	Keystrokes	Display	Answer	
a.	2nd [TRIG] = 60 =		sin 60° ≈	
b.	2nd [TRIG] ▶ ▶ = 60 =		cos 60° =	
c.	2nd [TRIG] ◀ ◀ = 60 =		tan 60° ≈	

Guided Practice **Complete the exercise. For △*PQR*, write the sine, cosine, and tangent ratios for ∠*P* and ∠*R*.**

1. For △*PQR*, write the sine, cosine, and tangent ratios for ∠*P* and ∠*R*.

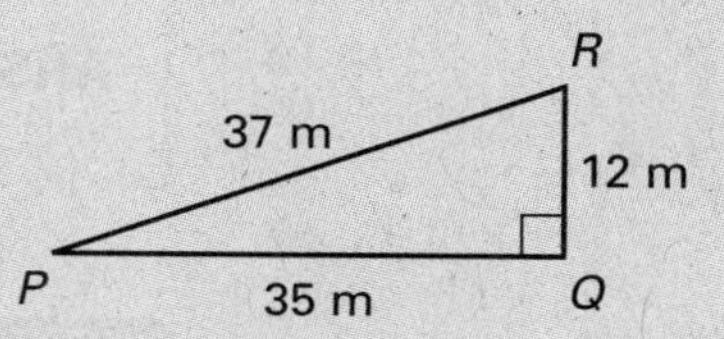

Use a calculator to approximate the expression. Round your answer to four decimal places.

2. sin 40°	**3.** tan 80°	**4.** cos 45°	**5.** sin 36°	**6.** tan 9°

EXAMPLE 3 Using a Cosine Ratio

When deciding which trigonometric ratio to use, look at the given values and the value you want to find.

Find the value of x in the triangle.

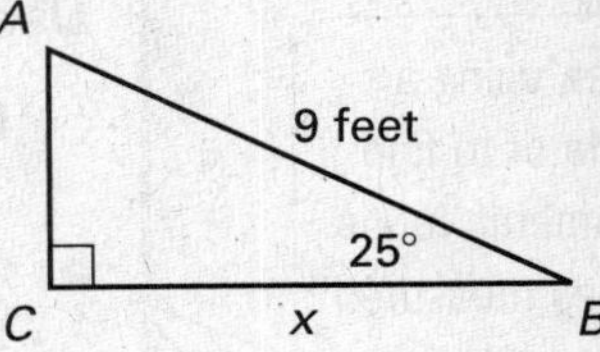

The length of the hypotenuse is 9 feet. The unknown side is adjacent to the given angle. Use the cosine of $\angle B$.

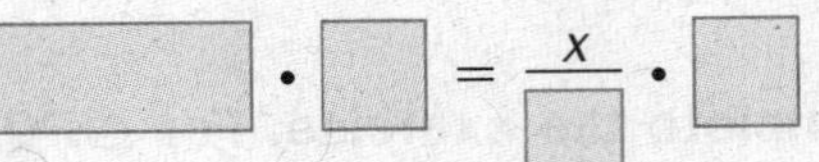

$\cos B = \frac{\text{adjacent}}{\text{hypotenuse}}$ Definition of cosine

$\cos 25° = \frac{x}{\square}$ Substitute.

$\square \cdot \square = \frac{x}{\square} \cdot \square$ Multiply each side by the same numb

$\square \approx \square$ Use a calculator.

ANSWER The value of x is about $\square$.

Guided Practice **Complete the exercise.**

7. Find the value of x in the triangle. Round your answer to the nearest hundredth of a centimeter.

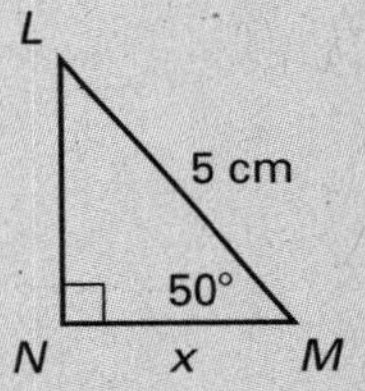

EXAMPLE 4 Using a Sine Ratio

Skateboarding A skateboard ramp is 45 inches long and makes a 38.5° angle with the ground. Find the height x of the skateboard ramp.

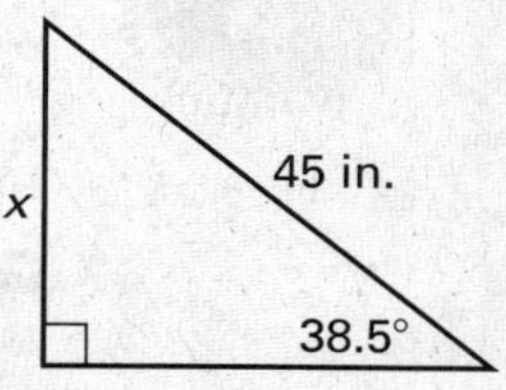

Solution

The unknown side is opposite the given angle. Use the sine ratio.

$\sin 38.5° = \frac{\text{opposite}}{\text{hypotenuse}}$ Definition of sine

$\sin 38.5° = \frac{x}{\square}$ Substitute.

$\square \cdot \square = \frac{x}{\square} \cdot \square$ Multiply each side by the same number.

$\square \approx x$ Use a calculator.

ANSWER The skateboard ramp is about $\square$ high.

EXAMPLE 5 Using a Tangent Ratio

Climbing A climbing net makes an angle of about 64° with the ground and attaches to a platform. The net extends horizontally about 6.3 feet. What is the height h of the platform?

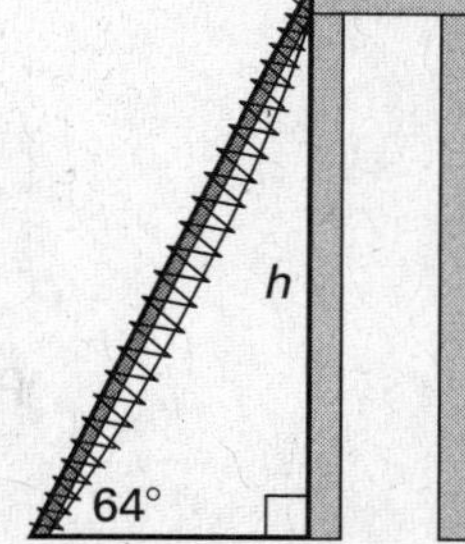

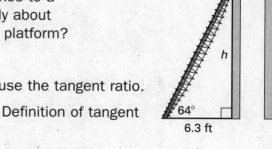

Solution

To find the height h of the platform, use the tangent ratio.

$\tan 64° = \frac{\text{opposite}}{\text{adjacent}}$ Definition of tangent

$\tan 64° = \square$ Substitute.

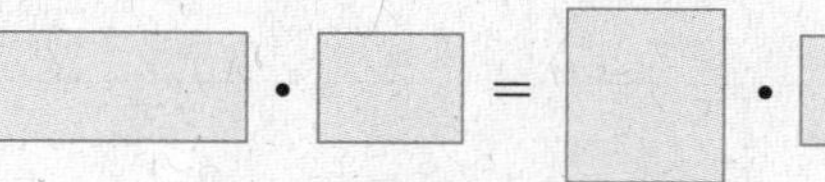

$\square \cdot \square = \square \cdot \square$ Multiply each side by the same number.

$\square \approx \square$ Use a calculator.

ANSWER The height of the platform is about $\square$.

Words to Review

Give an example of the vocabulary word.

Square root

Real number

Radical sign

Leg

Radical expression

Hypotenuse

Perfect square

Pythagorean theorem

Irrational number

Converse

Pythagorean triple

Sine

Trigonometric ratio

Tangent

Cosine

Review your notes and Chapter 9 by using the Chapter Review on pages 509–512 of your textbook.

Areas of Parallelograms and Trapezoids

Goal: Find the areas of parallelograms and trapezoids.

Vocabulary

Base of a parallelogram:

Height of a parallelogram:

Bases of a trapezoid:

Height of a trapezoid:

Area of a Parallelogram

Words The area of a parallelogram is the product of the base and the height.

$h = 4$ m

$b = 6$ m

Algebra $A =$ ______ **Numbers** $A =$ ______ • ______ $=$ ______ m^2

EXAMPLE 1 **Finding the Area of a Parallelogram**

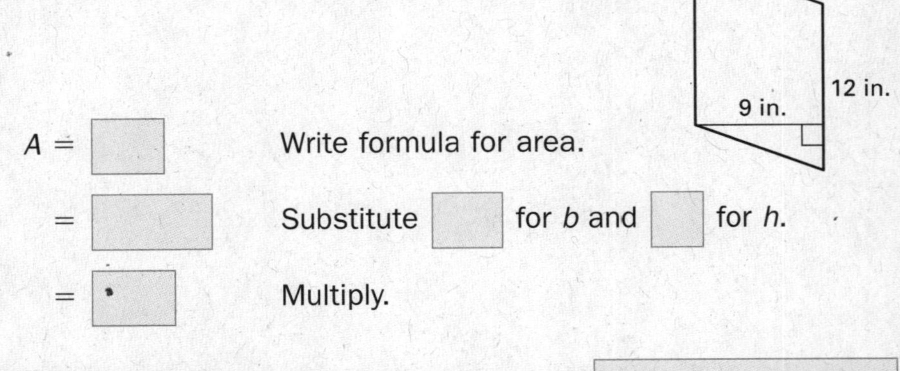

Find the area of the parallelogram.

$A =$ ______ Write formula for area.

$=$ ______ Substitute ______ for b and ______ for h.

$=$ ______ Multiply.

ANSWER The parallelogram has an area of ______.

Area of a Trapezoid

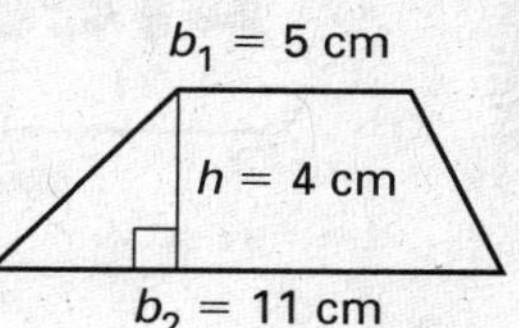

Words The area of a trapezoid is one half the product of the sum of the bases and the height.

Algebra $A = \square(b_1 + b_2)\square$

Numbers $A = \square(\square + \square)\square = \square$ cm^2

EXAMPLE 2 **Finding the Area of a Trapezoid**

Construction A deck floor is constructed in the shape of a trapezoid. What is its area?

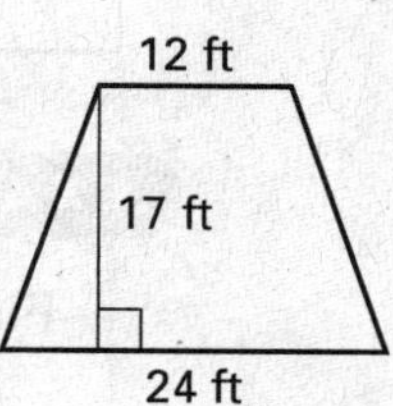

Solution

$A = \square(b_1 + b_2)\square$ Write formula for area of a trapezoid.

$= \square$ Substitute values for b_1, b_2, and h.

$= \square$ Multiply.

...es it matter which ...alues you choose ...r b_1 and b_2, 12 ft ...4 ft? Which property ...ports your answer?

ANSWER The deck floor has an area of $\square$.

Guided Practice **Sketch the quadrilateral and find its area.**

1. A parallelogram with base 13 feet and height 8 feet.

2. A trapezoid with bases 15 yards and 10 yards and height 6 yards.

Areas of Circles

Goal: Find the areas of circles.

Area of a Circle

Words The area of a circle is the product of π and the square of the radius.

Algebra $A =$ ____ **Numbers** $A =$ ____

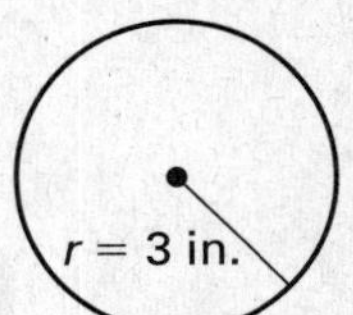

Finding the Area of a Circle

Find the area of a circle with a diameter of 14 centimeters.

Remember that the diameter is twice the radius.

$A =$ ____ Write formula for area of a circle.

$\approx$ ____ Substitute ____ for π and ____ for r.

$=$ ____ Evaluate using a calculator.

ANSWER The area is about ____.

Finding the Radius of a Circle

Find the radius of a circle that has an area of 706.5 square feet.

$A =$ ____ Write formula for area of a circle.

____ $\approx$ (____)r^2 Substitute ____ for A and ____ for π.

____ $\approx r^2$ Use a calculator to divide each side by ____.

____ $\approx r$ Take positive square root of each side.

____ $\approx r$ Evaluate square root.

ANSWER The radius of the circle is about ____.

Guided Practice **Find the unknown area or radius of the circle. Use 3.14 for π.**

1. $r = 9$ m, $A = \underline{?}$	**2.** $d = 11$ mi, $A = \underline{?}$	**3.** $A = 785\ \text{yd}^2$, $r = \underline{?}$

EXAMPLE 3 Solve a Multi-Step Problem

Flying Discs Find the area of the flying disc.

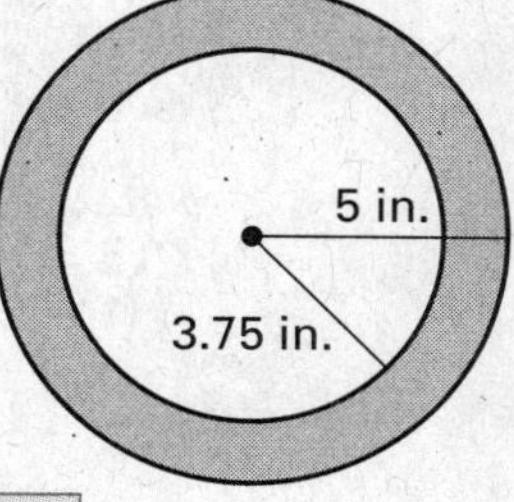

Solution

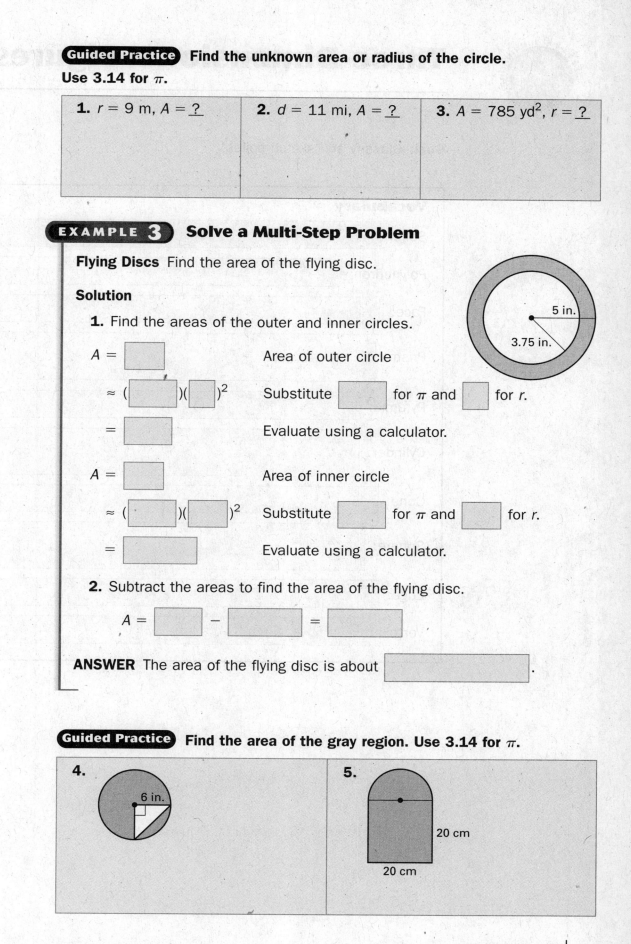

1. Find the areas of the outer and inner circles.

$A =$ ______ Area of outer circle

$\approx$ (______)(______)^2 Substitute ______ for π and ______ for r.

$=$ ______ Evaluate using a calculator.

$A =$ ______ Area of inner circle

$\approx$ (______)(______)^2 Substitute ______ for π and ______ for r.

$=$ ______ Evaluate using a calculator.

2. Subtract the areas to find the area of the flying disc.

$A =$ ______ $-$ ______ $=$ ______

ANSWER The area of the flying disc is about ______.

Guided Practice **Find the area of the gray region. Use 3.14 for π.**

4.

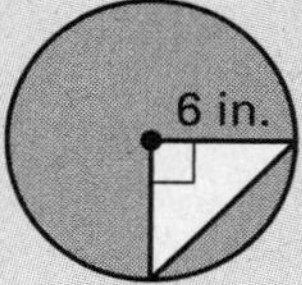

5.

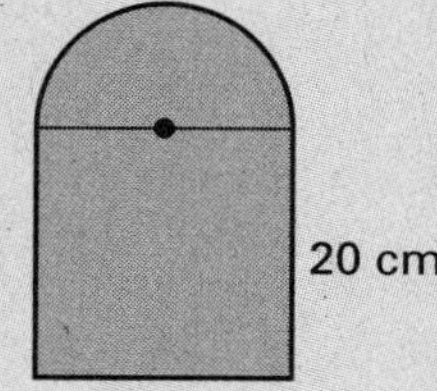

Three-Dimensional Figures

Goal: Classify and sketch solids.

Vocabulary

Solid:

Polyhedron:

Face:

Prism:

Pyramid:

Cylinder:

Cone:

Sphere:

Edge:

Vertex:

Classifying Solids

bases

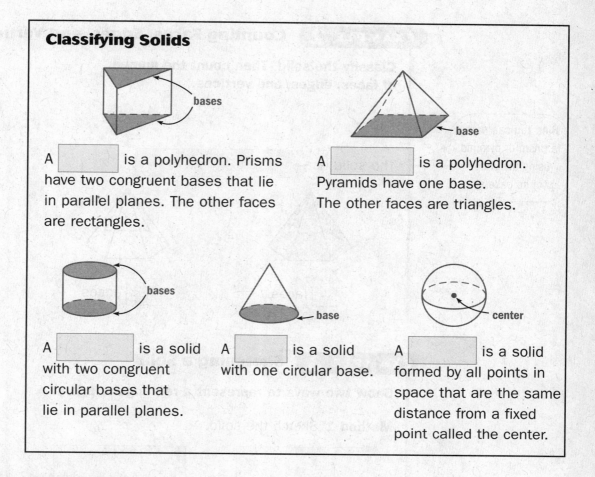

A ______ is a polyhedron. Prisms have two congruent bases that lie in parallel planes. The other faces are rectangles.

base

A ______ is a polyhedron. Pyramids have one base. The other faces are triangles.

bases

A ______ is a solid with two congruent circular bases that lie in parallel planes.

base

A ______ is a solid with one circular base.

center

A ______ is a solid formed by all points in space that are the same distance from a fixed point called the center.

EXAMPLE 1 Classifying Solids

Classify the solid and tell whether it is a polyhedron.

Think: Is the solid made up of all polygons?

The solid has ______ circular base, so it is a ______. It ______ a polyhedron, because a circle ______ a polygon.

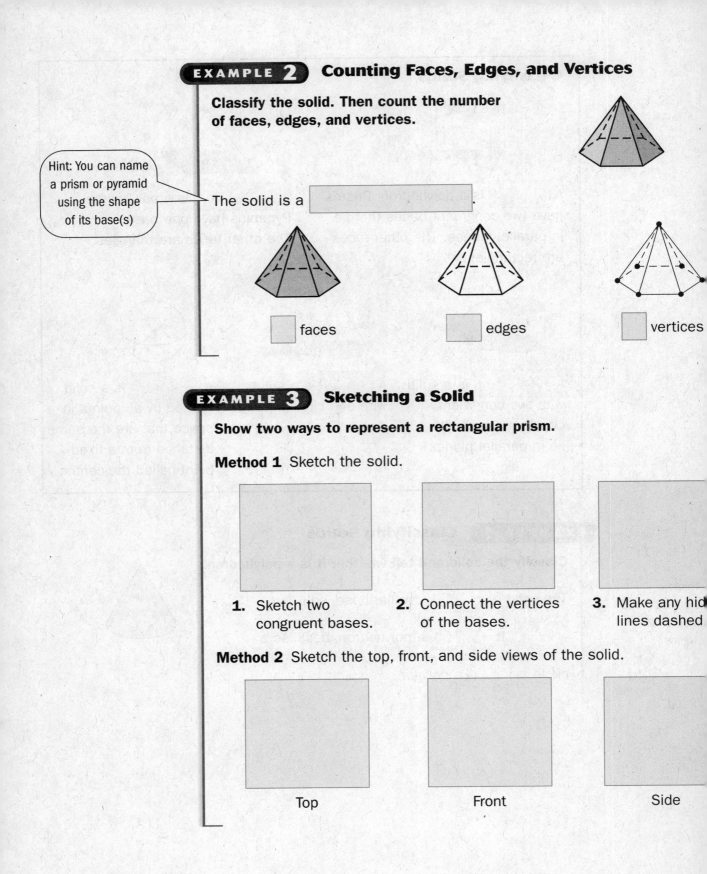

EXAMPLE 2 Counting Faces, Edges, and Vertices

Classify the solid. Then count the number of faces, edges, and vertices.

Hint: You can name a prism or pyramid using the shape of its base(s)

The solid is a ______.

______ faces ______ edges ______ vertices

EXAMPLE 3 Sketching a Solid

Show two ways to represent a rectangular prism.

Method 1 Sketch the solid.

1. Sketch two congruent bases.
2. Connect the vertices of the bases.
3. Make any hid lines dashed

Method 2 Sketch the top, front, and side views of the solid.

Top Front Side

Guided Practice **Classify the solid. Then tell whether it is a polyhedron.**

1. 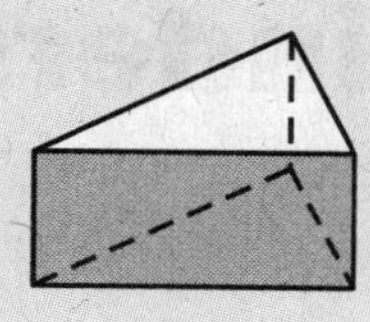	2. 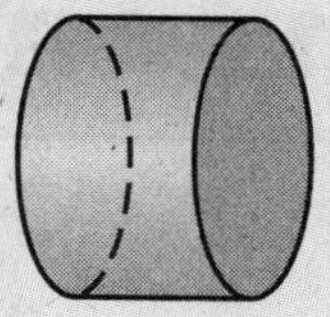	3. 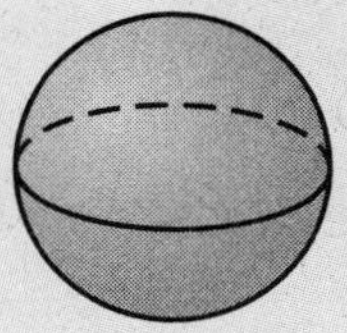

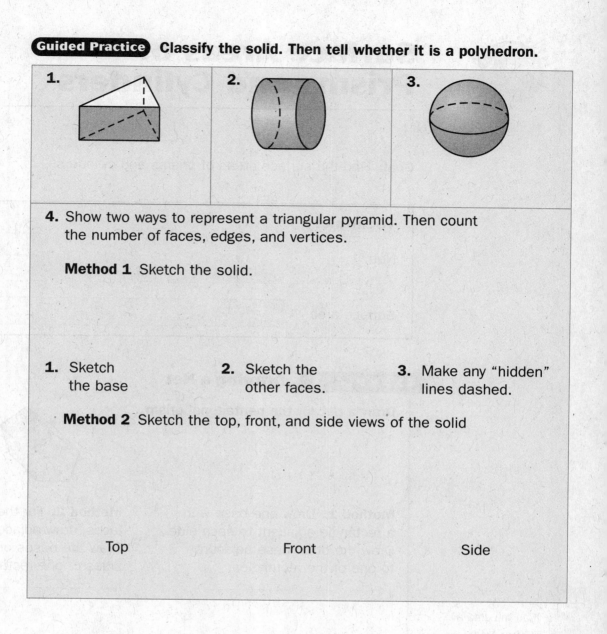

4. Show two ways to represent a triangular pyramid. Then count the number of faces, edges, and vertices.

Method 1 Sketch the solid.

1. Sketch the base

2. Sketch the other faces.

3. Make any "hidden" lines dashed.

Method 2 Sketch the top, front, and side views of the solid

Top

Front

Side

Surface Areas of Prisms and Cylinders

Goal: Find the surface areas of prisms and cylinders.

Vocabulary

Net:

Surface area:

EXAMPLE 1 **Drawing a Net**

Draw a net for the pentagonal prism.

Method 1: Draw one base with a rectangle adjacent to each side. Draw the other base adjacent to one of the rectangles.

Method 2: For the rectangular faces, draw adjacent rectangles. Draw the bases on opposite sides of one rectangle.

Can you draw a different net for the pentagonal prism?

EXAMPLE 2 Using a Net to Find Surface Area

Jewelry Box You are painting a jewelry box that is 12 inches long, 7 inches wide, and 7 inches tall. Before you begin painting, you need to find the surface area. What is the surface area of the jewelry box?

Solution

Draw a net of the jewelry box.

7 in. 7 in. 7 in. 12 in.

The area of each square face is ____ • ____ = ____

The area of each rectangular face is

There are ____ square faces and ____ rectangular faces, so the surface area is ____ • ____ + ____ • ____ = ____

ANSWER The surface area of the jewelry box is ____.

Surface Area of a Prism

Words The surface area of a prism is the sum of twice the area of a base and the product of the base's perimeter and the height.

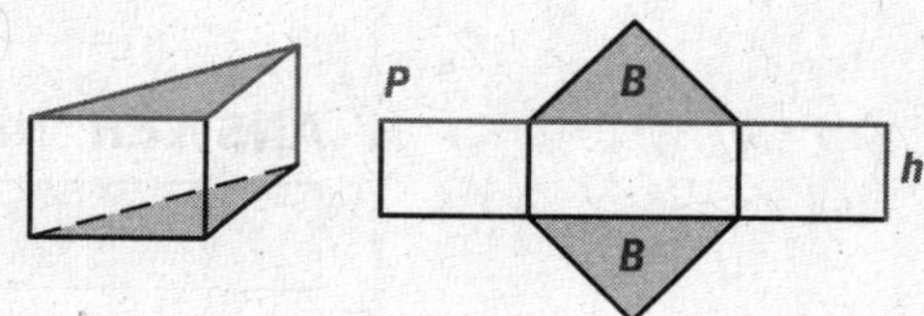

Algebra $S =$

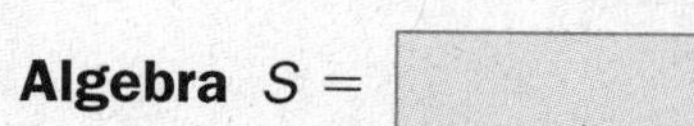

Think: What is the base of the prism?

EXAMPLE 3 Using a Formula to Find Surface Area

Find the surface area of the triangular prism.

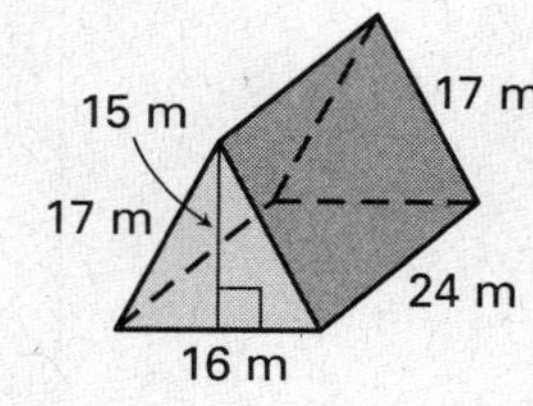

$S =$ ____

$=$ ____

$=$ ____

...ure that you write ...eight of the prism, not the height ...f the triangle.

ANSWER The surface area of the prism is ____.

Surface Area of a Cylinder

Words The surface area of a cylinder is the sum of twice the area of a base and the product of the base's circumference and the height.

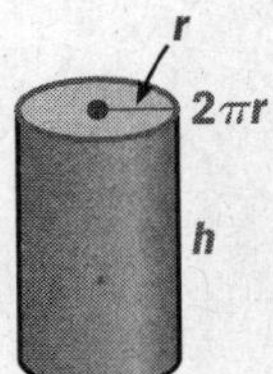

Algebra $S = 2$ 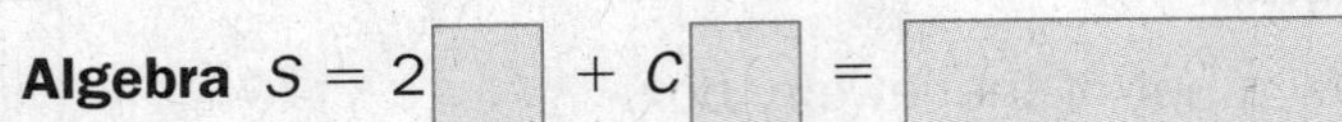 $+ C$ ___ $=$ ___

EXAMPLE 4 Standardized Test Practice

Tennis What is the surface area of the can of tennis balls?

Ⓐ 123 cm^2 Ⓑ 406 cm^2

Ⓒ 450 cm^2 Ⓓ 1029 cm^2

Solution

The radius is one half the diameter, so $r =$  cm.

$S =$  Write formula for surface area of a cylinder.

$S =$ ___ Substitute for r and h.

$\approx$  Evaluate using a calculator.

You can use the π key on your calculator instead of 3.14 when evaluating formulas.

ANSWER The surface area of the can of tennis balls is about ___. The correct answer is ___. Ⓐ Ⓑ Ⓒ

Guided Practice **Draw a net of the solid. Then find the surface area. Round to the nearest tenth.**

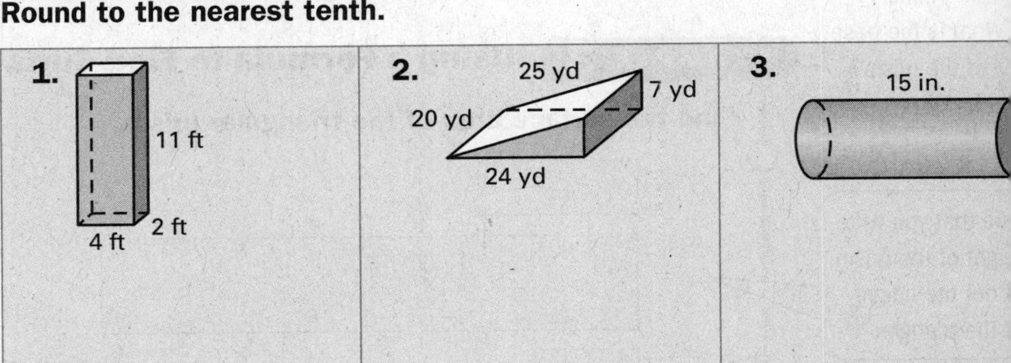

10.5

Surface Areas of Pyramids and Cones

Goal: Find the surface areas of pyramids and cones.

Vocabulary

Slant height: ____________

e pyramids in this
on have a regular
on as a base and
ruent triangles as
other faces. The
nt height is the
ne on any face
is not the base.

Surface Area of a Pyramid

Words The surface area of a regular pyramid is the sum of the area of the base and one half the product of the base perimeter and the slant height.

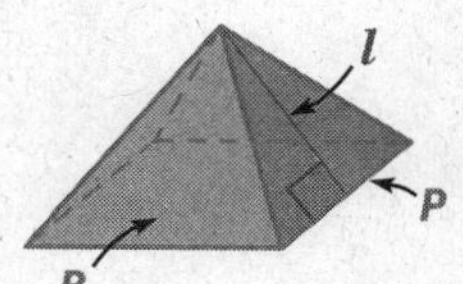

Algebra $S =$ 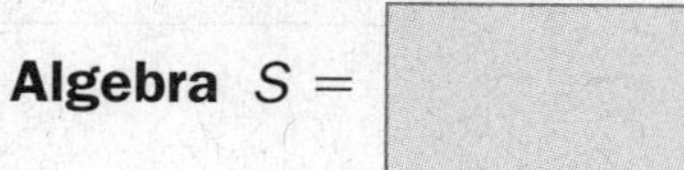

EXAMPLE 1 **Finding the Surface Area of a Pyramid**

Find the surface area of the regular pyramid.

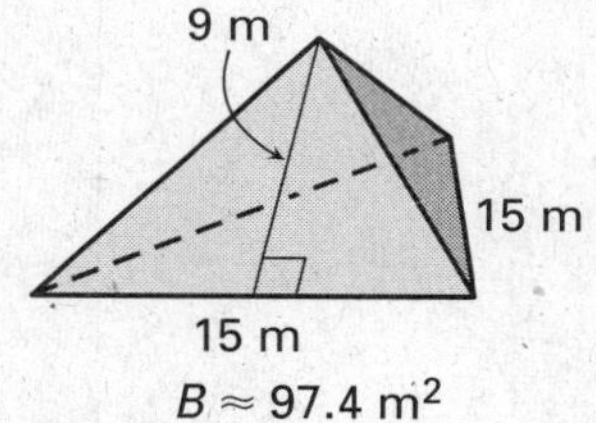

1. Find the perimeter of the base.

$P =$ ____ + ____ + ____ = ____

2. Substitute into the formula for surface area.

$S =$ ____ Write formula for surface area of a pyramid.

$\approx$  Substitute for B, P, and l.

$\approx$ ____ Simplify.

ANSWER The surface area is about ____________.

Surface Area of a Cone

Words The surface area of a cone is the sum of the area of the circular base and the product of pi, the radius of the base, and the slant height.

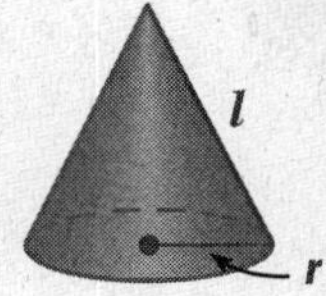

Algebra $S =$ ______

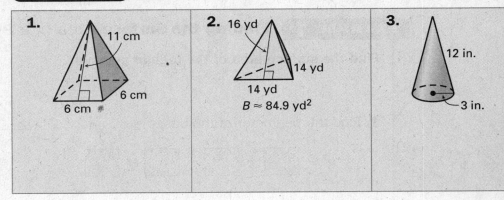

EXAMPLE 2 **Finding the Surface Area of a Cone**

Find the surface area of a cone with radius 7 feet and slant height 10

$S =$ ______ Write formula for surface area of a cone.

$\approx$ ______ Substitute for r and l.

$\approx$ ______ Evaluate using a calculator.

ANSWER The surface area is about ______.

Guided Practice **Find the surface area. Round to the nearest tenth.**

1.

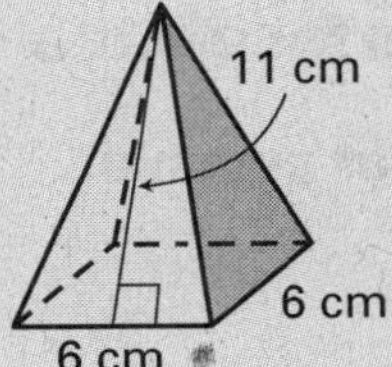

2.

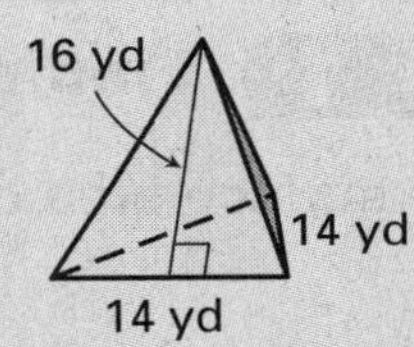

3.

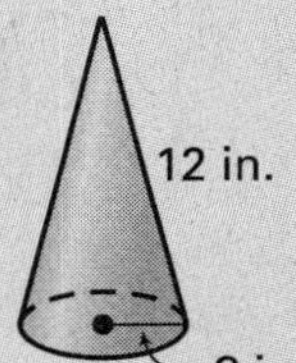

LESSON 10.6

Volumes of Prisms and Cylinders

Goal: Find the volumes of prisms and cylinders.

Vocabulary

Volume: ______

Volume of a Prism

Words The volume of a prism is the product of the area of the base and the height.

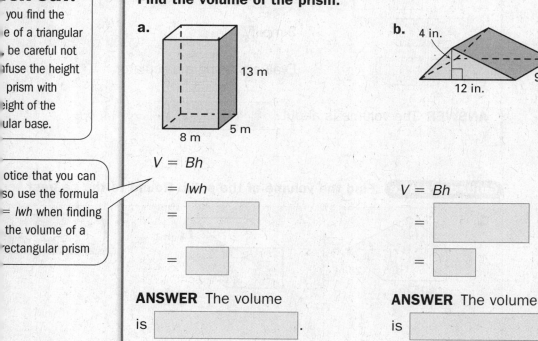

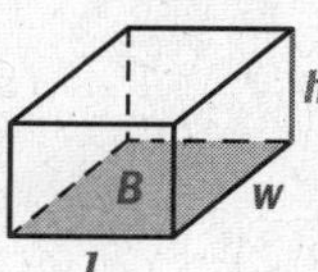

Algebra $V =$ ______

EXAMPLE 1 **Finding Volumes of Prisms**

WATCH OUT! When you find the volume of a triangular prism, be careful not to confuse the height of the prism with the height of the triangular base.

Find the volume of the prism.

a.

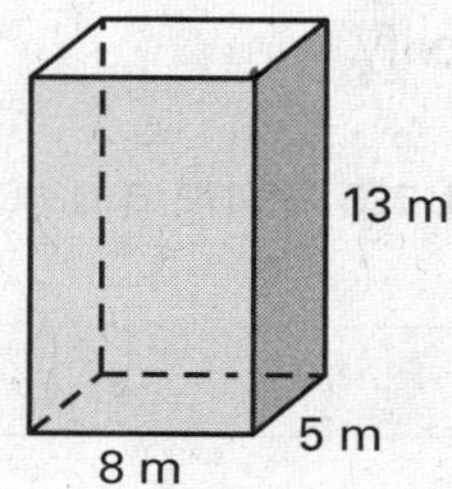

$V = Bh$

$= lwh$

$=$ ______

$=$ ______

Notice that you can also use the formula $V = lwh$ when finding the volume of a rectangular prism

ANSWER The volume is ______.

b.

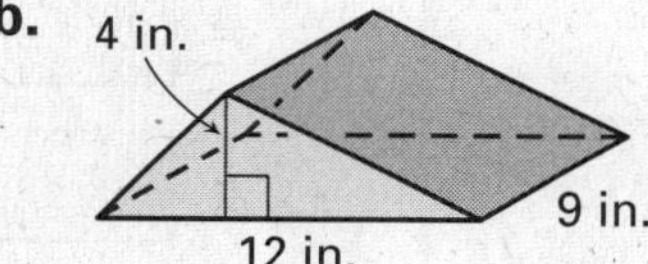

$V = Bh$

$=$ ______

$=$ ______

ANSWER The volume is ______.

Volume of a Cylinder

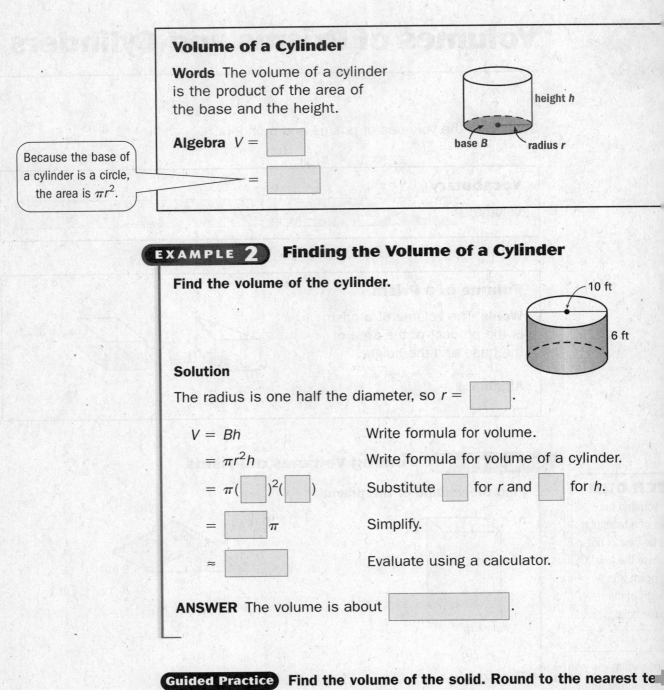

Words The volume of a cylinder is the product of the area of the base and the height.

height h

base B

radius r

Algebra $V =$ ____

$=$ ____

Because the base of a cylinder is a circle, the area is πr^2.

EXAMPLE 2 **Finding the Volume of a Cylinder**

Find the volume of the cylinder.

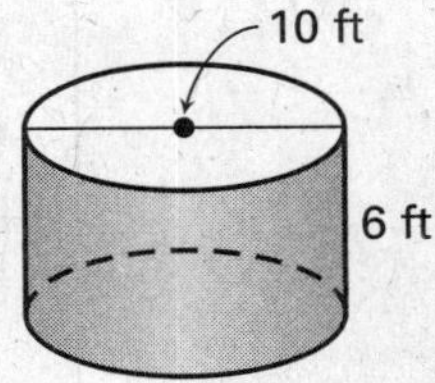

Solution

The radius is one half the diameter, so $r =$ ____.

$V = Bh$	Write formula for volume.
$= \pi r^2 h$	Write formula for volume of a cylinder.
$= \pi($ ____ $)^2($ ____ $)$	Substitute ____ for r and ____ for h.
$=$ ____ π	Simplify.
$\approx$ ____	Evaluate using a calculator.

ANSWER The volume is about ____.

Guided Practice **Find the volume of the solid. Round to the nearest te**

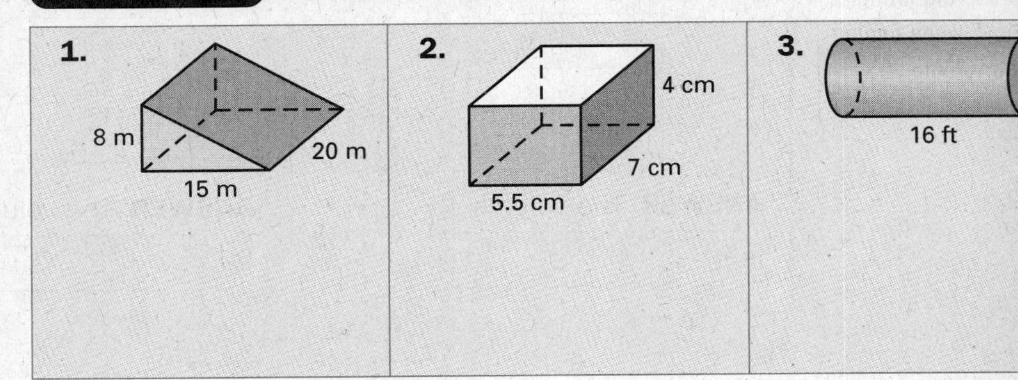

EXAMPLE 3 Comparing Volumes

Cheese At a grocery store, one type of cheddar cheese is sold in the shape of a rectangular prism, and another type is sold in the shape of a cylinder. Which shape of cheddar cheese has the greater volume?

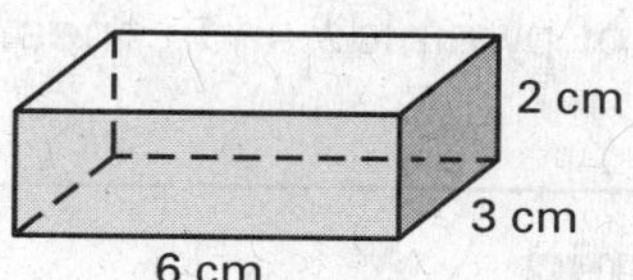

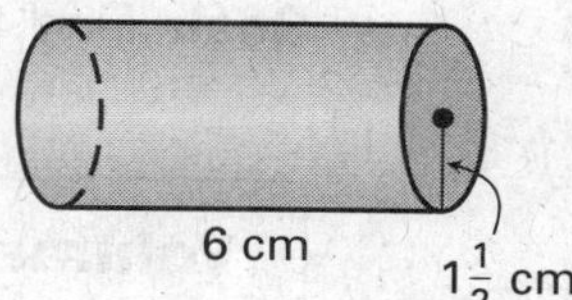

To decide which shape of cheddar cheese has the greater volume, find the volume of each shape.

en the abbreviation
a unit of measure
an exponent of 3,
ead the 3 as "cubic".
t^3 = cubic feet
^{3} = cubic inches

$V = Bh$

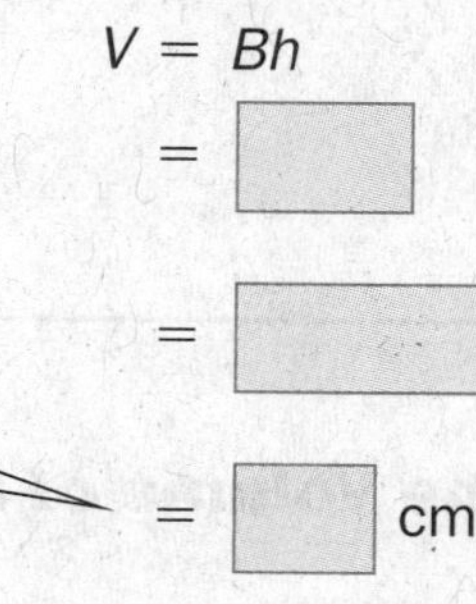

= ____

= ____

= ____ cm^3

$V = Bh$

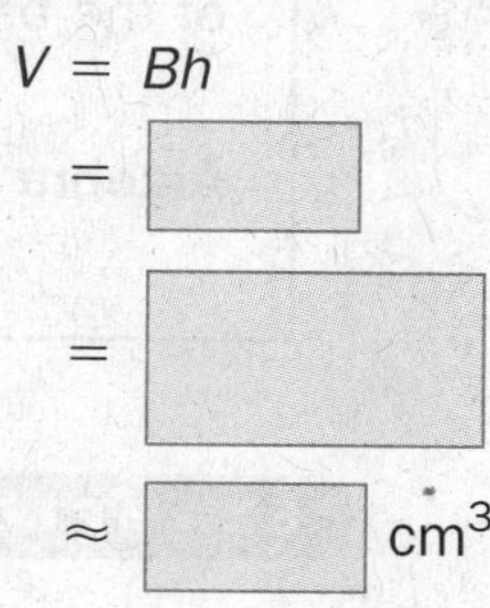

= ____

= ____

≈ ____ cm^3

ANSWER The ____ shape of cheddar cheese has the greater volume.

EXAMPLE 4 Standardized Test Practice

What happens to the volume of the cylinder shown when the dimensions are tripled?

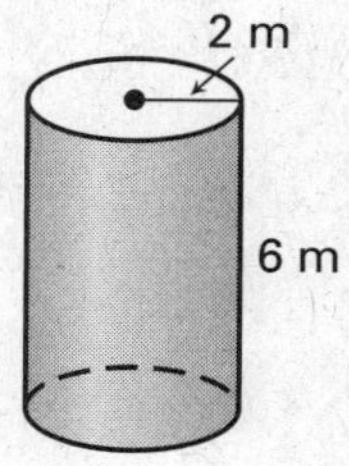

Ⓐ The volume is divided by 3.

Ⓑ The volume is multiplied by 3.

Ⓒ The volume is multiplied by 9.

Ⓓ The volume is multiplied by 27.

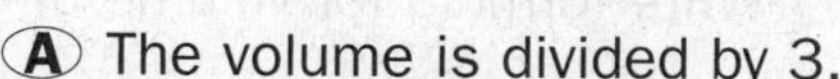

Solution

1. Find the volume of the cylinder.

$V = \pi r^2 h$

= ____ ____

= ____ $\pi\ m^3$

2. Find the volume of the cylinder when the dimensions are tripled.

$V = \pi r^2 h$

= ____ ____

= ____ $\pi\ m^3$

3. Compare the volumes

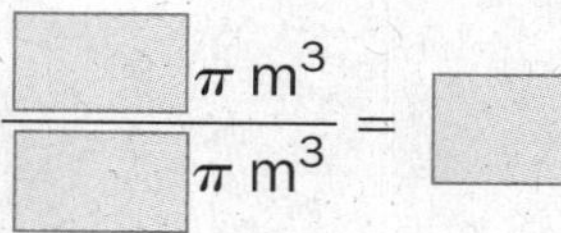

$\frac{\_\_\_\_\ \pi\ m^3}{\_\_\_\_\ \pi\ m^3} =$ ____

ANSWER When the dimensions are tripled, the volume is ____ by

____. The correct answer is ____. Ⓐ Ⓑ Ⓒ Ⓓ

Volumes of Pyramids and Cone

Goal: Find the volumes of pyramids and cones.

Remember that the height of a pyramid is different than the slant height of a regular pyramid.

Volume of a Pyramid

Words The volume of a pyramid is one third the product of the area of the base and the height.

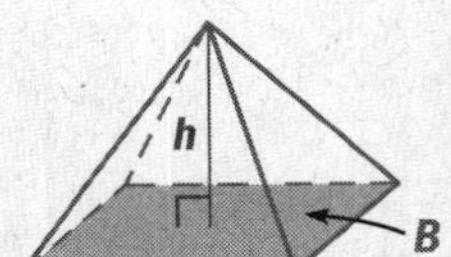

Algebra $V =$

EXAMPLE 1 Finding the Volume of a Pyramid

Paperweight A paperweight has the shape of a square pyramid. It has a height of 7 centimeters, and each side of its base measures 12 centimeters. What is the volume of the paperweight?

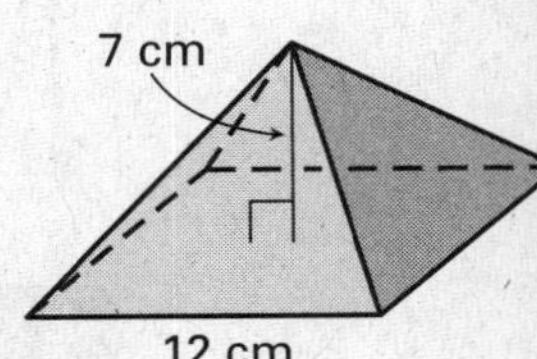

Solution

$V =$ Write formula for volume of a pyramid.

$=$  The base is square, so $B = s^2$.

$=$  Evaluate using a calculator.

ANSWER The paperweight has a volume of ______.

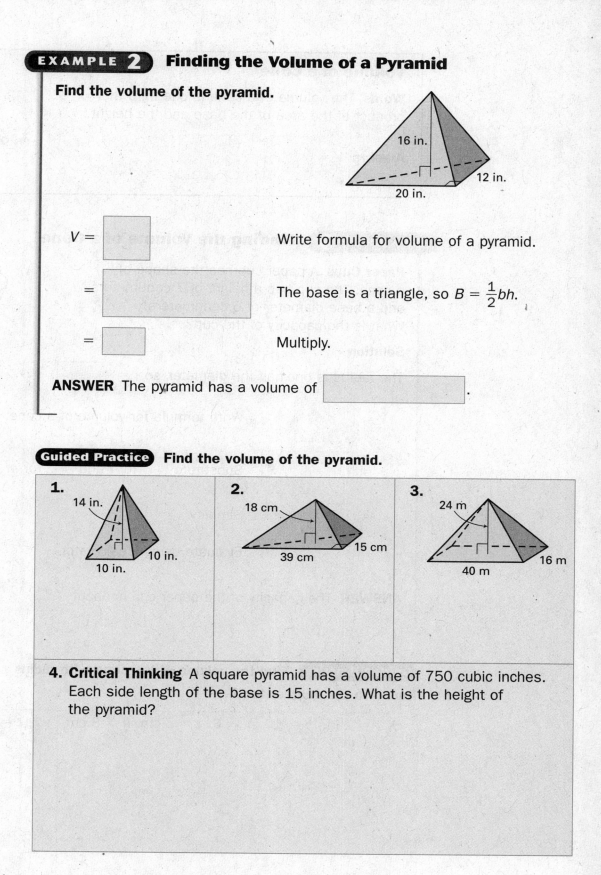

EXAMPLE 2 Finding the Volume of a Pyramid

Find the volume of the pyramid.

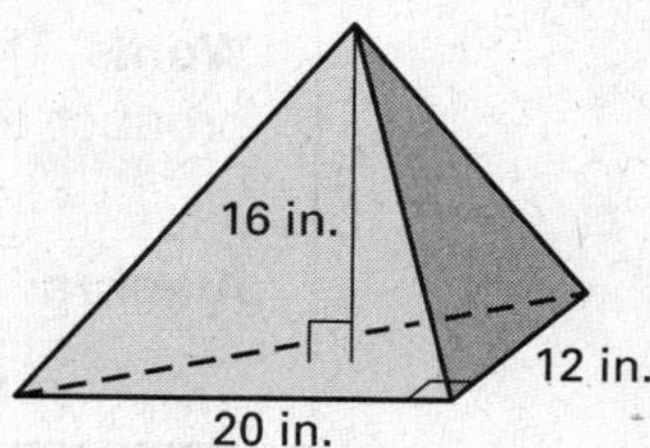

$V =$ [ ] Write formula for volume of a pyramid.

$=$ [ ] The base is a triangle, so $B = \frac{1}{2}bh$.

$=$ [ ] Multiply.

ANSWER The pyramid has a volume of [ ].

Guided Practice **Find the volume of the pyramid.**

1.

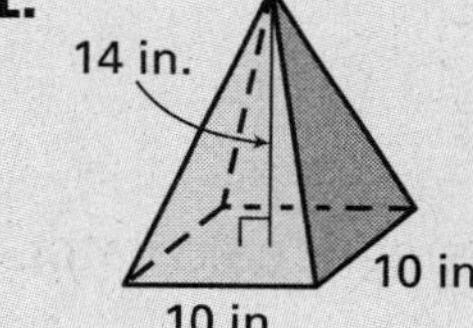

2.

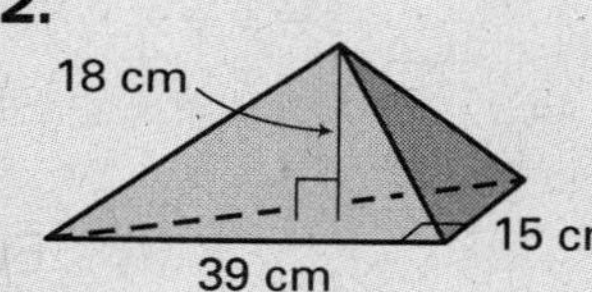

3.

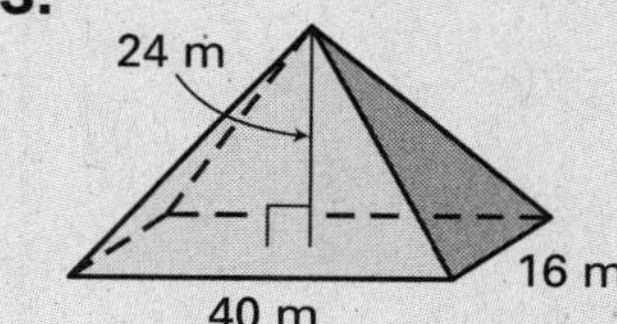

4. Critical Thinking A square pyramid has a volume of 750 cubic inches. Each side length of the base is 15 inches. What is the height of the pyramid?

Volume of a Cone

Words The volume of a cone is one third the product of the area of the base and the height.

Algebra $V =$ ______ $=$ ______

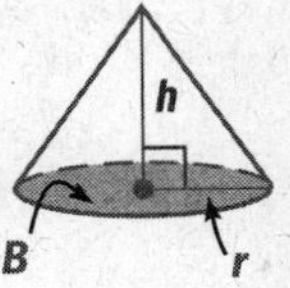

EXAMPLE 3 **Finding the Volume of a Cone**

Paper Cups A paper cup has the shape of a cone. The cup has a height of 7 centimeters and a base diameter of 6 centimeters. What is the capacity of the cup?

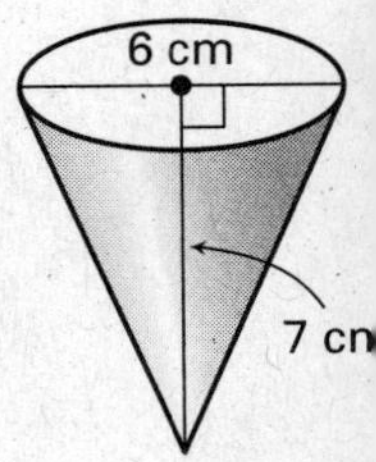

Solution

The radius is one-half the diameter, so $r =$ ______.

$V =$ ______	Write formula for volume of a cone.
$=$ ______	Substitute ______ for r and ______ for h.
$=$ ______	Simplify.
$\approx$ ______	Evaluate using a calculator.

ANSWER The capacity of the paper cup is about ______

Guided Practice **Find the volume of the cone with radius *r* and height *h*. Round to the nearest tenth.**

5. $r = 2$ in., $h = 10$ in.	6. $r = 8$ cm, $h = 8$ cm	7. $r = 20$ ft, $h = 6$

Words to Review

Give an example of the vocabulary word.

Base of a parallelogram

Polyhedron

Height of a parallelogram

Face

Bases of a trapezoid

Prism

Height of a trapezoid

Pyramid

Solid

Cylinder

Cone

Net

Sphere

Surface area

Edge

Slant height

Vertex

Volume

Review your notes and Chapter 10 by using the Chapter Review on pages 569–
of your textbook.

Relations and Functions

Goal: Use tables to represent functions.

Vocabulary

Relation:

Input:

Output:

Function:

Domain:

Range:

EXAMPLE 1 Identifying Functions

Tell whether the relation is a function. Explain your answer.

a. (4, 7), (2, 6), (4, −5), (2, −4)

ANSWER The relation ______ a function.

b.

Input	−1	0	1	2
Output	3	−3	−1	−1

ANSWER The relation ______ a function.

ATCH OUT!
function, two
erent inputs can
the same
out, but each
t must have
ctly *one* output.

Guided Practice **Tell whether the relation is a function.**

1. (−5, 2), (−2, 5), (−5, −2), (2, 5)

2.

Input	0	3	6	9
Output	12	8	4	2

EXAMPLE 2 Evaluating a Function

Arcade You have \$16 to spend at the arcade. You spend \$4 on food. Ea game costs \$0.50 to play. How many games can you play?

Solution

To solve the problem, use the function rule $C = 0.50g + 4$, where C is t amount you spend in dollars and g is the number of games you play. Firs make a table to determine how many games you can play.

Input g	Function	Output C
0	$C = 0.50($ ___ $) + 4$	___
8	$C = 0.50($ ___ $) + 4$	___
16	$C = 0.50($ ___ $) + 4$	___
24	$C = 0.50($ ___ $) + 4$	___

Because you have \$16 to spend, the domain of this function is 0, 1, 2, 3 ... ___. The range of this function is ___, ___ 5, 5.5, ... ___.

If an input value gives an output value that is close to the output value you want, then choose a number close to your original input value.

ANSWER You can play ___ games.

EXAMPLE 3 Writing a Function Rule

Write a function rule that relates *x* and *y*.

Input	Output
−5	−8
−3	−6
−1	−4
1	−2
3	0

(Inputs increase by +2 each row.)

To write a function rule, try to find an equation of the form $y = ax + b$. You can look at differences in the function to find values of a and b.

1. The value of a is $\frac{\text{change in output}}{\text{\_\_\_}}$.

$a = $ ___ $=$ ___ $\qquad y =$ ___ $x + b$

2. To find b, choose an input-output pair to substitute for x and y.

Let $(x, y) = ($ ___ $, 0)$ $\qquad 0 =$ ___ $($ ___ $) + b$, so $b =$ ___

When choosing an input-output pair, if possible, choose a pair that has a zero to make the calculations easier.

ANSWER A function rule that relates x and y is ___.

✓ **Check** ___ $=$ ___ $\qquad$ Substitute $(1, -2)$ in function rule.

Scatter Plots

Goal: Make and interpret scatter plots.

Vocabulary

Scatter plot:

EXAMPLE 1 **Making a Scatter Plot**

Tree Height The table shows the height of a tree each year for six years. Make a scatter plot of the data.

Year	1	2	3	4	5	6
Height (cm)	60	115	165	210	250	285

Solution

1. Plot the ordered pairs from the table.

(1, 60), ______, ______,

______, (5, 250), ______

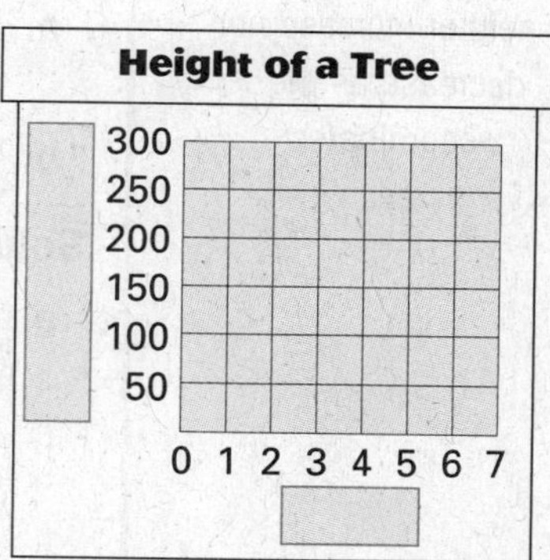

2. Label the horizontal and vertical axes.

Put ______ on the horizontal axis

and ______ on the vertical axis.

Guided Practice Make a scatter plot of the data.

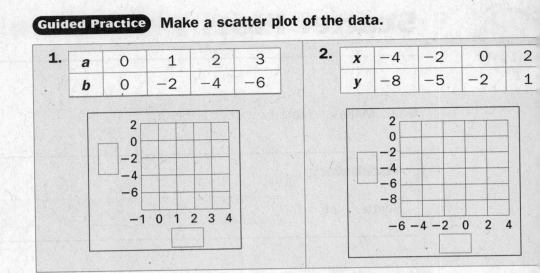

1.

a	0	1	2	3
b	0	−2	−4	−6

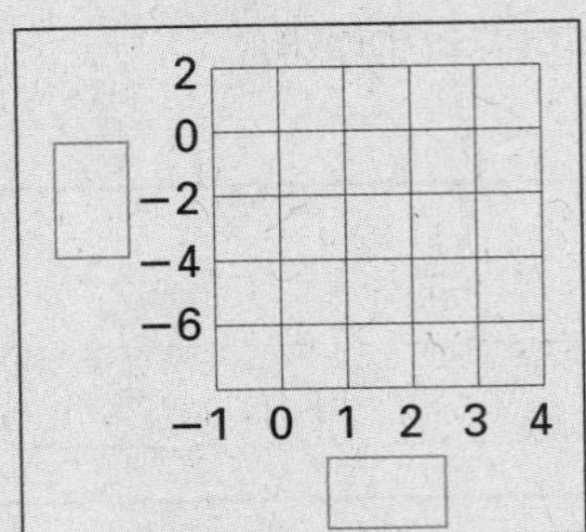

2.

x	−4	−2	0	2
y	−8	−5	−2	1

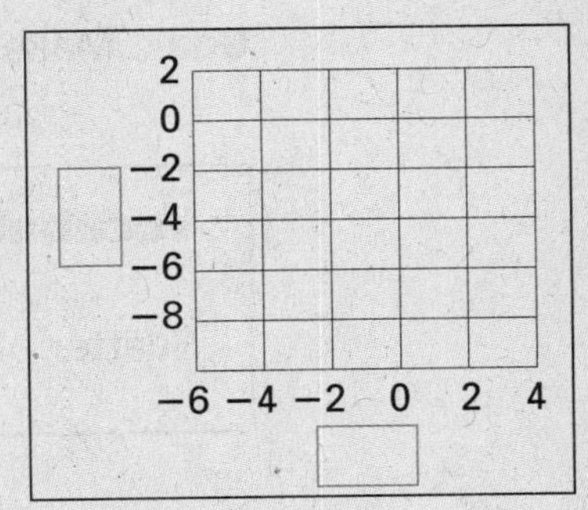

EXAMPLE 2 Interpreting a Scatter Plot

DVD Player The table shows how the cost of a DVD player has changed

Number of months on shelf x	0	3	6	9	12	15
Price y	\$215	\$210	\$199	\$184	\$167	\$140

Think: Do the y-coordinates increase, decrease, or neither increase nor decrease as the x-coordinates increase?

a. Make a scatter plot of the data. Tell whether x and y have a *positive relationship*, a *negative relationship*, or *no relationship*.

b. Estimate the price of the DVD player after 18 months on the shelf.

Solution

a. In the scatter plot, the y-coordinates ________ as the x-coordinates increase.

ANSWER The quantities have a ________ relationship.

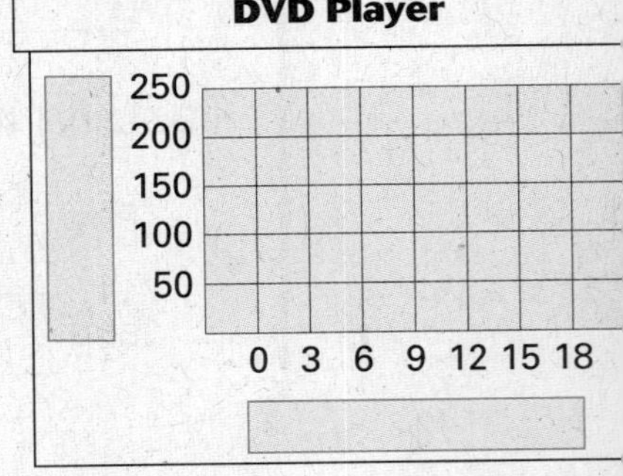

b. To estimate the price of the DVD player after 18 months, draw a curve that shows the overall pattern of the data. The curve looks like it will pass through the point (18, ________).

Graph each ordered pair. Then draw a curve through the points.

ANSWER The price of the DVD player after 18 months on the shelf is about ________.

Equations in Two Variables

Goal: Find solutions of equations in two variables.

Vocabulary

Solution of an equation in two variables:

EXAMPLE 1 **Standardized Test Practice**

Bowling At a bowling alley, it costs \$5 to rent shoes plus \$3 per game. The total cost can be modeled by the equation $C = 5 + 3g$, where C is the total cost, in dollars, and g is the number of games bowled. Which table shows some possible total costs for bowling?

Ⓐ

g	1	2	3	4
C	\$3	\$6	\$9	\$12

Ⓑ

g	1	2	3	4
C	\$8	\$11	\$14	\$17

Ⓒ

g	1	2	3	4
C	\$3	\$8	\$13	\$18

Ⓓ

g	1	2	3	4
C	\$8	\$16	\$24	\$32

Solution

Substitute several values of g into the equation and solve for C. Then identify that table that contains the solutions.

g-value	**Substitute for g.**	**Solve for C.**	**Solution**
$g = 1$	$C = 5 + 3(\quad)$	$C =$	
$g = 2$	$C = 5 + 3(\quad)$	$C =$	
$g = 3$	$C = 5 + 3(\quad)$	$C =$	
$g = 4$	$C = 5 + 3(\quad)$	$C =$	

ANSWER The correct answer is ___.    

EXAMPLE 2 Checking Solutions

Tell whether (5, −8) is a solution of $4x - y = 12$.

$4x - y = 12$ Write original equation.

$4($ ____ $) -$ ____ $\stackrel{?}{=} 12$ Substitute ____ for x and ____ for y.

____ $\stackrel{?}{=} 12$ Simplify.

____ $\neq 12$ Solution ____ check.

ANSWER The ordered pair (5, −8) ____ a solution of $4x - y = 12$.

EXAMPLE 3 Finding Solutions of an Equation

Write the equation $6x + 2y = 16$ in function form. Then list four solut

1. Rewrite the equation in function form.

$6x + 2y = 16$ Write original equation.

____ = ____ ____ from each side.

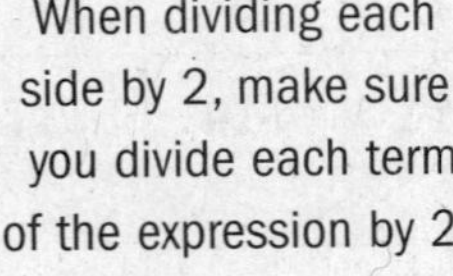

When dividing each side by 2, make sure you divide each term of the expression by 2.

$y =$ ____ Divide each side by ____.

2. Substitute several values of x into the equation and solve for y.

***x*-value**	**Substitute for *x*.**	**Solve for *y*.**	**Solution**
$x = -1$	$y = 8 - 3($ ____ $)$	$y =$ ____	____
$x = 0$	$y = 8 - 3($ ____ $)$	$y =$ ____	____
$x = 1$	$y = 8 - 3($ ____ $)$	$y =$ ____	____
$x = 2$	$y = 8 - 3($ ____ $)$	$y =$ ____	____

Generally, an equation involving two variables has an infinite number of solutions.

ANSWER Four solutions are ____, ____, ____, and ____

Guided Practice **Tell whether the ordered pair is a solution of the equation.**

1. $y = -3x - 5$; $(-4, 7)$	**2.** $-7y + x = -7$; $(-1, -14)$

List four solutions of the equation.

3. $y = -5x + 11$	**4.** $18x - 3y = 9$

Graphs of Linear Equations

Goal: Learn to sketch the graph of a linear equation.

Vocabulary

Linear equation:

EXAMPLE 1 Graphing a Linear Equation

Graph $y = \frac{1}{3}x - 1$.

1. Choose several values to substitute for x. Then evaluate to find y and make a table of values.

x	−6	−3	0	3	6
y	−3	−2	−1	0	1

2. List the solutions as ordered pairs.

, , , ,

3. Plot the ordered pairs. Then draw a line through them.

Make sure the arrowheads are drawn on the graph. They indicate that the line extends forever in both directions.

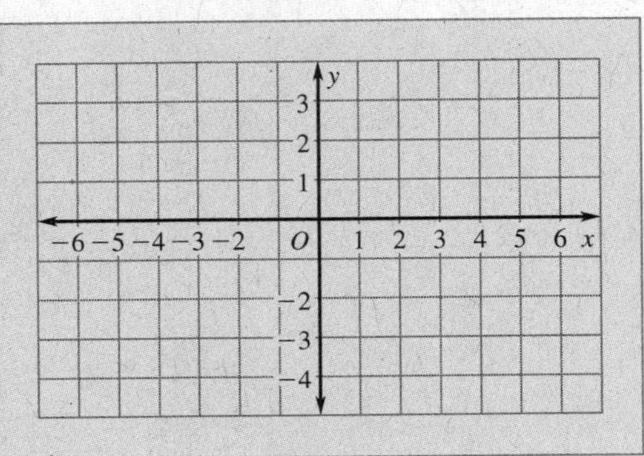

ANSWER The line is the graph of $y = \frac{1}{3}x - 1$.

Guided Practice **Graph the linear equation.**

1. $y = x - 7$

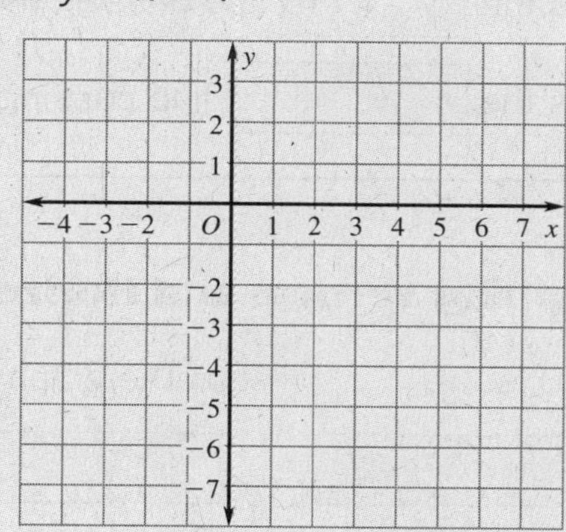

2. $2x + y = 3$

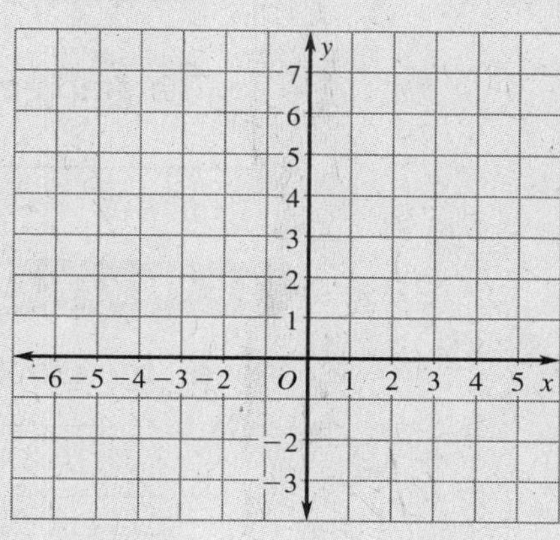

EXAMPLE 2 Using the Graph of a Linear Equation

Music Lessons You are taking music lessons. The book used for the lessons costs $15. If you are charged $7.50 per lesson, you can model the total cost c of your lessons in dollars using the equation $c = 7.5n + 15$, where n is the number of lessons.

a. Graph $c = 7.5n + 15$.

b. Estimate how many lessons you will take for the total cost of your lessons to be $75.

Think:
…e graph of the …ction through the points is a ray, and … a line. Can you explain why?

Solution

a. Make a table of values.

n	0	2	4	6	8
c	15	30	45	60	75

Plot each solution and draw a ray through the points.

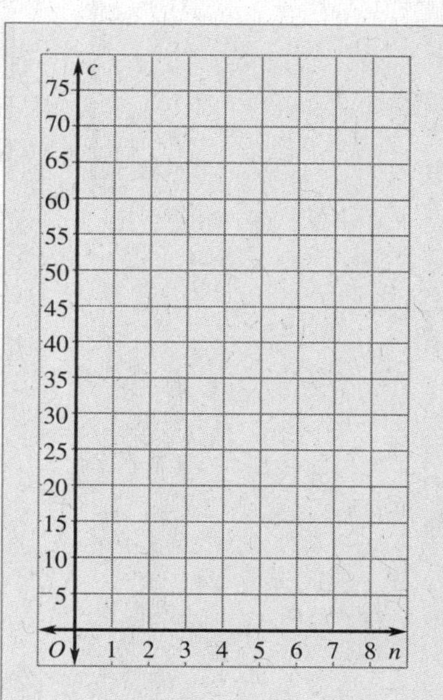

b. The graph shows that it will take ☐ lessons for the total cost of your lessons to be $75.

Vertical and Horizontal Lines

The graph of $x = a$ is the ______ line passing through $(a, 0)$.

The graph of $y = b$ is the ______ line passing through $(0, b)$.

EXAMPLE 3 Graphing Vertical and Horizontal Lines

WATCH OUT!
A vertical line *does not* represent a function, because one input has infinitely many outputs. A horizontal line *does* represent a function.

a. The graph of $x = 6$ is the ______

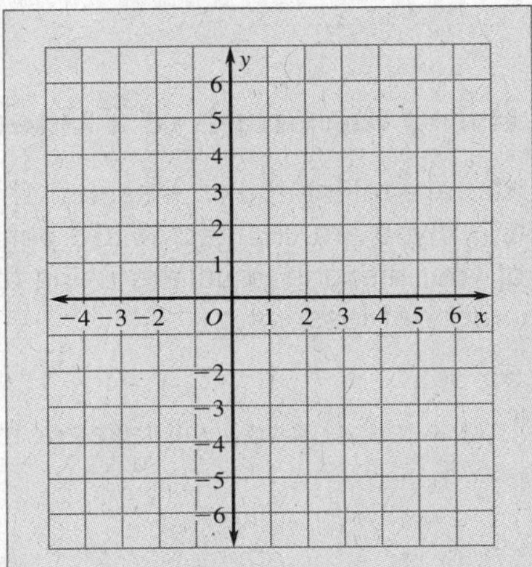

For all values of y, the x-value is 6.

b. The graph of $y = -3$ is the ______

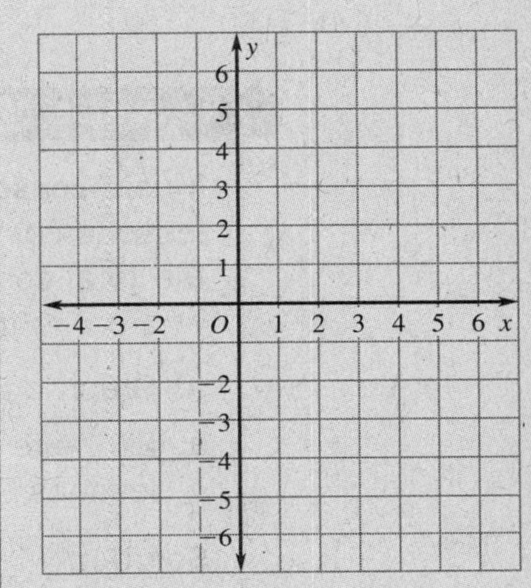

For all values of x, the y-value is -3.

Using Intercepts

Goal: Find *x*- and *y*-intercepts of a line.

Vocabulary

x-intercept: ____

y-intercept: ____

Finding Intercepts

To find the *x*-intercept of a graph, substitute 0 for ____ into the equation of the line and solve for ____.

To find the *y*-intercept of a graph, substitute 0 for ____ into the equation of the line and solve for ____.

EXAMPLE 1 Finding Intercepts

Find the intercepts of the graph of $y = \frac{3}{4}x - 6$.

To find the ____, let $y = 0$ and solve for *x*.

$y = \frac{3}{4}x - 6$

____ $= \frac{3}{4}x - 6$

____ $= \frac{3}{4}x$

____ $= x$

To find the ____, let $x = 0$ and solve for *y*.

$y = \frac{3}{4}x - 6$

$y = \frac{3}{4}$ ____ $- 6$

$y =$ ____ $- 6$

$y =$ ____

ember that the
epts of a line are
pers, not points.

ANSWER The *x*-intercept is ____ and the *y*-intercept is ____.

The graph of the equation contains the points ____ and ____.

EXAMPLE 2 Using Intercepts to Graph a Line

Graph the line with an *x*-intercept of −1 and a *y*-intercept of −4.

The *x*-intercept is −1, so plot the point ______. The *y*-intercept is −4, so plot the point ______.

Draw a line through the two points.

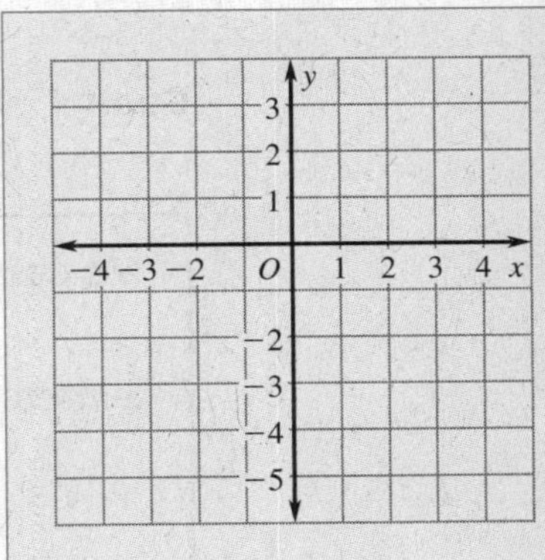

Guided Practice **Find the intercepts of the graph of the equation. Then graph the line using the intercepts.**

1. $4x + y = -3$

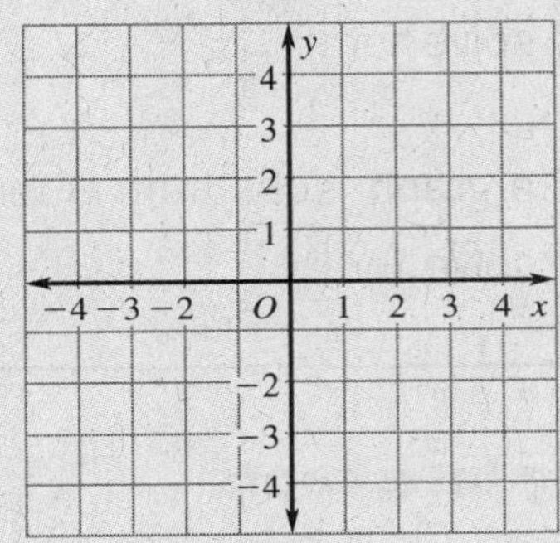

2. $6x - 2y = -2$

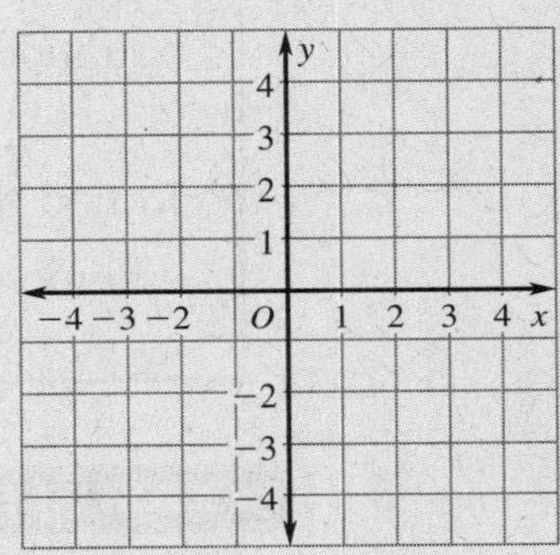

3. $-3x - y = -15$

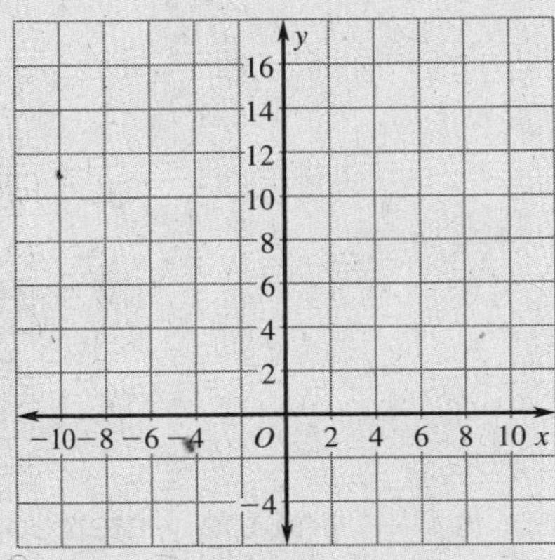

4. $12x - 6y = 18$

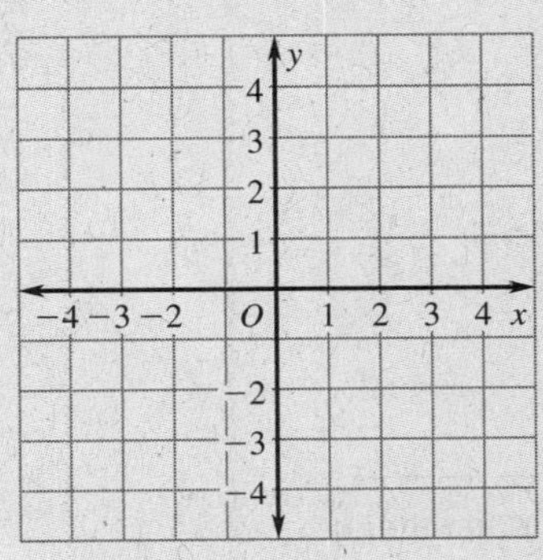

EXAMPLE 3 Using and Interpreting Intercepts

Fundraising You sell pizzas and subs to raise money for a field trip. Each pizza sells for $4 and each sub sells for $6. You raise $60. Graph the equation $4x + 6y = 60$, where x is the number of pizzas you sell and y is the number of subs you sell. What do the intercepts represent?

Solution

1. Find the *x*-intercept.

To find the *x*-intercept,

let ______ = 0 and solve for ______.

$$4x + 6y = 60$$

______ + ______ = 60

______ = 60

______ = ______

2. Find the *y*-intercept.

To find the *y*-intercept,

let ______ = 0 and solve for ______.

$$4x + 6y = 60$$

______ + ______ = 60

______ = 60

______ = ______

3. The *x*-intercept is ______ and the *y*-intercept is ______. So the points ______ and ______ are on the graph. Plot these points and draw a line through them.

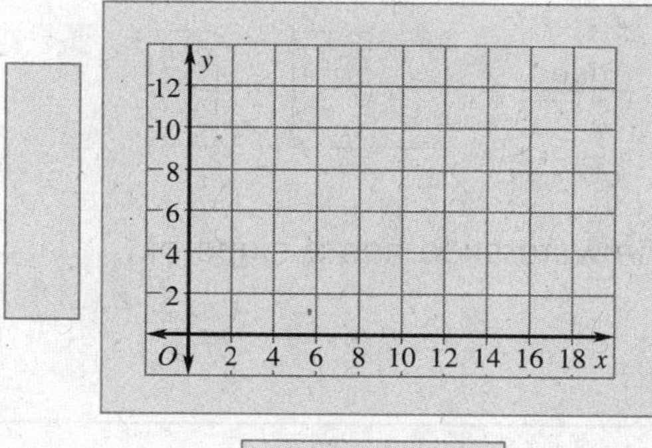

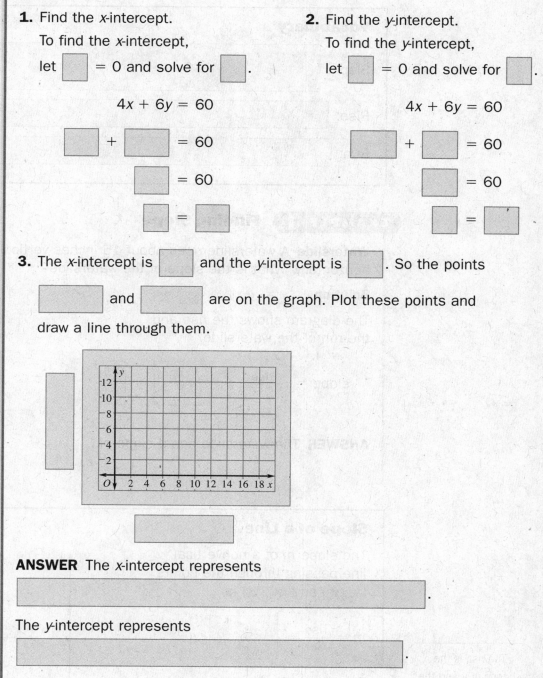

ANSWER The *x*-intercept represents

______.

The *y*-intercept represents

______.

LESSON 11.6

Slope

Goal: Find and interpret slopes of lines.

Vocabulary

Slope:

Rise:

Run:

EXAMPLE 1 Finding Slope

Waterslide A waterslide rises about 15 inches vertically for every 12 inc horizontally. What is the slope of the waterslide?

Solution

The diagram shows the rise and the run of the waterslide.

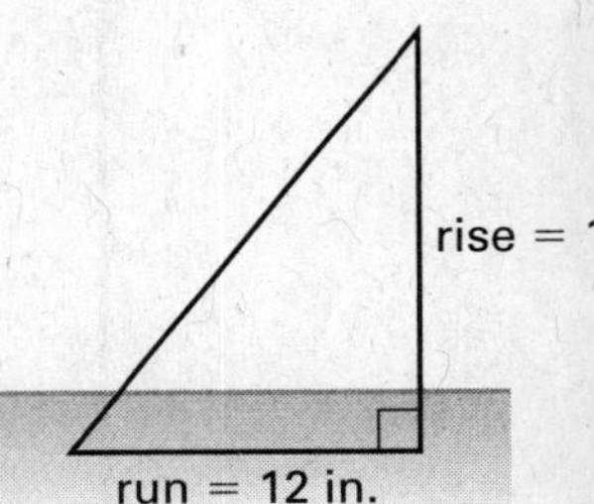

slope = $\frac{\text{rise}}{}$ = ___ = ___

ANSWER The waterslide has a slope of ___.

Slope of a Line

The slope m of a nonvertical line passing through the points (x_1, y_1) and (x_2, y_2) is

$m = \frac{\text{rise}}{\text{run}} =$ ___

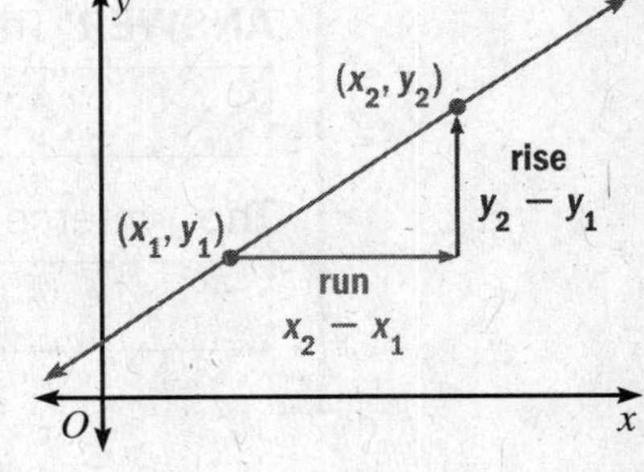

The rise is the change in y and the run is the change in x.

The slope of a line is the same no matter which two points you choose to use in the formula.

EXAMPLE 2 Positive and Negative Slope

Find the slope of the line.

a.

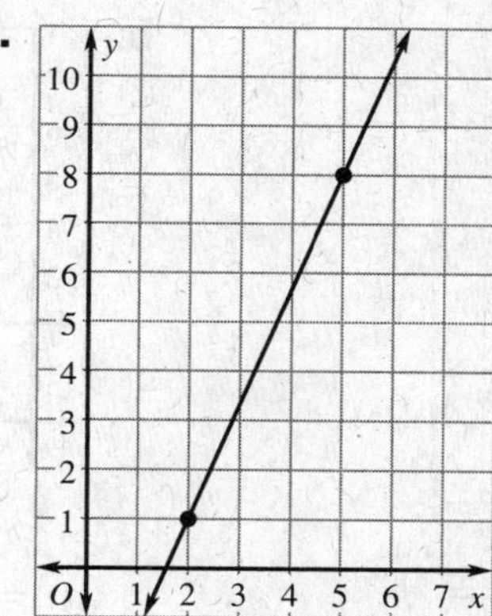

$m = \dfrac{\text{rise}}{\text{run}} =$ ______

$=$ ______

$=$ ______

Choose which points will be $, y_1)$ and (x_2, y_2)

ANSWER The slope is ______.

b.

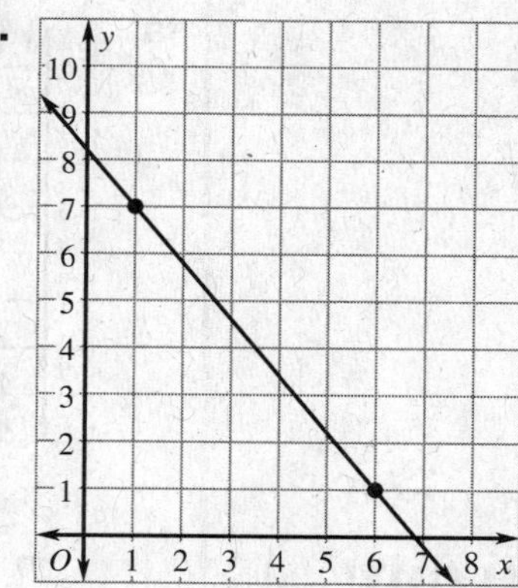

$m = \dfrac{\text{rise}}{\text{run}} =$ ______

$=$ ______

$=$ ______ or ______

ANSWER The slope is .

Guided Practice **Find the slope of the line passing through the points.**

1. (0, 2), (5, 5)	**2.** (9, 4), (1, 10)	**3.** (1, −6), (−4, 4)

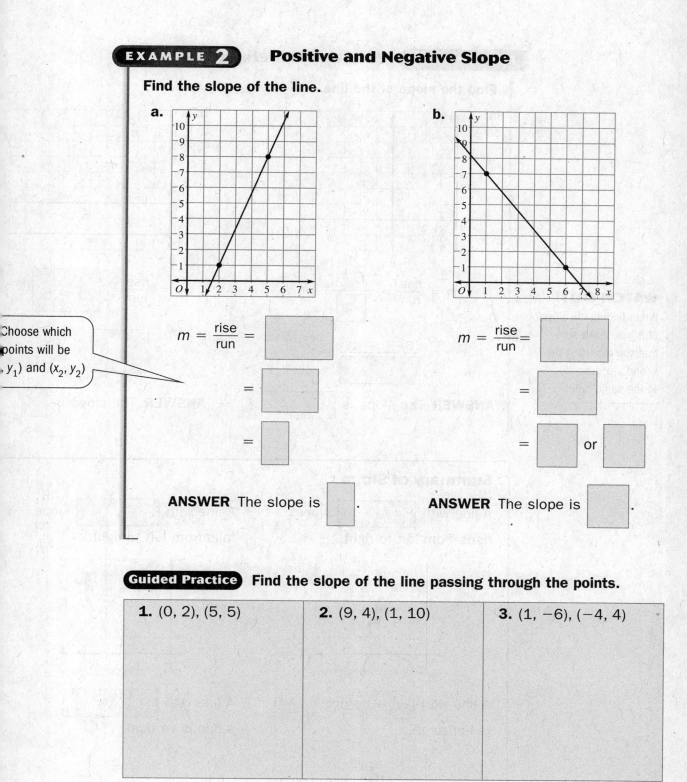

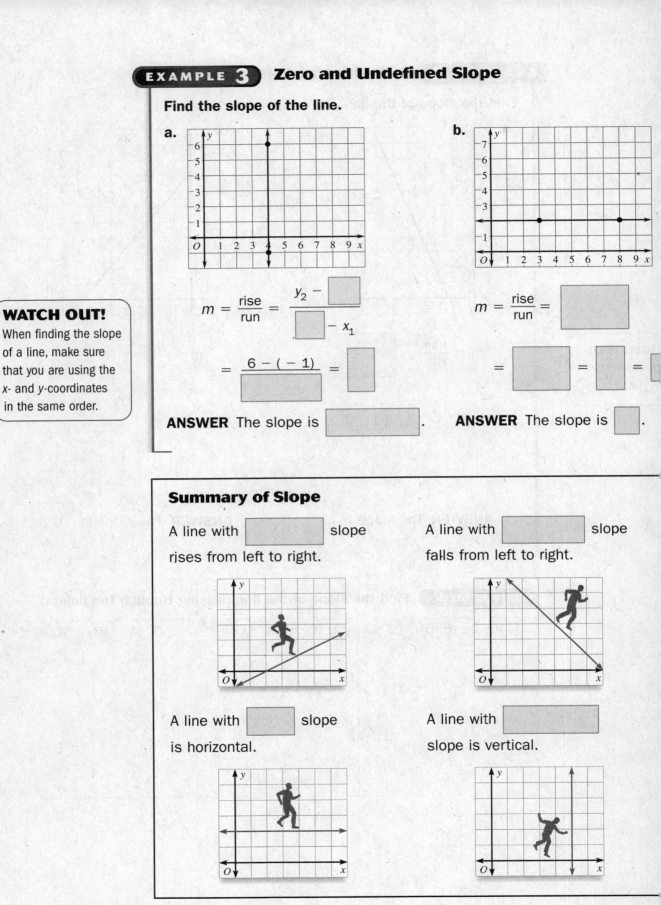

EXAMPLE 3 Zero and Undefined Slope

Find the slope of the line.

a.

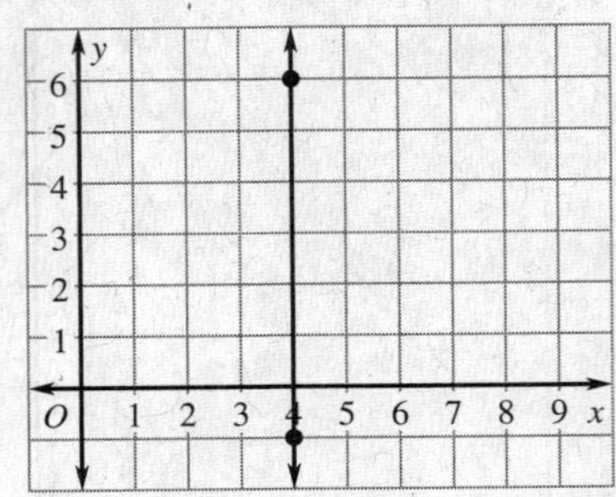

$m = \frac{\text{rise}}{\text{run}} = \frac{y_2 - \square}{\square - x_1}$

$= \frac{6 - (-1)}{\square} = \square$

ANSWER The slope is ______.

b.

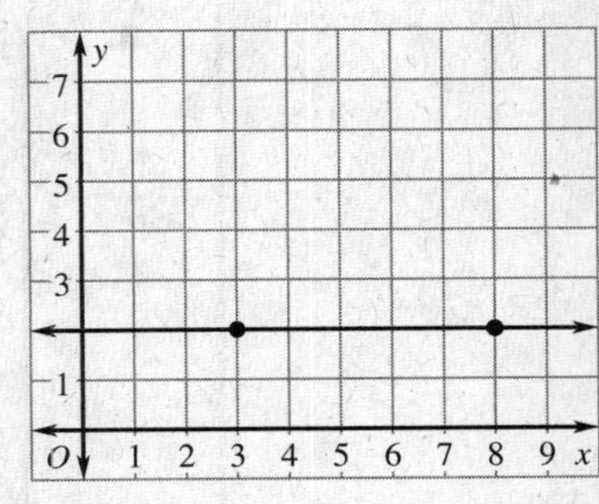

$m = \frac{\text{rise}}{\text{run}} = \square$

$= \square = \square = \square$

ANSWER The slope is ______.

WATCH OUT!
When finding the slope of a line, make sure that you are using the x- and y-coordinates in the same order.

Summary of Slope

A line with ______ slope rises from left to right.

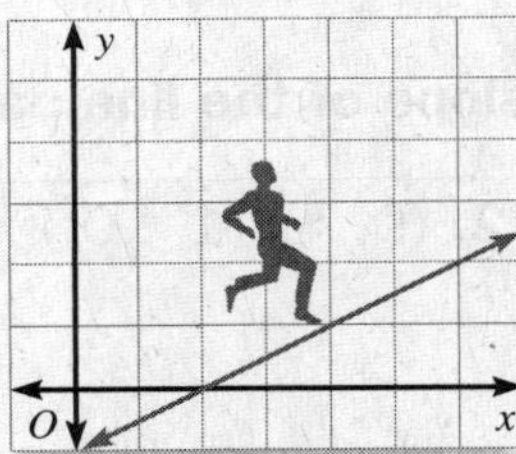

A line with ______ slope falls from left to right.

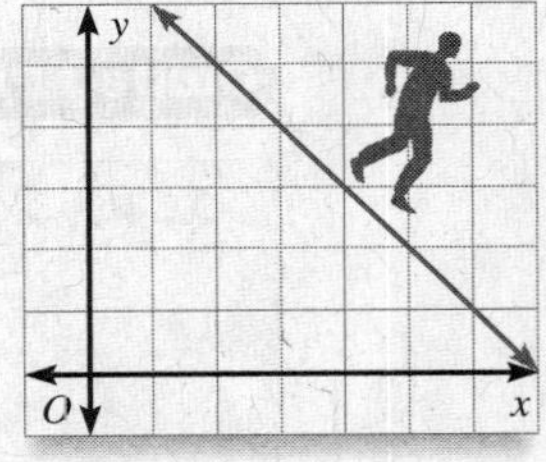

A line with ______ slope is horizontal.

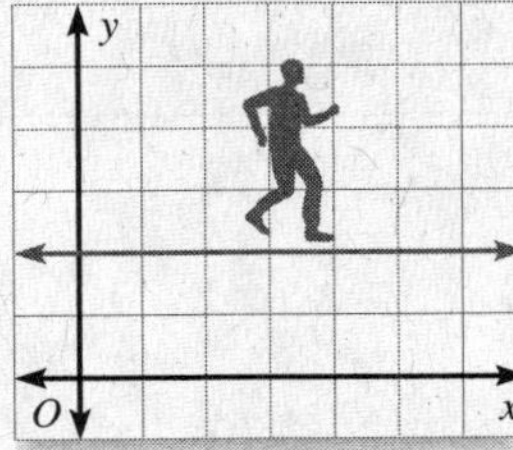

A line with ______ slope is vertical.

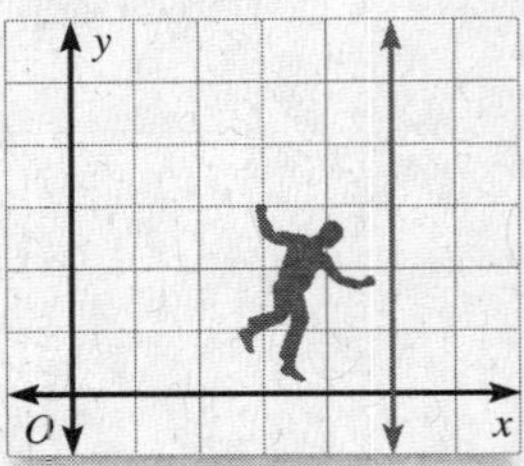

Slope-Intercept Form

Goal: Write and graph equations in slope-intercept form.

Slope-Intercept Form

Words The linear equation $y = mx + b$ is written in slope-intercept form. The ______ is m. The ______ is b.

Algebra $y = mx + b$ **Numbers** $y = 4x + 1$

EXAMPLE 1 **Identifying Slopes and y-Intercepts**

Find the slope and y-intercept of the graph of the equation.

a. $y = -x + 7$ **b.** $-9x + 3y = -6$

Solution

a. The equation $y = -x + 7$ can be written as $y =$ ______ $x + 7$.

ANSWER The line has a slope of ______ and a y-intercept of ______.

b. Write the equation $-9x + 3y = -6$ in slope-intercept form.

$-9x + 3y = -6$	Write original equation.
$3y =$ ______	______ to each side.
$y =$ ______	______ each side by 3.

The equation $y =$ ______ can be written as $y =$ ______ $x +$ ______.

ANSWER The line has a slope of ______ and a y-intercept of ______.

EXAMPLE 2 Graphing Using Slope-Intercept Form

Graph the equation $y = \frac{1}{4}x + 5$.

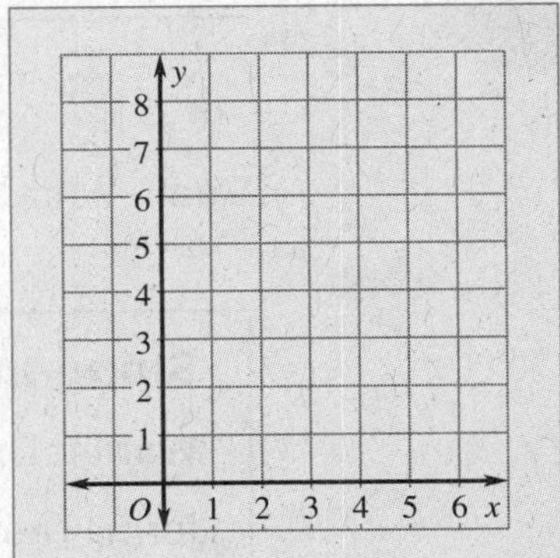

Solution

> Once you plot the second point, you can check that it is correct by substituting the coordinates of the point into the original equation.

1. The y-intercept is 5, so plot the point ______.

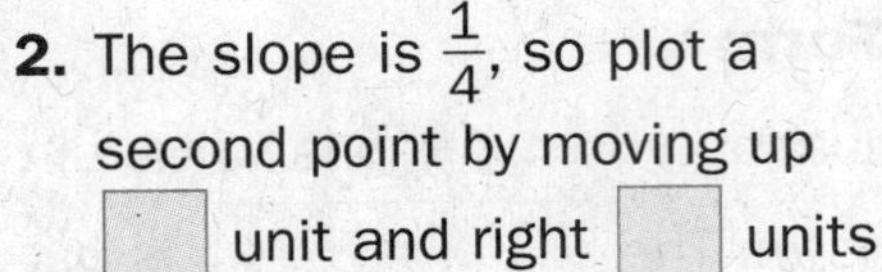

2. The slope is $\frac{1}{4}$, so plot a second point by moving up ______ unit and right ______ units.

3. Draw a line through the points.

Guided Practice **Find the slope and y-intercept of the graph of the equa**
Then graph the equation.

1. $y = 4x + 3$

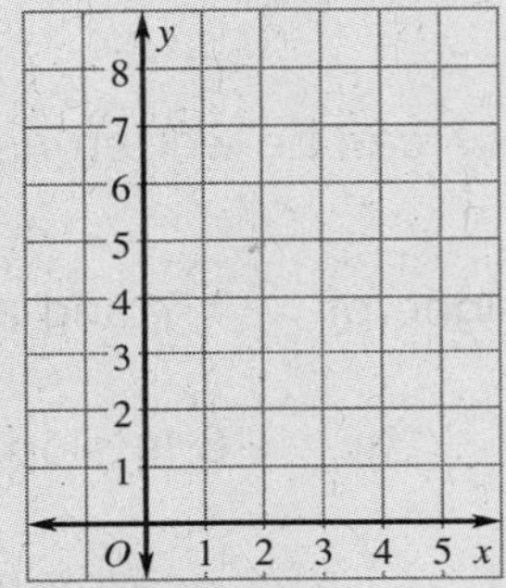

2. $x - y = 8$

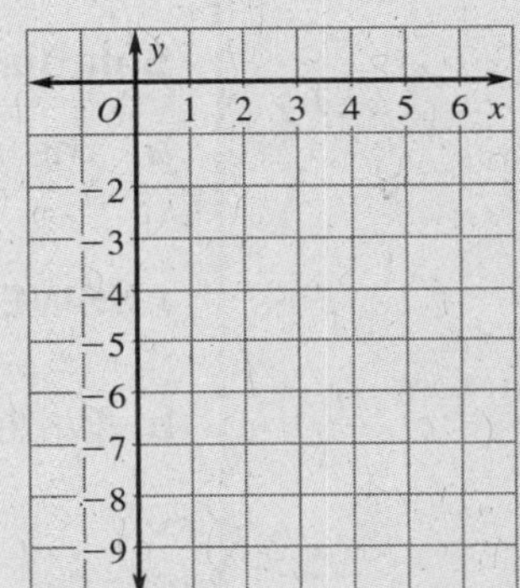

3. $y = -\frac{2}{3}x$

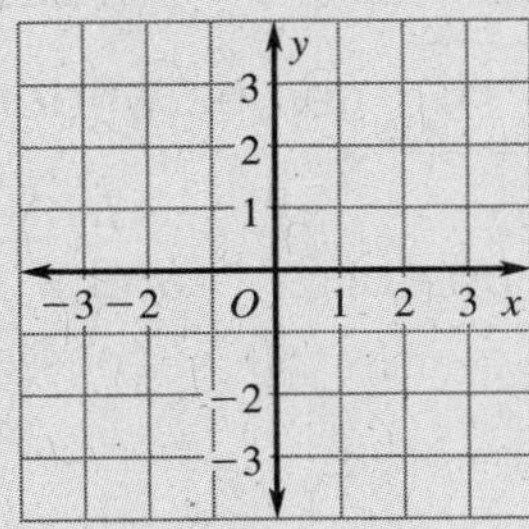

4. $2y = 5x + 6$

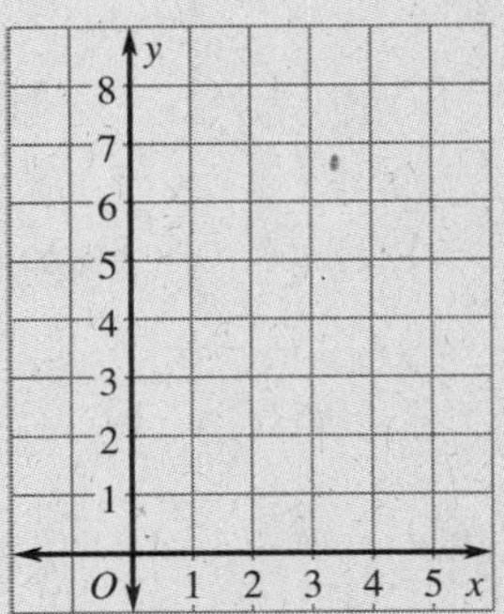

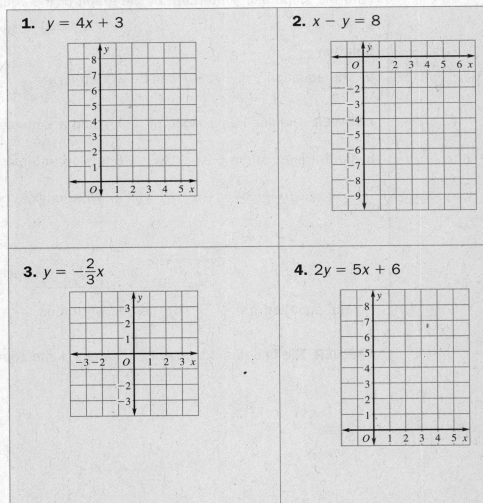

EXAMPLE 3 Writing a Function Rule

Money You have \$37 in your bank account. Every month you put \$12 into your account. If you don't spend any of the money that you put into your account, what equation can you use to find how much money you will have in your account after 10 months?

Solution

You can write an equation in slope-intercept form to find how much money you will have in your account after 10 months.

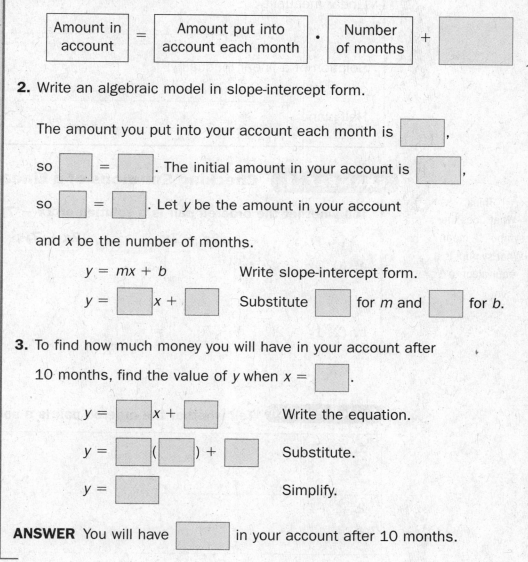

1. Write a verbal model.

Amount in account	=	Amount put into account each month	•	Number of months	+	☐

2. Write an algebraic model in slope-intercept form.

The amount you put into your account each month is ☐, so ☐ = ☐. The initial amount in your account is ☐, so ☐ = ☐. Let y be the amount in your account and x be the number of months.

$y = mx + b$ Write slope-intercept form.

$y =$ ☐ $x +$ ☐ Substitute ☐ for m and ☐ for b.

3. To find how much money you will have in your account after 10 months, find the value of y when $x =$ ☐.

$y =$ ☐ $x +$ ☐ Write the equation.

$y =$ ☐ (☐) + ☐ Substitute.

$y =$ ☐ Simplify.

ANSWER You will have ☐ in your account after 10 months.

Graphs of Linear Inequalities

Goal: Graph linear inequalities.

Vocabulary

Linear inequality:

Solution of a linear inequality:

Half-plane:

EXAMPLE 1 **Checking Solutions of a Linear Inequality**

Think:
What does the symbol $\ngtr$ mean? What symbol is it equivalent to?

Tell whether the ordered pair is a solution of $2x - 7y > -3$.

(x, y)	$2x - 7y$	$2x - 7y \overset{?}{>} -3$	Conclusion
a. (0, 0)	2( ) − 7( ) =	−3	(0, 0) a solution.
b. (2, 1)	2( ) − 7( ) =	$\ngtr$ −3	(2, 1) a solution.

Guided Practice **Tell whether the ordered pair is a solution of $4x + 5y$ ≤**

1. (0, 0)

2. (1, −1)

3. (−3, 2)

4. (−1, 1)

Graphing Linear Inequalities

1. Change the inequality symbol to "______." Graph the ______.
   Use a ______ line for < or >. Use a ______ line for ≤ or ≥.
2. Test a point in one of the ______ to check whether it is a solution of the inequality.
3. If the test point ______ a solution, shade its half-plane. If the test point ______ a solution, shade the other half-plane.

EXAMPLE 2 Graphing a Linear Inequality

Graph $y - 6x \geq 8$.

1. Change ≥ to = and write the equation in slope-intercept form.

$y - 6x$ ______ 8   Replace ______ with ______ sign.

______ ______ to each side.

Graph the line that has a slope of ______ and a y-intercept of ______.

Because the inequality is ≥, use a ______ line.

…member that a …d line indicates … points on a line … solutions of an …uality. A dashed … indicates that …nts on the line … *not* solutions.

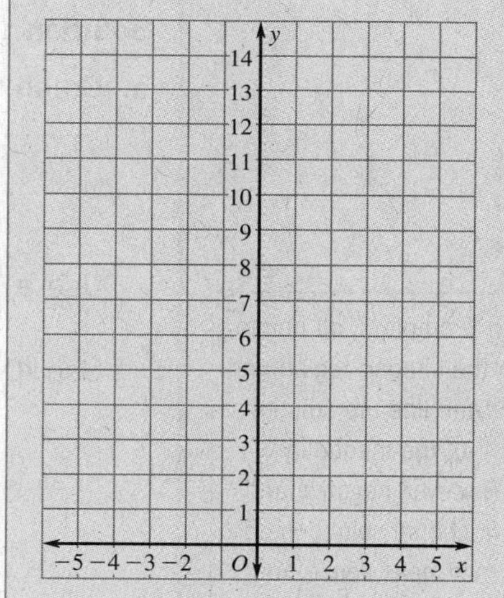

… can use an point … on the line as a …point. Using (0, 0) …nvenient because …s substituted for …each variable.

2. Use (0, 0) as a test point. Substitute the point into the original inequality.

$y \geq 6x + 8$

______ $\overset{?}{\geq}$ 6______ + 8

______ (0, 0) ______ a solution.

3. Shade the half-plane that ______ contain (0, 0).

Guided Practice Graph the inequality.

5. $y > x - 9$

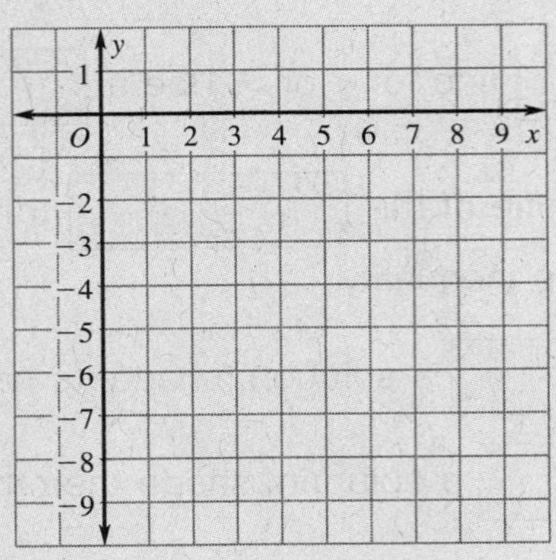

6. $\frac{1}{8}x + y \leq 5$

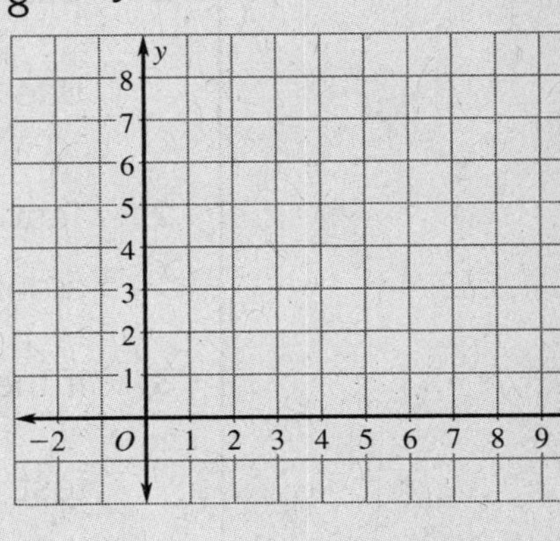

EXAMPLE 3 Using the Graph of a Linear Inequality

Pictures You go to the photo center to buy photo enlargements. You have $45 to spend. Each 5 × 7 enlargement costs $1 and each 8 × 10 enlargement costs $3. The inequality $x + 3y \leq 45$, where x represents the number of 5 × 7 prints and y represents the number of 8 × 10 prints models this situation. How many enlargements can you buy with $45?

a. Graph the inequality.

b. Use the graph to find a solution. Then interpret the solution.

Solution

a. Graph the equation

_______________.

Use a _______ line.

Use (0, 0) as a test point.

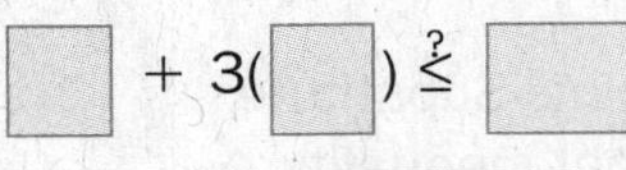

_______ ✓

Shade the half-plane

that _______ (0, 0).

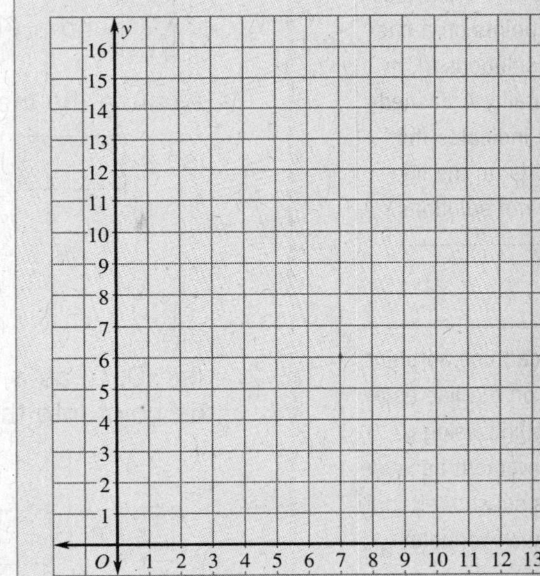

In Example 3, all points in the shaded region and on the line are solutions of the inequality. However, negative and fractional solutions do not make sense. You cannot buy a negative number of items, and you cannot buy a part of an item.

b. One solution is (3, _______). This means that you can buy 3 5 × 7 enlargments and _______ 8 × 10 enlargements.

Words to Review

Give an example of the vocabulary word.

Relation

Range

Input

Scatter plot

Output

Solution of an equation in two variables

Function

Linear equation

Domain

x-intercept

y-intercept

Slope-intercept form

Slope

Linear inequality

Rise

Solution of a linear inequality

Run

Half-plane

Review your notes and Chapter 11 by using the Chapter Review on pages 636–6
of your textbook.

Stem-and-Leaf Plots

Goal: Make and interpret stem-and-leaf plots.

Vocabulary

Stem-and-leaf plot: ________

EXAMPLE 1 Making a Stem-and-Leaf Plot

Snowboarding The scores of the top 15 finishers of a snowboard half pipe competition are shown below. How can the data be displayed to show the distribution of the scores?

38.4, 40.6, 37.8, 38.9, 41.7, 39.2, 37.1, 41.4,

40.5, 38.8, 40.9, 39.3, 41.2, 38.3, 37.1

Solution

You can display the scores in a stem-and-leaf plot.

1. Identify the stems and leaves. The scores range from ________ through ________. Let the ________ be the digits in the tens' and ones' places. Let the ________ be the tenths' digits.
2. Write the stems first. Then record each score by writing its tenths' digit on the same line as its corresponding stem. Include a key that shows what the stems and leaves represent.
3. Make an ordered stem-and-leaf plot.

The leaves for each stem are listed in order from least to greatest.

Unordered Plot

____	____	____	____	
____	____	____	____	____
____	____	____		
____	____	____	____	
____	____	____	____	

Key: 38 | 4 = ________

Ordered Plot

____	____	____	____	
____	____	____	____	____
____	____	____		
____	____	____	____	
____	____	____	____	

Key: 38 | 4 = ________

Guided Practice **Make an ordered stem-and-leaf plot of the data.**

1. Baseball pitch speeds (mi/h): 86, 83, 74, 95, 89, 97, 68, 88, 72, 97
94, 85, 70, 89, 80, 93, 91, 84

EXAMPLE 2 Interpreting a Stem-and-Leaf Plot

In a stem-and-leaf plot, a stem can be one or more digits. A leaf is usually a single digit.

Movies The stem-and-leaf plot at the right shows the ages of people in a movie theater. Use the stem-and-leaf plot to describe the data. What interval includes the most ages?

Stem	Leaves
0	5 6 7 7 8 8 8 9 9
1	0 0 0 1 1 2 2 2 3 3 4 5
2	0 2 8 9
3	3 7
4	8
5	1

Key: 2 | 0 =

Solution

The oldest person is ____ years old and the youngest person is ____ years old. So the range of ages is ____ years. Most of the ages are in the ____–____ interval.

EXAMPLE 3 Making a Double Stem-and-Leaf Plot

Swimming The data below show the number of laps swum during practice by swimmers on two different swim teams. Overall, which team swam more laps?

Dolphins: 19, 25, 31, 26, 17, 25, 26, 18, 23, 19, 25, 24

Sharks: 18, 25, 9, 15, 30, 24, 17, 18, 22, 16, 28, 19

Solution

You can use a double stem-and-leaf plot to compare the number of laps swum.

Dolphins Sharks

Key: 1 | 3 | 0 represents ____ and ____.

ANSWER The ____ swim team swam more laps because it had more swimmers swim a number of laps in the ____.

Guided Practice Complete the following exercises.

2. Make an ordered double stem-and-leaf plot to compare the times, in minutes, that two friends spent online in the last week.
Omar: 35, 26, 30, 48, 55, 13, 38
Joseph: 46, 15, 68, 0, 44, 49, 32

3. In general, who spent the most time online in the last week, Omar or Joseph?

Box-and-Whisker Plots

Goal: Make and interpret box-and-whisker plots.

Vocabulary

Box-and-whisker plot:

Lower quartile:

Upper quartile:

Lower extreme:

Upper extreme:

EXAMPLE 1 Making a Box-and-Whisker Plot

Towers The heights, in feet, of the world's tallest towers are listed below. Show how the lengths are distributed by making a box-and-whisker plot.

1214 1535 1230 1149 1815 1369 1403 1362 1762 1

Solution

If a data set has an odd number of values, then the median is not included in either half of the data when determining the quartile values.

1. Order the data to find the median and the quartiles.

$$\text{Median} = \frac{\square + \square}{2} = \square$$

Lower half | Upper half

1149 ☐ ☐ ☐ ☐ | ☐ ☐ ☐ 1762

Lower quartile = ☐ Upper quartile = ☐

2. Plot these values below a number line that includes the extremes.

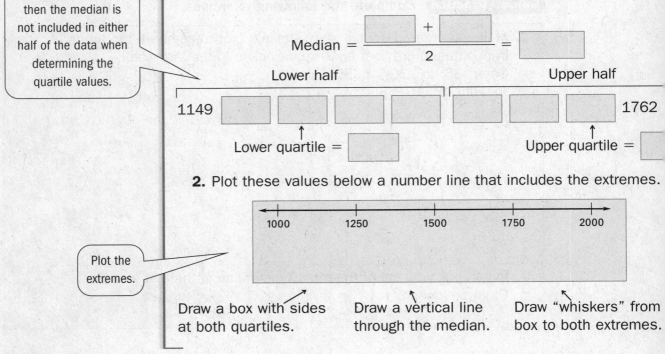

1000 1250 1500 1750 2000

Plot the extremes.

Draw a box with sides at both quartiles.

Draw a vertical line through the median.

Draw "whiskers" from box to both extremes.

EXAMPLE 2 Interpreting Box-and-Whisker Plots

Home Buying Your friend's family is buying a home. The box-and-whisker plots show how much homes cost, in thousands of dollars, in two regions in your city.

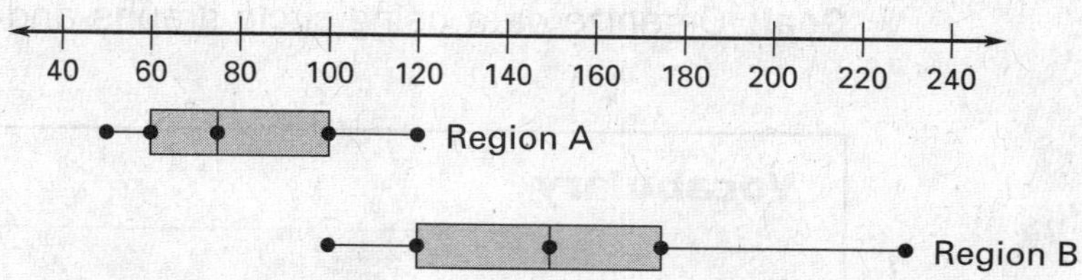

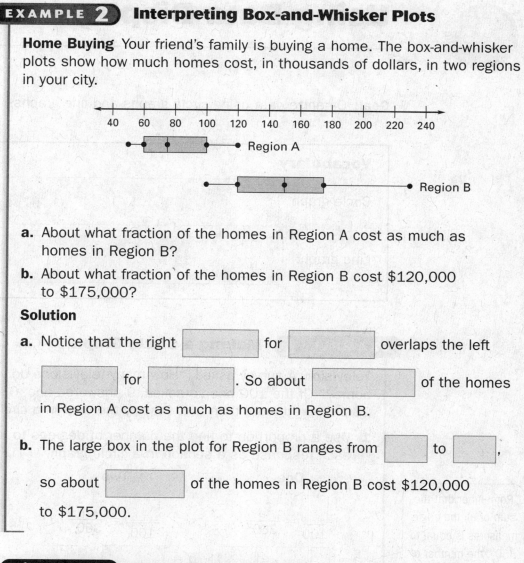

a. About what fraction of the homes in Region A cost as much as homes in Region B?

b. About what fraction of the homes in Region B cost $120,000 to $175,000?

Solution

a. Notice that the right ______ for ______ overlaps the left ______ for ______. So about ______ of the homes in Region A cost as much as homes in Region B.

b. The large box in the plot for Region B ranges from ______ to ______, so about ______ of the homes in Region B cost $120,000 to $175,000.

Guided Practice Use a box-and-whisker plot.

1. In the morning, you wait in line to ride the roller coasters for 34, 23, 28, 36, 15, 32, 40, and 27 minutes. In the afternoon, you wait in line to ride the roller coasters for 55, 29, 45, 61, 25, 43, 70, and 41 minutes. Make a box-and-whisker plot of the data for each part of the day.

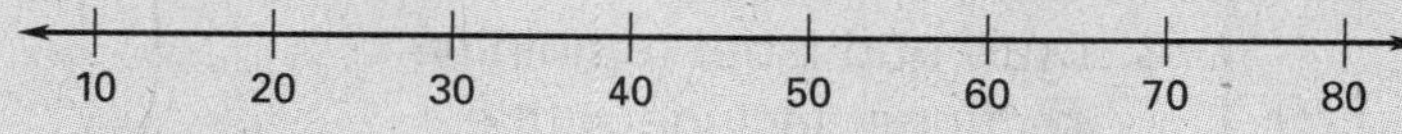

2. During which part of the day do you wait in line longer?

3. About how often do you wait in line 25–30 minutes during each part of the day?

Using Data Displays

Goal: Organize data using circle graphs and line graphs.

Vocabulary

Circle graph:

Line graph:

EXAMPLE 1 **Making a Circle Graph**

Television A survey asked, "How many televisions do you have in your home?" Of the 100 people asked, 9 answered one, 63 answered two, a 28 answered more than two. Display the data in a circle graph.

1. Use a proportion to find the number of degrees to use to represent each response as a section in a circle graph.

One	**Two**	**Three**
$\frac{\square}{100} = \frac{a}{360^\circ}$	$\frac{\square}{100} = \frac{b}{360^\circ}$	$\frac{\square}{100} = \frac{c}{360^\circ}$
$a = \square \approx \square$	$b = \square \approx \square$	$c = \square \approx \square$

Remember that the sum of all the angle measures is equal to 360°, the number of degrees in a circle.

2. Draw a circle. Show its center.
3. Use a protractor to draw the first angle measure. Then label the section.
4. Draw and label remaining sections. Include a title.

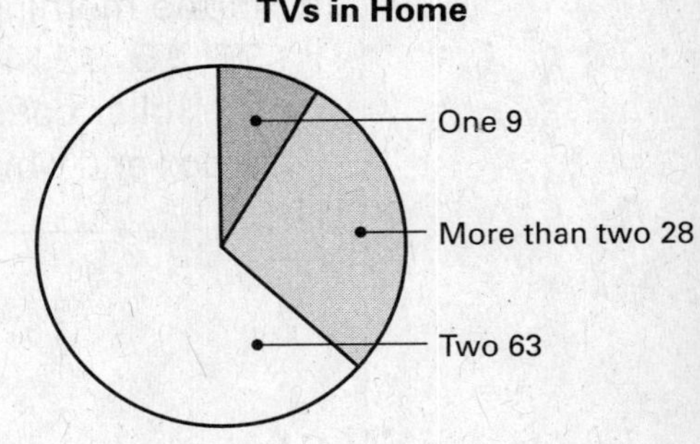

In Example 1, you can draw the two smaller angles first. Then the remaining section of the circle will have the measure of the largest angle.

ANSWER The graph shows that the majority of people have ______ televisions in their homes.

EXAMPLE 2 Making a Line Graph

Zoo The table shows the number of visitors, in hundred thousands, to a zoo. Make a line graph of the data.

Year	1995	1996	1997	1998	1999	2000	2001
Visitors (100,000)	2.4	3.5	4.3	5.8	7.1	7.9	8.6

1. Draw and label the horizontal and vertical scales. Include a title.
2. Plot a point for each data pair.
3. Draw line segments to connect the points.

The graph shows ____________ over time.

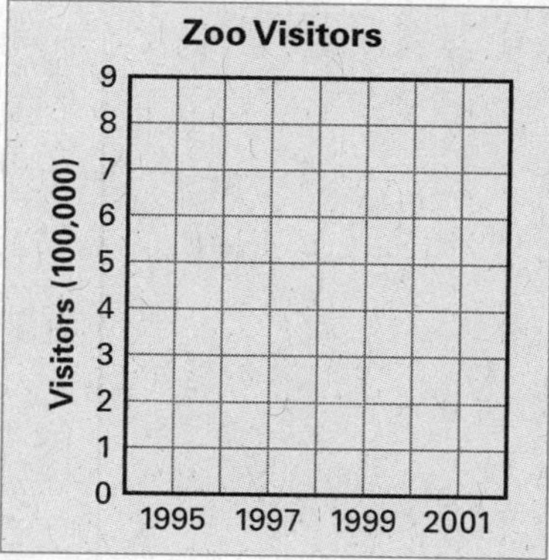

Guided Practice **Use the table of sales data.**

1. Make a circle graph of the data for Week 2. What does the graph show?

Gasoline Sales			
Week	**1**	**2**	**3**
87 octane	71%	64%	79%
89 octane	22%	30%	16%
93 octane	7%	6%	5%

2. Make a line graph of the data for 93 octane gasoline. What does the graph show?

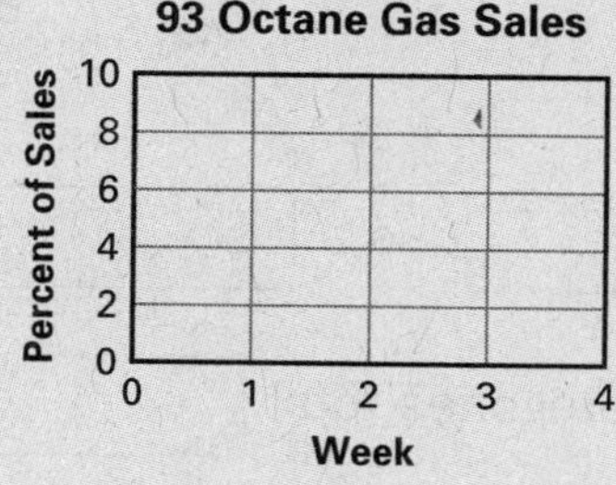

Using Appropriate Data Displays

Use a ________ to represent data as parts of a ________.

Use a ________ to display data over ________.

Use a ________ to ________ a data set.

Use a ________ to show the data's distribution in quarters, using the median, ________, and ________.

Use a ________ to display data in distinct categories.

Use a ________ to display data in overlapping categories

Use a ________ to compare the ________ of data that are grouped in equal intervals.

EXAMPLE 3 **Choosing a Data Display**

Choose an appropriate display for the data.

a. The table below shows the percent of holiday shopping done in stores, through catalogs, and online.

Shopping	Percent
Stores	52%
Catalogs	37%
Online	11%

b. The table below shows the results of a survey that aske people what film speed they use in their cameras.

Film speed	Percent
100	20%
200	68%
400	53%
800	15%

Solution

a. The percents total ________, so a ________ is appropriate.

b. The percents in the categories total ________ ________.

An appropriate display for the data is a ________.

Counting Methods

Goal: Use counting methods to count the number of choices.

Vocabulary

Tree diagram:

EXAMPLE 1 **Making a Tree Diagram**

Sandwiches You are choosing a sub. You can choose white (Wi) or wheat (We) for the bread and ham (H), turkey (T), steak (S), meatball (M), or bologna (B) for the meat. How many subs are possible?

Solution

You can use a tree diagram to count the number of possible subs.

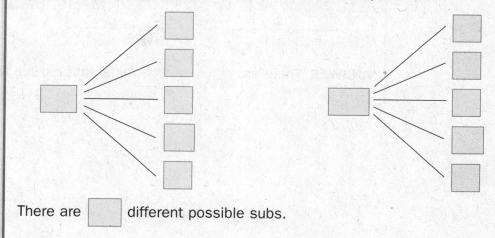

There are ______ different possible subs.

The Counting Principle

If one event can occur in *m* ways, and for each of these a second event can occur in *n* ways, then the number of ways that the two events can occur together is ______.

This principle can be extended to three or more events.

EXAMPLE 2 Using the Counting Principle

Camping A campground provides a variety of activities for its campers. In the morning, you can choose fishing, a nature walk, a canoe trip, or arts and crafts. In the afternoon, you can choose swimming, hiking, a wagon ride, or a bike trip. To count the number of different pairs of activities you can participate in, use the counting principle.

Solution

☐ · ☐ = ☐ Counting principle

morning afternoon

ANSWER You can participate in ☐ different pairs of activities.

EXAMPLE 3 Using the Counting Principle

License Plates A license plate starts with 3 letters and then has 3 digi
How many different license plates are possible?

Solution

☐ · ☐ · ☐ · ☐ · ☐ · ☐ = ☐ Coun
princi

letters digits

ANSWER There are ☐ different possible license plates.

Guided Practice **Count the choices.**

1. An ice cream shop sells one-topping sundaes made of chocolate, vanilla, or chocolate-vanilla twist ice cream with hot fudge, strawberry, caramel, or pineapple topping. Use a tree diagram to find how many different one-topping sundaes are possible.

2. In Example 3, suppose that the license plate may not use any repeated letters or digits. How many different license plates are possible? Explain.

EXAMPLE 4 Solve a Multi-Step Problem

Spinner You and two friends each spin the spinner shown at the right. What is the probability that you each spin the same shape?

Solution

1. List the *favorable* outcomes. There are ___:

2. Use the counting principle to find the number of *possible* outcomes.

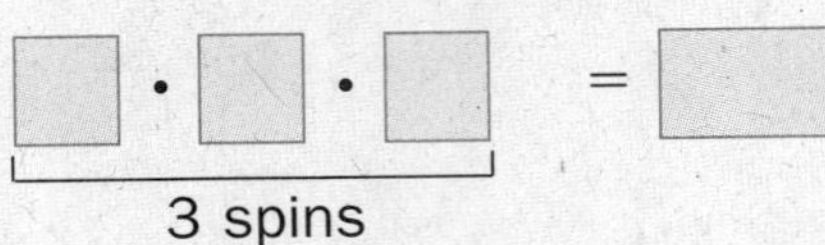

$\square \cdot \square \cdot \square = \square$

3 spins

3. Then use the formula for finding probability.

$$\frac{\text{Number of } \square \text{ outcomes}}{\text{Number of } \square \text{ outcomes}} = \square = \square$$

ANSWER The probability that you each spin the same shape is ___.

Permutations

Goal: Use permutations to count possibilities.

Vocabulary

Permutation:

Factorial:

EXAMPLE 1 **Counting Permutations**

Movies Four friends go to a movie. You can use the counting principle to count the number of permutations of 4 seats. This is the number of different orders in which 4 friends can be seated in the theater.

Solution

You can use $n!$ find the number of permutations of n objects.

Choices for 1st seat		Choices for 2nd seat		Choices for 3rd seat		Choices for 4th seat		
☐	·	☐	·	☐	·	☐	=	☐

ANSWER The four friends can sit in ☐ different orders.

Guided Practice **Evaluate the factorial.**

1. 2!	**2.** 5!	**3.** 7!	**4.** 8!

EXAMPLE 2 **Counting Permutations**

Spelling Bee Eighteen contestants are entered in a spelling bee. You can use the counting principle to count how many ways the top two finishers can advance to the finals.

Solution

Choices for top finisher		Choices for runner-up		
☐	·	☐	=	☐

ANSWER There are ☐ ways the top two finishers can advance.

Permutations

Algebra The number of permutations of n objects taken r at a time can be written as $\_\_P\_\_$ and evaluated using $\frac{n!}{\_\_!}$.

Numbers $_6P_4 = \frac{\_\_}{\_\_!} = \_\_ = \frac{\_\_ \cdot \not{2} \cdot \not{1}}{\not{2} \cdot \not{1}} = \_\_$

EXAMPLE 3 **Evaluating a Permutation**

Science Club Two students are chosen from the 8 students in your sch Science Club. One of the students will attend a science fair and the oth will compete in a science academic challenge. To find how many differe ways the students can be chosen, find $_8P_2$.

Solution

$_8P_2 = \frac{\_\_}{\_\_!} = \_\_$ Use permutation formula.

In Example 3, you can write 8! as 8 • 7 • 6! and cancel both 6 factorials.

$= \frac{\_\_}{\_\_}$ Divide out comm factors.

$= \_\_$ Multiply.

Guided Practice **Find the number of permutations.**

5. $_7P_4$	6. $_8P_3$	7. $_3P_3$	8. $_{11}P_2$

9. In Example 1, you found the number of permutations of 4 seats tak how many at a time? Explain.

Combinations

Goal: Use combinations to count possibilities.

Vocabulary

Combination:

EXAMPLE 1 **Listing Combinations**

Pizza A pizza shop is having a special on large pizzas with 2 toppings. You want to order your pizza with 2 different toppings. You can choose from pepperoni (P), sausage (S), green peppers (G), onions (O), olives (L), and mushrooms (M). How many different pizzas can you order?

Solution

List all possible pizzas with 2 different toppings. Then cross out any duplicate groupings that represent the same pizza.

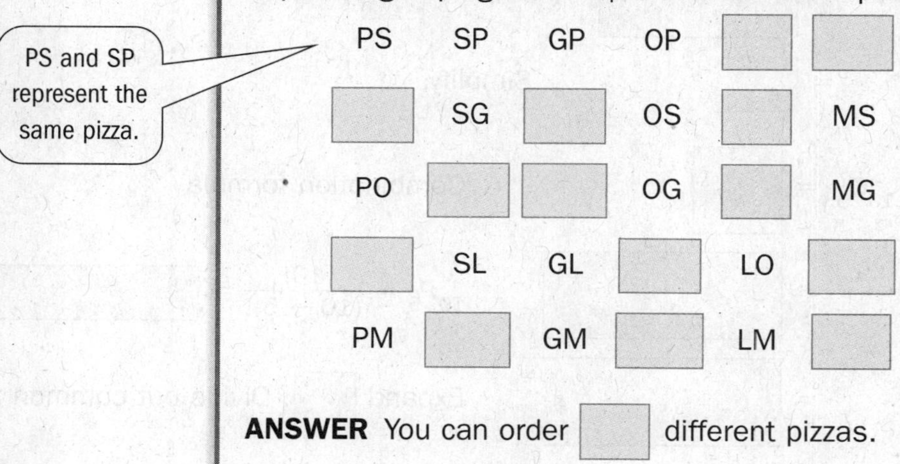

ANSWER You can order ______ different pizzas.

Guided Practice **Complete the exercise.**

1. In Example 1, the complete list shows the number of permutations of 6 items chosen 2 at a time. How many items would be in the complete list if you had to choose from 8 toppings?

Combination Notation

Words To find the number of combinations of n objects taken r at a time divide the number of permutations of n objects taken r at a time by $r!$.

Algebra ${}_nC_r =$

Numbers ${}_8C_6 =$

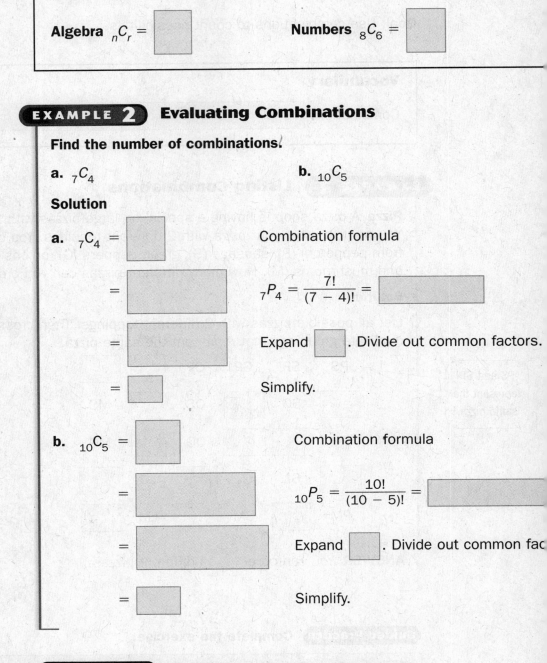

EXAMPLE 2 **Evaluating Combinations**

Find the number of combinations.

a. ${}_7C_4$

b. ${}_{10}C_5$

Solution

a. ${}_7C_4 =$ Combination formula

$=$ ${}_7P_4 = \frac{7!}{(7-4)!} =$

$=$ Expand . Divide out common factors.

$=$ Simplify.

b. ${}_{10}C_5 =$ Combination formula

$=$ ${}_{10}P_5 = \frac{10!}{(10-5)!} =$

$=$ Expand . Divide out common fac

$=$ Simplify.

Guided Practice **Find the number of combinations.**

2. ${}_5C_3$	3. ${}_8C_2$	4. ${}_9C_9$	5. ${}_7C_1$

EXAMPLE 3 **Permutations and Combinations**

Tell whether the possibilities can be counted using a *permutation* or *combination*. Then write an expression for the number of possibilities.

a. Bouquet A flower shop sells red, pink, white, peach, and yellow roses. You want to choose 3 of these colors to make a bouquet. How many different bouquets can you make?

b. Cheerleading Six cheerleaders are going to form a pyramid. In how many different ways can the cheerleaders be placed in the pyramid?

Mutate means to change. For permutations, you count changes in order of items. For combinations, objects combined in any order represent the same group.

Solution

a. Order ______ important in choosing the flowers, so the possibilities can be counted by evaluating ______.

b. Because the cheerleaders can be placed in different positions in the pyramid, order ______ important. So the possibilities can be counted by evaluating ______.

Probability and Odds

Goal: Find the odds in favor of events.

Vocabulary

Complementary events:

Unfavorable outcome:

Odds:

EXAMPLE 1 **Finding Probabilities**

CDs Your CD player has a random play feature in which songs are playe[d in] any order. You play a CD that has 10 songs using the random play featu[re].

a. What is the probability that your favorite song on the CD is played firs[t]?

b. What is the probability that your favorite song on the CD is not played first?

The probability that Event A occurs and the probability that Event A does not occur have a sum of 1 because they are complementary events.

Solution

a. P(favorite song is first) $= \dfrac{\text{Number of } \_\_\_\_ \text{ outcomes}}{\text{Number of } \_\_\_\_ \text{ outcomes}} = \_\_\_\_$

b. P(favorite song is not first) $= 1 - P$(favorite song is first)

$= 1 - \_\_\_\_$

$= \_\_\_\_$

Guided Practice **You are given the probability that an event will occur. Find the probability that the event will not occur.**

1. $P(A) = \frac{2}{3}$	**2.** $P(A) = 0.15$	**3.** $P(A) = 54\%$	**4.** $P(A) = \frac{3}{8}$
5. The 12 letters in the word PENNSYLVANIA are each written on pieces of paper and put in a bag. What is the probability of randomly drawing an N from the bag? What is the probability of randomly not drawing an N?			

EXAMPLE 2 Finding Odds

Restaurants The results of a survey asking your class to name their favorite type of restaurant are shown at the right. What are the odds in favor of a randomly chosen student from your class naming *diner*?

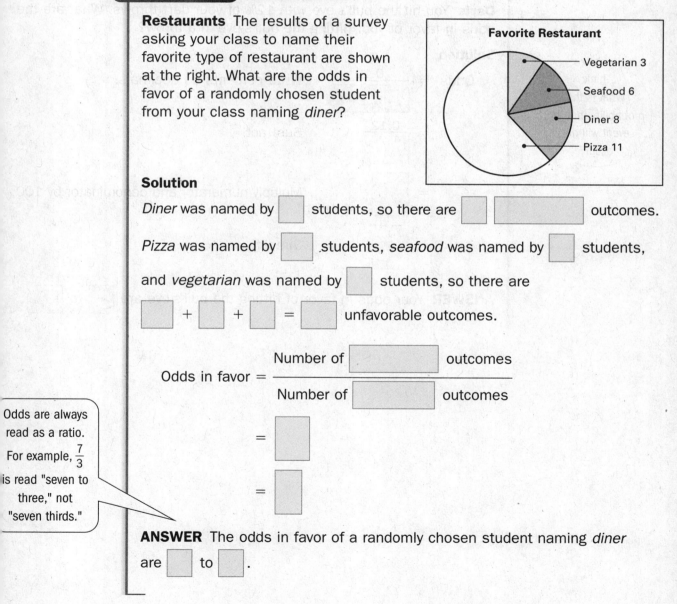

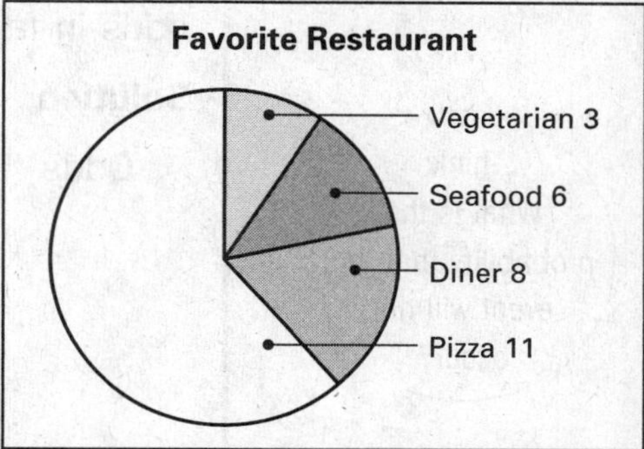

Solution

Diner was named by ☐ students, so there are ☐ ☐ outcomes.

Pizza was named by ☐ students, *seafood* was named by ☐ students, and *vegetarian* was named by ☐ students, so there are

☐ + ☐ + ☐ = ☐ unfavorable outcomes.

Odds in favor = $\frac{\text{Number of } \square \text{ outcomes}}{\text{Number of } \square \text{ outcomes}}$

= ☐

= ☐

Odds are always read as a ratio. For example, $\frac{7}{3}$ is read "seven to three," not "seven thirds."

ANSWER The odds in favor of a randomly chosen student naming *diner* are ☐ to ☐.

Guided Practice **You choose a tile at random from a bag of 26 letter tiles labeled A through Z. Find the odds in favor of the event.**

6. You choose a D.	**7.** You choose a consonant.

EXAMPLE 3 Finding Odds Using Probability

Darts You hit the bull's-eye with 12% of your dart throws. What are the odds in favor of your hitting the bull's-eye in a throw?

Think: What is the probability that the event will not occur?

Solution

Odds $= \dfrac{0.12}{\square}$ Write percents as decimals.

$= \dfrac{0.12}{\square}$ Subtract.

$= \square$ Multiply numerator and denominator by 100.

$= \square$ Simplify.

ANSWER Your odds in favor of hitting the bull's-eye are ____ to ____.

Independent and Dependent Events

Goal: Study independent and dependent events.

Vocabulary

Compound events:

Independent events:

Dependent events:

EXAMPLE 1 **Independent and Dependent Events**

Tell whether the events are *independent* or *dependent*.

a. You toss a coin. Then you toss the coin again.

b. Your teacher randomly chooses a student to go to the board. The student remains at the board when your teacher randomly chooses another student to go to the board.

Solution

a. The result of the first toss does not affect the result of the second toss, so the events are ______.

b. There is one fewer student to choose from when the teacher chooses another student, so the events are ______.

Probability of Independent Events

Words For two independent events, the probability that both events occu

is the ______ of the probabilities of the events.

Algebra If events A and B are independent, then

$P(\text{A and B}) =$ ______.

EXAMPLE 2 **Standardized Test Practice**

History Report Each student in your history class is to write a report on one of the 50 United States. Each student randomly chooses a state. What is the probability that you and the student who sits behind you randomly choose the same state?

Ⓐ $\frac{1}{2500}$ Ⓑ $\frac{1}{1250}$ Ⓒ $\frac{1}{50}$ Ⓓ $\frac{1}{25}$

Solution

The choices are ______ events, because choosing one state does not affect the probability of choosing another state.

So the probability of each event is ______.

$P(\text{state and same state}) = P(\text{state}) \cdot P(\text{same state})$

$= \_\_\_ \cdot \_\_\_ = \_\_\_$

ANSWER The probability that you both choose the same state is ______

The correct answer is ______. Ⓐ Ⓑ Ⓒ Ⓓ

Probability of Dependent Events

Words For two dependent events, the probability that both events occur is the ______ of the probability of the first event and the probability of the second event given that the first event also occurs.

Algebra If events A and B are dependent, then

$P(\text{A and B}) =$ ______.

EXAMPLE 3 Finding Probability of Dependent Events

Carnival You are playing a balloon popping game at a carnival. There are 19 red, 15 blue, 12 yellow, and 14 green balloons. You randomly pop balloons by throwing darts at them. What is the probability that the first two balloons you pop are yellow?

Solution

Find the probability that the first and second balloons you pop are yellow. Then multiply.

you explain why the
ts are dependent?

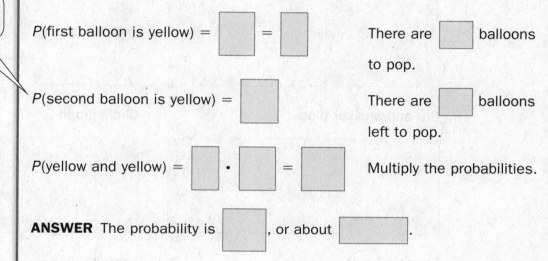

P(first balloon is yellow) = ___ = ___ There are ___ balloons to pop.

P(second balloon is yellow) = ___ There are ___ balloons left to pop.

P(yellow and yellow) = ___ • ___ = ___ Multiply the probabilities.

ANSWER The probability is ___, or about ___.

Guided Practice **Find the probability.**

1. You roll a number cube twice. Find the probability of getting two odd numbers.

2. In Example 3, find the probability that the first two balloons you pop are blue.

Words to Review

Give an example of the vocabulary word.

Stem-and-leaf plot

Upper extreme

Box-and-whisker plot

Circle graph

Lower quartile

Line graph

Upper quartile

Tree diagram

Lower extreme

Permutation

Factorial

Odds

Combination

Compound events

Complementary events

Independent events

Unfavorable outcome

Dependent events

Review your notes and Chapter 12 by using the Chapter Review on pages 704–708 of your textbook.

LESSON 13.1

Polynomials

Goal: Simplify polynomials by combining like terms.

Vocabulary

Polynomial:

Binomial:

Trinomial:

Standard form:

EXAMPLE 1 **Writing Polynomials in Standard Form**

Write the polynomial in standard form. Classify the polynomial.

If you do not see an exponent with a variable, then its exponent is 1. $3x = 3x^1$

a. $3x - 8 + 4x^2$

$= 3x$ ___ (___) $+ 4x^2$ Write subtraction as addition.

$=$ ___ $+$ ___ $+$ (___) Order terms with decreasing exponents.

ANSWER The polynomial ___ has ___ terms, so it is a ___.

b. $-x - 2x^5$

$= -x$ ___ (___) Write subtraction as addition.

$= -2x^5 + ($ ___ $)$ Order terms with decreasing exponents.

ANSWER The polynomial ___ has ___ terms, so it is a ___.

Guided Practice **Write the polynomial in standard form and classify it.**

1. $9 + a^2 - 5a$	2. $-7 + 10m^3$	3. $-8p^2 - p - 6p^4 + p^3$

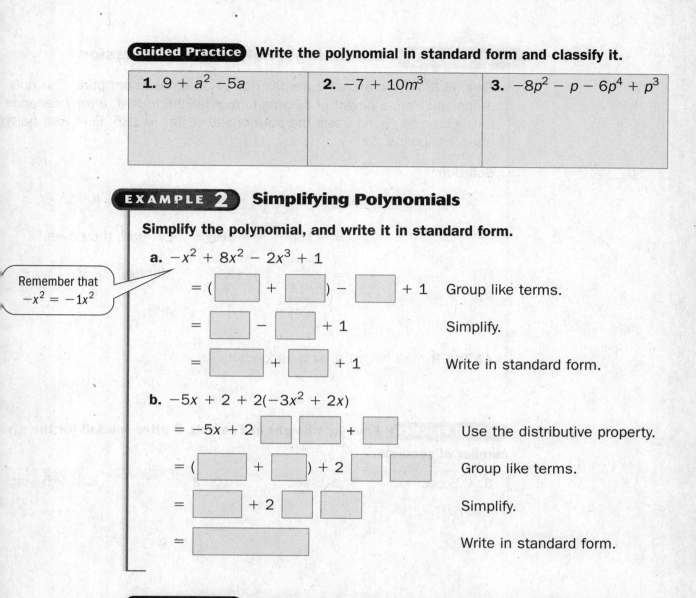

EXAMPLE 2 Simplifying Polynomials

Simplify the polynomial, and write it in standard form.

Remember that $-x^2 = -1x^2$

a. $-x^2 + 8x^2 - 2x^3 + 1$

$= (\square + \square) - \square + 1$ Group like terms.

$= \square - \square + 1$ Simplify.

$= \square + \square + 1$ Write in standard form.

b. $-5x + 2 + 2(-3x^2 + 2x)$

$= -5x + 2 \square \square + \square$ Use the distributive property.

$= (\square + \square) + 2 \square \square$ Group like terms.

$= \square + 2 \square \square$ Simplify.

$= \square$ Write in standard form.

Guided Practice **Simplify the polynomial and write it in standard form.**

4. $-10 + n^3 - 4n - 9n^3$	5. $-6q^4 - 3q^2 + 2q^3 + 11q^4$
6. $-2(t^2 + 5t - 1) - 7t^2$	7. $-15b^3 + b^4 + 3(b^3 - 4b)$

EXAMPLE 3 Evaluating a Polynomial Expression

Freefall Ride You are on a freefall ride at an amusement park. The ride drops you from a height of 185 feet. Your height, in feet, after t seconds falling, can be found using the polynomial $-16t^2 + 185$. Find your heigh after 3 seconds.

Solution

$-16t^2 + 185 = -16(\quad)^2 + 185$ Substitute for t.

$= -16(\quad) + 185$ Evaluate the power.

$= \quad + 185$ Multiply.

$= \quad$ Add.

ANSWER Your height after 3 seconds is ______.

Guided Practice **Find your height in Example 3 after you fall for the give number of seconds.**

8. 0.5 sec	**9.** 1.5 sec	**10.** 2 sec	**11.** 2.5 sec

Adding and Subtracting Polynomials

Goal: Add and subtract polynomials.

EXAMPLE 1 Adding Polynomials Vertically

Find the sum $(5x^3 - x^2 + 6x - 4) + (7x^2 - 10x - 1)$.

	____	____	____	____	____	$- 4$
$+$			____	____	____	$- 1$
			____			

Write the second polynomial under the first.
Arrange like terms in columns.

Add like terms.

EXAMPLE 2 Adding Polynomials Horizontally

Find the sum $(-3y^2 - 8y + 1) + (-4y^2 + 12y - 2)$.

$(-3y^2 - 8y + 1) + (-4y^2 + 12y - 2)$

$= -3y^2$ ____ ____ ____ ____ ____ ____ $+ 1 - 2$ Group like terms.

$=$ ____ Combine like terms.

hen you regroup
ns, you must move
subtraction or an
ition sign with the
m that follows it.

Guided Practice **Find the sum.**

1. $(-2a^2 + 6a + 9) + (a^2 - 3a - 5)$

2. $(7s^2 - s + 4) + (5s^2 - 8s - 11)$

3. $(-p^3 + 4p^2 - p - 3) + (-2p^2 + p - 2)$

4. $(-5n^2 + 3n - 1) + (-n^2 - 4n + 1)$

EXAMPLE 3 Subtracting Polynomials Vertically

Find the difference $(2x^3 - 9x^2 + x - 5) - (4x^3 - 3x^2 + 8)$.

Solution

1. Find the opposite of the second polynomial.

$-(4x^3 - 3x^2 + 8) =$ ______

2. Find the sum $(2x^3 - 9x^2 + x - 5) + ($ ______ $)$.

$2x^3 \quad - \quad 9x^2 \quad + \quad x - \quad 5$ Write the second polynomial under the first.

$+$ ____ ____ ____ ____ ____ Arrange like terms in columns.

______ Add like terms.

Guided Practice **Find the difference.**

5. $(3b^2 + 2b - 7) - (3b^2 + 15b - 4)$

6. $(6y^2 - y) - (2y^2 + 5y + 9)$

7. $(r^2 - 8r - 1) - (-10r^2 - 7r + 5)$

8. $(-2m^3 - 4m^2 + m + 3) - (4m^3 + m - 3)$

EXAMPLE 4 Finding the Area of a Board

Football Toss In a football toss game, footballs are thrown through a circular hole in a board, as shown at the right. Write a polynomial expression for the area of the board.

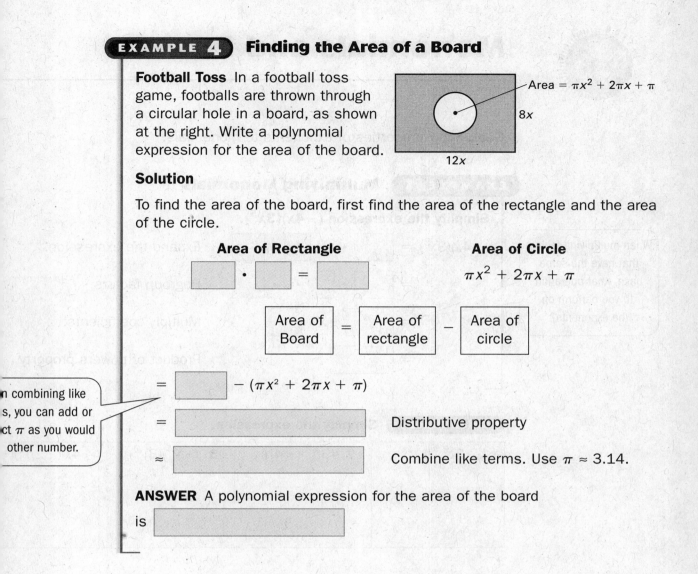

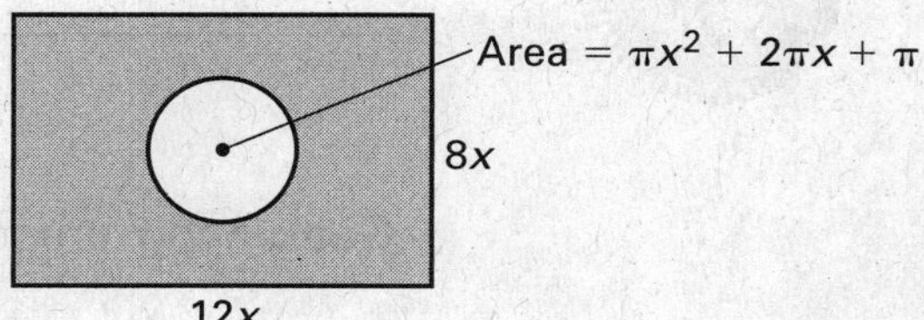

Solution

To find the area of the board, first find the area of the rectangle and the area of the circle.

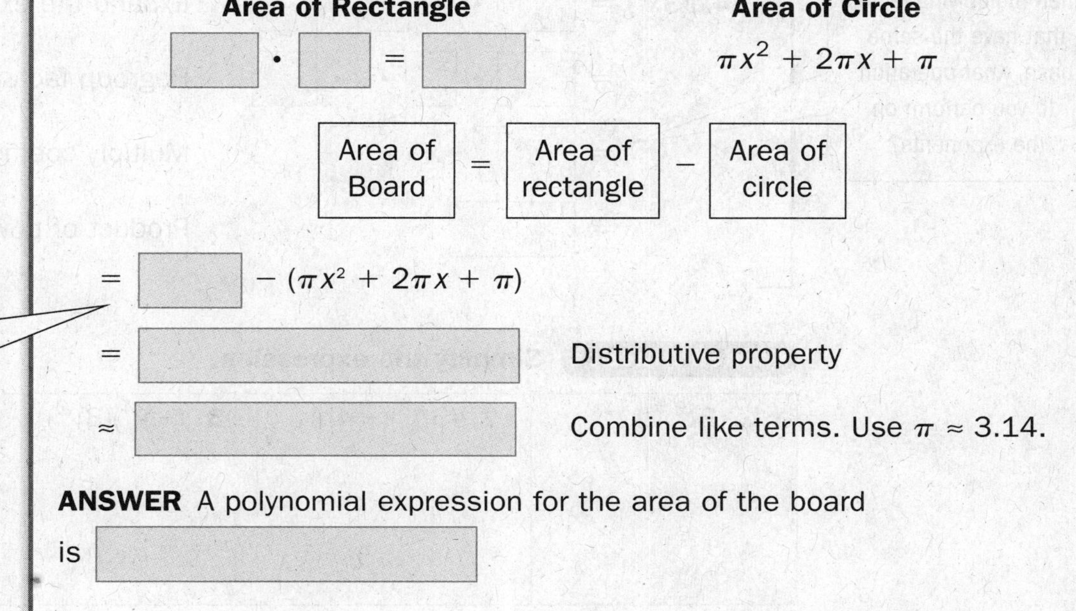

Area of Rectangle
Area of Circle
$\pi x^2 + 2\pi x + \pi$
Area of Board = Area of rectangle − Area of circle
$- (\pi x^2 + 2\pi x + \pi)$
Distributive property
Combine like terms. Use $\pi \approx 3.14$.
ANSWER A polynomial expression for the area of the board is
n combining like
s, you can add or
ct π as you would
other number.

LESSON 13.3

Monomials and Powers

Goal: Apply properties of exponents to monomials.

EXAMPLE 1 Multiplying Monomials

Simplify the expression $(-4x)(3x^5)$.

When multiplying factors that have the same base, what operation do you perform on the exponents?

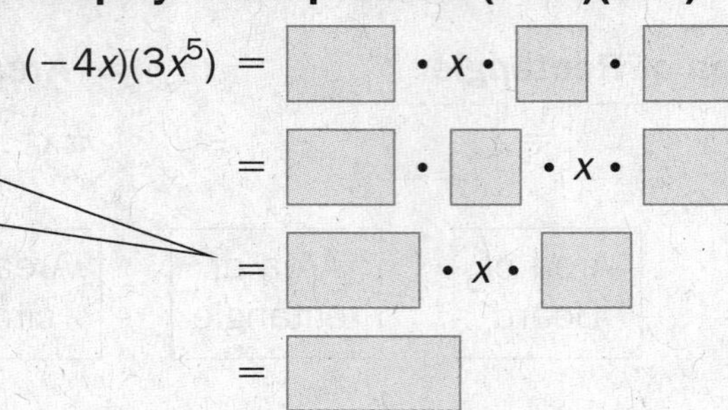

$(-4x)(3x^5) =$ ____ $\cdot\, x \,\cdot$ ____ $\cdot$ ____ Expand the expression.

$=$ ____ $\cdot$ ____ $\cdot\, x \,\cdot$ ____ Regroup factors.

$=$ ____ $\cdot\, x \,\cdot$ ____ Multiply coefficients.

$=$ ____ Product of powers property

Guided Practice **Simplify the expression.**

1. $(2t^2)(t)$	**2.** $(5n^3)(-4n)$	**3.** $(-y^4)(3y^6)$	**4.** $(-2p^5)(-$

EXAMPLE 2 Using the Distributive Property

Simplify the expression $-5n^2(2n + 3)$.

$-5n^2(2n + 3)$

$= ($ ____ $)($ ____ $) + ($ ____ $)($ ____ $)$ Distributive property

$=$ ____ Product of powers property

Guided Practice **Simplify the expression.**

5. $4y^2 - 7y$	**6.** $-6m(2m - 1)$	**7.** $-q^2(9q^2 + 2)$	**8.** $t^4(-3t +$

Power of a Product Property

Words To simplify a power of a product, find the ______ of each factor and ______.

Algebra $(ab)^m = \square \cdot \square$ **Numbers** $(2 \cdot 3)^4 = \square \cdot \square$

EXAMPLE 3 **Simplifying a Power of a Product**

Circle When a circle with radius r is projected against a wall, the radius is tripled. Write an expression for the area of the projected circle.

Solution

The radius of the projected circle is three times the radius of the projected circle. So, the radius of the projected circle is ______.

Use the formula $A = \pi r^2$.

$A = \pi(\square)^2$ Substitute radius of projected circle.

$= \pi(\square \cdot \square)$ Power of a product property

$= \pi \cdot \square \cdot \square)$ Evaluate the power.

$= \square$ Multiply.

ANSWER An expression for the area of the projected circle is $A = \square$

Power of a Power Property

Words To simplify a power of a power, ______ exponents.

Algebra $(a^m)^n = a^{\square}$ **Numbers** $(4^2)^3 = 4^{\square} = \square$

EXAMPLE 4 Simplifying a Power of a Power

Simplify the expression $(6y^5)^2$.

$(6y^5)^2 = \square \cdot (\square)^{\square}$ Power of a product property

$= \square \cdot y^{\square}$ Power of a power property

$= \square$ Simplify.

Guided Practice **Simplify the expression.**

9. $(2^3)^3$	**10.** $(x^4)^5$	**11.** $(7n^6)^2$	**12.** $(p^2q^3)^4$

Multiplying Binomials

Goal: Multiply binomials.

EXAMPLE 1 Multiplying Binomials with a Table

Find the product $(4x + 1)(7x - 5)$ and simplify.

Write the first polynomial on the left of the table.

Write the second polynomial above the table.

Multiply to fill the table.

	$7x$	____
____	____	____
1	$7x$	____

The product is ____ ____ ____ $+ 7x$ ____ ____. Combine like terms.

ANSWER The product is ____.

EXAMPLE 2 Multiplying Binomials Vertically

Find the product $(-2x + 9)(3x + 2)$ and simplify.

	$-2x + 9$	Write the first binomial.
$\times$	$3x + 2$	Write the second binomial.
	____ + ____	Multiply $2(-2x + 9)$.
	____ + ____	Multiply $3x(-2x + 9)$.
	____	Add.

EXAMPLE 3 Multiplying Binomials Horizontally

Geometry Write an expression for the area of the square shown at the right. Then expand the expression and simplify.

$x - 8$

$x - 8$

Solution

An expression for the area of the square is ______. To expand the expression, multiply 2 binomials.

Use the formula for the area of a square: $A = s^2$.

______ $= (x - 8)(x - 8)$ Write two binor

$=$ ___ $(x - 8) -$ ___ $(x - 8)$ Distributive pro

$=$ ___ ___ ___ $-$ ___ ___ ___ Distributive pro

$=$ ______ Combine like te

Guided Practice **Find the product and simplify.**

1. $(t + 4)(t + 8)$	2. $(m - 3)(m - 6)$	3. $(-5y + 1)(4y -$

EXAMPLE 4 Multiplying with the FOIL Method

Find the product $(6x + 5)(-2x - 1)$ and simplify.

F First	+	O Outer	+	I Inner	+	L Last	
___ $\cdot$ (___)	+	___ $\cdot (-1)$	+	$5 \cdot$ (___)	+	___ $\cdot (-1)$	Group terms.
___	+	(___)	+	(___)	+	(___)	Multiply.
___							Combine like terms.

Guided Practice **Find the product and simplify.**

4. $(a + 2)(-3a + 2)$	**5.** $(p - 9)(p - 4)$	**6.** $(7n - 5)(2n + 5)$

Non-Linear Functions

Goal: Use function notation and graph non-linear functions.

Vocabulary

Function notation:

Vertical line test:

EXAMPLE 1 **Using Function Notation**

Model Rocket You launch a model rocket. The height of the rocket, in fe
is given by the equation $h = -16t^2 + 150t$, where t is the time in secor
after you launch the rocket. Write a function that models the height of th
rocket x seconds after you launch it. Use the function to find the height
the model rocket 3.5 seconds after you launch it.

Solution

Let $f(x)$ = height in feet and x = time in seconds.

____ = -16 ____ + 150 ____		Write the height equation in function notation.
$f(3.5) = -16($ ____ $)^2 + 150($ ____ $)$		Substitute 3.5 for x.
$f(3.5) = -16($ ____ $)$ + ____		Evaluate.
$f(3.5)$ = ____		Simplify.

ANSWER The function is ____. The height of the model rocket is ____ after 3.5 seconds.

Guided Practice **Rewrite using function notation.**

1. $y = 6x^2$	2. $y = -x^2 + 3$	3. $y = -\frac{1}{4}x^2$

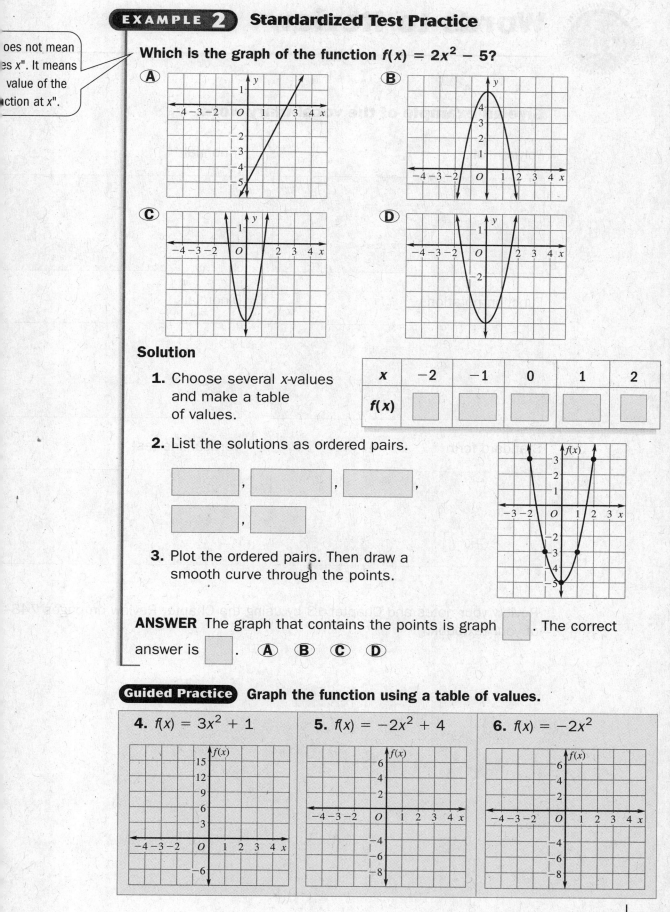

oes not mean
es x". It means
value of the
ction at x".

EXAMPLE 2 **Standardized Test Practice**

Which is the graph of the function $f(x) = 2x^2 - 5$?

Ⓐ

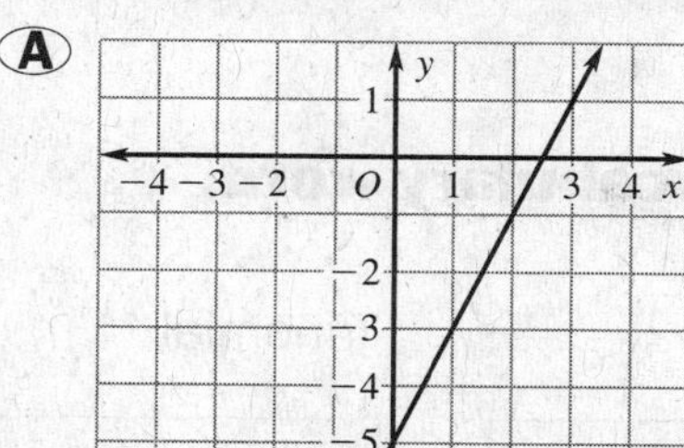

Ⓑ

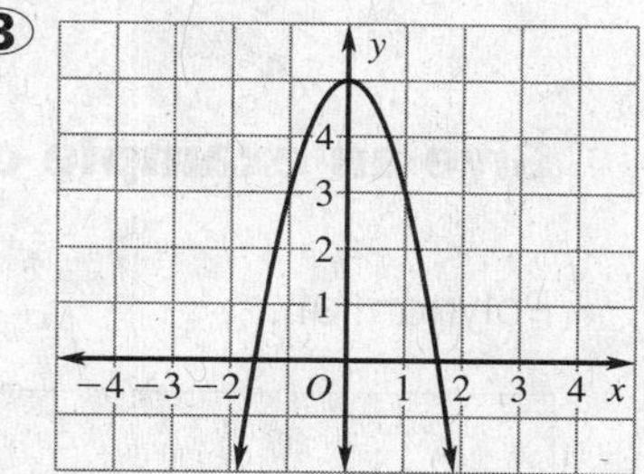

Ⓒ

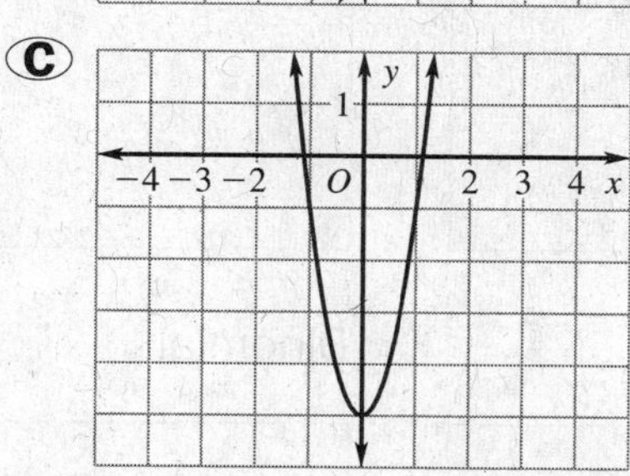

Ⓓ

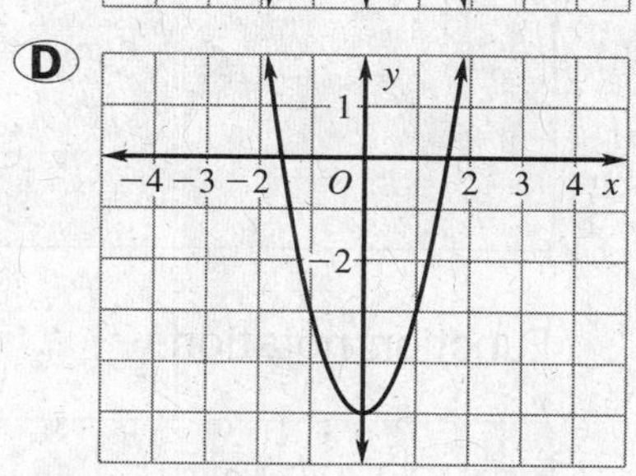

Solution

1. Choose several *x*-values and make a table of values.

x	−2	−1	0	1	2
f(x)					

2. List the solutions as ordered pairs.

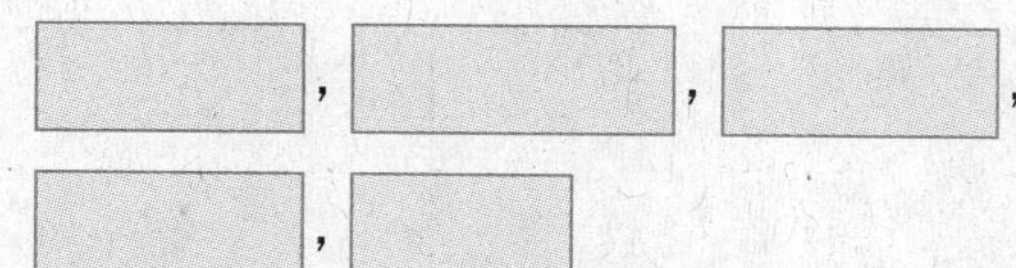

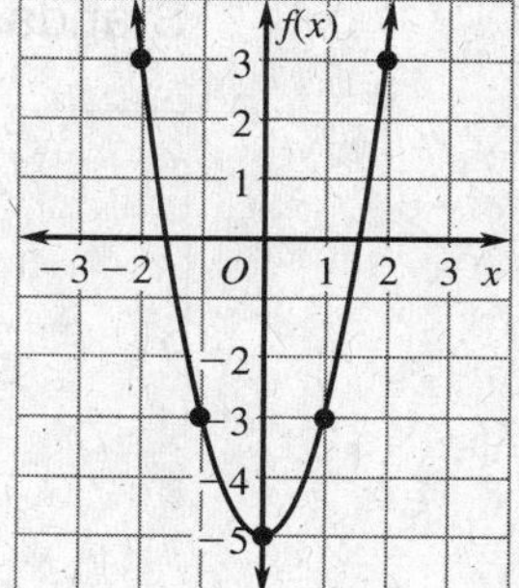

3. Plot the ordered pairs. Then draw a smooth curve through the points.

ANSWER The graph that contains the points is graph ____. The correct answer is ____. Ⓐ Ⓑ Ⓒ Ⓓ

Guided Practice **Graph the function using a table of values.**

4. $f(x) = 3x^2 + 1$

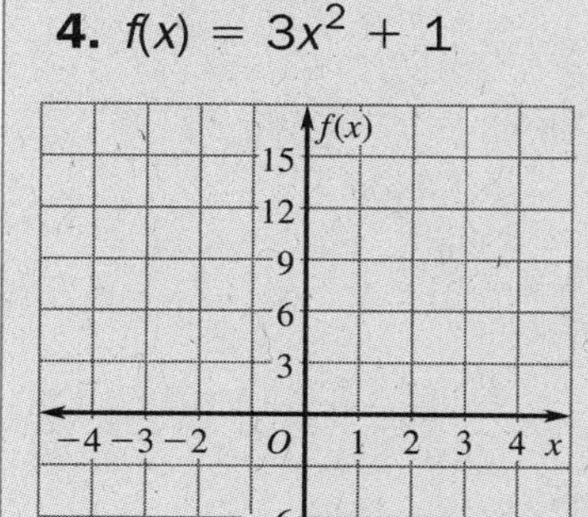

5. $f(x) = -2x^2 + 4$

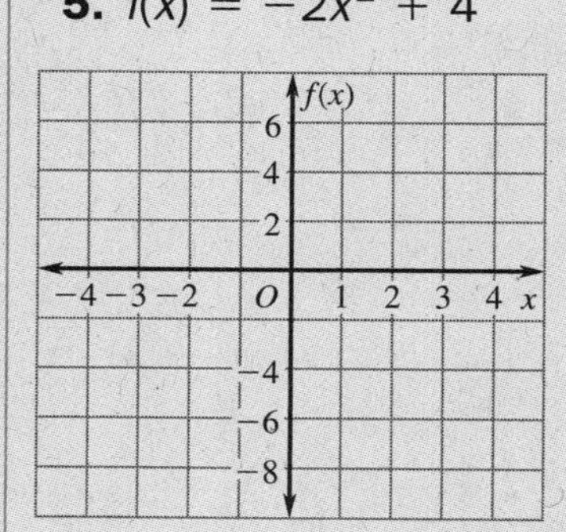

6. $f(x) = -2x^2$

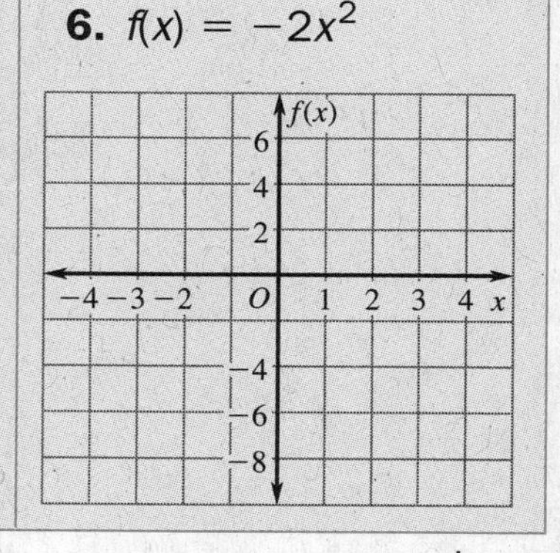

Words to Review

Give an example of the vocabulary word.

Polynomial

Trinomial

Function notation

Binomial

Standard form

Vertical line test

Review your notes and Chapter 13 by using the Chapter Review on pages 748– of your textbook.